S0-AQK-454

✿ **HAESE & HARRIS PUBLICATIONS**

Mathematics

for the international student
Mathematical Studies SL

Mal Coad

Glen Whiffen

John Owen

Robert Haese

Sandra Haese

Mark Bruce

International Baccalaureate
Diploma Programme

Mal Coad
Glen Whiffen
Glenn Smith
Alison Ryan
Robert Haese
Sandra Haese
Tom van Dulken

 Haese & Harris Publications

EXAM PREPARATION & PRACTICE GUIDE

MATHEMATICS FOR THE INTERNATIONAL STUDENT
International Baccalaureate Mathematical Studies SL Course
EXAM PREPARATION & PRACTICE GUIDE

Mal Coad	B.Ec, Dip.T.
Glen Whiffen	B.Sc., B.Ed.
Glenn Smith	B.Ed., Dip.T.
Alison Ryan	B.Sc., M.Ed.
Robert Haese	B.Sc.
Sandra Haese	B.Sc.
Tom van Dulken	B.Sc.(Hons), Ph.D.

Haese & Harris Publications
3 Frank Collopy Court, Adelaide Airport, SA 5950, AUSTRALIA
Telephone: +61 8 8355 9444, Fax: + 61 8 8355 9471
Email: info@haeseandharris.com.au
Web: www.haeseandharris.com.au

National Library of Australia Card Number & ISBN 978-1-876543-99-0

© Haese & Harris Publications 2006

Published by Raksar Nominees Pty Ltd
3 Frank Collopy Court, Adelaide Airport, SA 5950, AUSTRALIA

First Edition   2006   *Reprinted 2008*

Artwork by Piotr Poturaj and David Purton
Cover design by Piotr Poturaj
Computer software by David Purton

Typeset in Australia by Susan Haese (Raksar Nominees). Typeset in Times Roman 9/10

The Guide has been developed independently of the International Baccalaureate Organization (IBO). The Guide is in no way connected with, or endorsed by, the IBO.

This book is copyright. Except as permitted by the Copyright Act (any fair dealing for the purposes of private study, research, criticism or review), no part of this publication may be reproduced, stored in a retrieval system, or transmitted in any form or by any means, electronic, mechanical, photocopying, recording or otherwise, without the prior permission of the publisher. Enquiries to be made to Haese & Harris Publications.

Copying for educational purposes: Where copies of part or the whole of the book are made under Part VB of the Copyright Act, the law requires that the educational institution or the body that administers it, has given a remuneration notice to Copyright Agency Limited (CAL). For information, contact the Copyright Agency Limited.

Acknowledgements: While every attempt has been made to trace and acknowledge copyright, the authors and publishers apologise for any accidental infringement where copyright has proved untraceable. They would be pleased to come to a suitable agreement with the rightful owner.

The authors and publishers would like to thank all those teachers who have read the proofs of this book and offered advice and encouragement.

Special thanks to John Bush for his detailed advice and criticism in the early stages of planning the Exam Preparation & Practice Guides. Others who offered to read and comment on the proofs include: Irene Owen, Paula Waldman, Julie Mortensen, Margie Karbassioun, Jane Kerr, Susan Cox, Andrew Spray, Mark Banner-Martin, Brendan Watson, Wallis Green, Andrzej Cichy, Marie-Therese Filippi, Robb Sloan, Bill O'Brien, Mark Willis, Edward Kemp, Peter Joseph, Sonja Bartholomew, Jim Napolitano, Myrricia Holmann, Rema George, Alexina Coad. To anyone we may have missed, we offer our apologies.

The publishers wish to make it clear that acknowledging these teachers does not imply any endorsement of this book by any of them, and all responsibility for the content rests with the authors and publishers.

FOREWORD

This Guide aims to help you prepare for the IB Mathematical Studies SL final examinations. It should be used in conjunction with your textbook and other material suggested by your teacher.

- While using this guide you will need to refer to your information booklet. The formulas and tables are not given in the guide. It is essential that you become familiar with the layout and content of the booklet.

The Guide covers Topics 2-8 in the syllabus. Each topic begins with a concise summary of key facts and includes a number of worked examples linked to the main concepts. This is intended to complement your textbook. Following each summary is a set of twenty five "short questions" and eight "long questions" which can be used to consolidate your knowledge by reminding you of the fundamental skills required for the topic.

The best way to consolidate your mathematical understanding is by being active. This includes summarising the topics in an effective way and attempting questions.

This Guide also offers five specimen examinations with each examination divided into Paper 1 and Paper 2 questions. Each Paper 1 has fifteen questions to be completed within 90 minutes; each Paper 2 has five questions also to be completed within 90 minutes. The specimen examinations reflect a balanced assessment of the course.

Fully worked solutions are provided for every question in the topic section of the Guide. Detailed markschemes are provided for each paper in the specimen examinations. In many situations alternative solutions exist which are accepted.

Try to complete the specimen examinations under examination conditions. Getting into good habits will reduce pressure during the examination.

- It is important that you persevere with a question, but sometimes it is a good strategy to move on to other questions and return later to ones you have found challenging. Time management is very important during the examination and too much time spent on a difficult question may mean that you do not leave yourself sufficient time to complete other questions.

- Use a pen rather than a pencil, except for graphs and diagrams.

- If you make a mistake draw a single line through the work you want to replace. Do not cross out work until you have replaced it with something you consider better.

- Set your work out clearly with full explanations don't take shortcuts.

- Diagrams and graphs should be sufficiently large, well labelled and clearly drawn.

- Remember to leave answers correct to three significant figures unless an exact answer is more appropriate or a different level of accuracy is requested in the question. Answers involving money can be given to 2dp, 3sf or to the nearest integer.

Get used to reading the questions carefully.

- Ensure that you understand the "command terms" used in this course and what each means in regard to what is required in response to a question. Check for key words in the question. If the word "hence" appears, then you must use the result you have just obtained. "Hence, or otherwise" means that you can use any method you like, although it is likely that the best method uses the previous result.

- Rushing into a question may mean that you miss subtle points. Underlining key words may help.

- Questions in the examination are often set so that, even if you cannot get through one part, the question can still be picked up in a later part.

After completing a specimen examination, identify areas of weakness.

- Return to your notes or textbook and review the topic.

- Ask your teacher or a friend for help if further explanation is needed.

- Summarise each topic. Summaries that you make yourself are the most valuable.

- Test yourself, or work with someone else to help improve your knowledge of a topic.

- If you have had difficulty with a question, try it again later. Do not just assume that you know how to do it once you have read the solution. It is important that you work on weaker areas, but do not neglect the other areas.

Your graphics display calculator is an essential aid.

- Make sure you are familiar with the operation of all the modes of your calculator that you will be using.

- In trigonometry questions remember to check that the gdc is in degrees.

- Become familiar with common error messages and how to respond to them.

- For quadratic and higher order polynomials and for periodic functions remember to check for all solutions in a given domain.

- Important features of graphs may be revealed by zooming in or out.

- Asymptotic behaviour is not always clear on a gdc screen; don't just rely on appearances. As with all aspects of the gdc reflect on the reasonableness of the results.

- Are your batteries fresh?

We hope this guide will help you structure your examination preparation effectively. Remember that good examination techniques will come from good examination preparation.

We welcome your feedback:

web: http://haeseandharris.com.au

email: info@haeseandharris.com.au

TABLE OF CONTENTS

SUMMARY
NUMBER SETS

- Natural Numbers $\quad \mathbb{N} = \{0, 1, 2, 3, 4, ...\}$

- Integers $\qquad\quad \mathbb{Z} = \{...., -2, -1, 0, 1, 2, ...\}$

- Rational Numbers $\quad \mathbb{Q} = \{\frac{p}{q} \mid p, q \in \mathbb{Z}, \ q \neq 0\}$

- Real Numbers $\qquad \mathbb{R} = \{\text{all real numbers}\}$
  These are numbers that can be placed on a number line.

The Venn diagram shows the relationship between the sets.

You must understand and be able to use:

▶ Prime numbers, prime factors, common factors, multiples.

▶ Universal Set, subsets, complements, intersection, union.

▶ Venn diagrams and the link to Topic 3 (Sets, Logic and Probability).

Example:

For $U = \{n \in \mathbb{Z} \mid 0 < n < 10\}$, $A = \{\text{prime numbers}\}$, and $B = \{\text{even numbers}\}$:

a List the elements of each set.

b Represent the sets A and B on a Venn diagram.

c Find the number of elements in $A \cap B$, $A \cup B$ and $(A \cup B)'$.

d Write down an element of B.

e Write down a subset of B.

Solution:

a $U = \{1, 2, 3, 4, 5, 6, 7, 8, 9\}$, $A = \{2, 3, 5, 7\}$ and $B = \{2, 4, 6, 8\}$

b

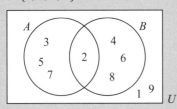

c $A \cap B = \{2\}$, $A \cup B = \{2, 3, 4, 5, 6, 7, 8\}$
and $(A \cup B)' = \{1, 9\}$
$\therefore \quad n(A \cap B) = 1 \quad n(A \cup B) = 7 \quad n(A \cup B)' = 2$

d An element of B is 4 (or 6 or 8 or 2).

e A subset of B is $\{2, 4\}$, for example.

APPROXIMATION AND ESTIMATION

You must be familiar with and use:

▶ Rounding: e.g., $1.50 = 2$ (nearest whole number)
$\qquad\qquad\qquad 1.49 = 1$ (nearest whole number)

▶ Significant figures:
  The significant figures are counted from the first left hand non-zero digit.

  e.g., count from the 3 in the following examples.
  $$345\,600 = 346\,000 \ (3 \text{ s.f.})$$
  $$\text{and } 0.003\,456 = 0.00346 \ (3 \text{ s.f.})$$

PERCENTAGE ERROR

$$\text{Percentage error} = \frac{\text{approximate value } - \text{ exact value}}{\text{exact value}} \times 100\%$$

Note: Some % answers work out to be negative. We convert these to the positive.

Example:

A length of rope, measured exactly as 7.45 m, is stated as 7.4 m long on the packaging. Find the percentage error caused by the rounding.

Solution:

$$\% \text{ error} = \frac{7.4 - 7.45}{7.45} \times 100 = -0.671\%$$

So, the percentage error is 0.671%.

STANDARD FORM (SCIENTIFIC NOTATION)

Standard form is $\quad a \times 10^k \quad$ where $\quad 1 \leqslant a < 10 \quad$ and $\quad k \in \mathbb{Z}$.

Note that

- 2565 in standard form is 2.565×10^3
- 3.04×10^{-3} as a decimal is $0.003\,04$

SI UNITS
You must understand and be able to use:

▶ Metric conversion e.g., convert $5.3 \text{ g} = 530 \text{ cg}$

▶ Areas and Volumes e.g., $8 \text{ m} \times 5 \text{ m} = 40 \text{ m}^2$

▶ Formulae e.g., converting temperature units

▶ Units such as cms^{-1} (cm/s)
  These arise when doing divisions such as $\frac{\text{distance}}{\text{time}}$

  Example:

  Given $\text{speed} = \frac{\text{distance}}{\text{time}}$, find the time taken for a car travelling at an average speed of 70 kmh^{-1} to cover 245 km.

  Solution: $\quad \text{speed} = \frac{\text{distance}}{\text{time}}$
  $$\therefore \quad 70 = \frac{245}{t}$$
  $$\therefore \quad t = \frac{245}{70}$$
  $$\therefore \quad t = 3.5 \text{ hours}$$

SEQUENCES

These are sequences of numbers such as

23, 27, 31, 35, 39, ... or 24, 12, 6, 3, 1.5, ... say

In general, we write: $u_1, u_2, u_3, u_4, u_5, ...$

Special sequences are:

- **Arithmetic**
  with common difference, $d = u_2 - u_1 = u_3 - u_2 = ...$
  and $u_n = u_1 + (n - 1)d$

- **Geometric**
  with common ratio $r = \frac{u_2}{u_1} = \frac{u_3}{u_2} = ...$
  and $u_n = u_1 r^{n-1}$

Example 1:

Find the common difference or common ratio in these sequences:

a 4, 13, 22, 31, ... **b** $\frac{1}{2}$, 1, 2, 4, ...

Solution: **a** This is arithmetic as
$$13 - 4 = 22 - 13 = 31 - 22 = 9 \quad \therefore \quad d = 9$$

b This is geometric as $\frac{4}{2} = \frac{2}{1} = \frac{1}{\frac{1}{2}} = 2 \quad \therefore \quad r = 2$

Example 2:

Which term of the sequence $3, 7, 11, \ldots$ is 119?

Solution:

The sequence is arithmetic with $u_1 = 3$, $d = 4$,

Now $\quad u_n = u_1 + (n-1)d$

$\therefore \quad 119 = 3 + (n-1) \times 4$

$\therefore \quad n = 30 \quad$ {using a gdc}

SERIES

A series is the addition of the terms of a sequence.

That is $\quad u_1 + u_2 + u_3 + u_4 + \ldots$

These formulae can be used to find the **sum** of a series:

- **Arithmetic:** $\quad S_n = \dfrac{n}{2}(2u_1 + (n-1)d) \quad$ or

$$S_n = \dfrac{n}{2}(u_1 + u_n)$$

- **Geometric:** $\quad S_n = \dfrac{u_1(r^n - 1)}{r - 1} \quad$ or

$$S_n = \dfrac{u_1(1 - r^n)}{1 - r}$$

APPLICATIONS FOR SEQUENCES AND SERIES

Applications involve:

- ▶ Simple and Compound Interest
- ▶ Growth and Decay

Example:

A 50 g sample of radioactive material decreases in weight by 3.2% per annum. Calculate the number of years it will take for the sample to weigh less than 20 g.

Solution:

The decay is geometric with

$u_1 = 50$, $\quad u_n = 20 \quad$ and $\quad r = 96.8\% = 0.968$

Using $\quad u_n = u_1 \times r^{n-1} \quad$ we have the equation

$20 = 50 \times (0.968)^{n-1}$

$\therefore \quad n = 29.173 = 30$ years $\quad$ {using a gdc}

SIMULTANEOUS EQUATIONS

An example is: $\qquad 2a + b = 7$

$\qquad\qquad\qquad 3a + 2b = 11$

These may be solved using

- Substitution
- Elimination
- a gdc

    (The use of the gdc is emphasised in the syllabus.)

The solution is $\quad a = 3$, $\quad b = 1$.

QUADRATIC EQUATIONS

These are equations of the form $\quad ax^2 + bx + c = 0$.

You must understand and be able to use:

- ▶ methods to solve equations of the form $ax^2 + bx + c = 0$
- ▶ terms such as factors, zeros and roots

    Example: $\quad 6x^2 - x - 2 = 0 \qquad$ is a quadratic equation

    $\qquad\qquad (2x + 1)(3x - 2) = 0 \quad$ is its factored form

    $\qquad\qquad x = -\tfrac{1}{2}$ are $\tfrac{2}{3} \qquad$ are its roots or solutions

- ▶ a gdc to solve quadratic equations

You must understand and be able to:

- ▶ write equations in terms of x
- ▶ use algebra to solve problems

TOPIC 2 – NUMBER AND ALGEBRA (SHORT QUESTIONS)

1 a List the elements of the following sets:
  - **i** $A = \{x \in \mathbb{Z} \mid -2 < x < 3\}$
  - **ii** $B = \{\text{prime numbers less than } 15\}$
  - **iii** $C = \{x \in \mathbb{R} \mid x^2 = 8\}$

  b State whether the following statements are true or false.
  - **i** All rational numbers are integers.
  - **ii** $4 - p > 4 + p$, $\quad p \in \mathbb{Z}^-$.
  - **iii** $\mathbb{N} = \{0, 1, 2, 3, \ldots\}$

2 Place the following numbers in the appropriate Venn diagram.
2.5, π, -3, $\tfrac{8}{5}$, 0, $\sqrt{25}$

3 $U = \{\text{natural numbers less than } 12\} \quad A = \{\text{multiples of } 3\}$
$B = \{\text{factors of } 10\}$
List the elements of: **a** $A \cap B$ **b** $A \cup B$ **c** $(A \cup B)'$.

4 a Draw a number line to represent the set
$X = \{x \in \mathbb{R} \mid -3 \leqslant x \leqslant 3\}$

  b Use a number line to clearly represent each of the following:
  - **i** $x < -1$ **ii** $0 \leqslant x < 2$ **iii** $x \geqslant 2$

5 $U = \{n \in \mathbb{N} \mid 1 \leqslant n \leqslant 12\}$
$P = \{\text{odd numbers}\}$, $\quad Q = \{\text{factors of } 12\} \quad$ and
$R = \{\text{multiples of } 5\}$
List the elements of

a	$P \cap Q$	**b**	$(P \cap Q) \cup R$
c	$Q \cap R$	**d**	$P' \cap (Q \cup R)$

6 The information below shows the number of different types of movies available for hire. $P = \{\text{comedy}\}$, $Q = \{\text{romance}\}$, $R = \{\text{adventure}\}$

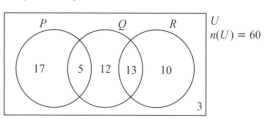

Find

a	$n(P)$	**b**	$n(P \cup Q)$	**c**	$n(Q \cap R)$
d	$n((P \cup Q \cup R)')$	**e**	$n(Q')$	**f**	$n(P \cap R)$

7 a A number of IB students study English or Spanish or both English and Spanish. 25 study Spanish and 18 study English. If 6 students study both languages, how many IB students are there?

  b An international school offers its programme in both French and English languages. 60% of the students study in the English language programme and 76% study in the French language programme. What percentage of the students take lessons in both languages?

  c In a class of 25 students, 20% do not study art or drama. 13 students study art and 9 students study drama. How many students study both art and drama?

8 Evaluate $\sqrt{\dfrac{32.76}{3.95 \times 2.63}}$, giving your answer:

  a correct to 3 decimal places

  b correct to the nearest whole number

  c correct to 3 significant figures

  d in standard form.

9 The speed of light is approximately $186\,280$ miles per second. Assume the distance from Mars to Earth is approximately $195\,000\,000$ km.

  a Given that mile : kilometre $= 1 : 1.609$, determine the speed of light in kilometres per minute. Give your answer to 3 significant figures.

  b Express your answer to **a** using scientific notation (standard form).

  c If a light source on Mars is ignited, how many minutes will it be before it is seen through a telescope on Earth?

10 **a** A measurement of 5.645 cm is rounded, correct to 3 significant figures.

    i Write down the actual error caused by rounding.

    ii Calculate the relative error.

    iii Calculate the percentage error.

  b The speedometer of a car has an error of 3.2% at 70 km per hour.

    i What is the actual error?

    ii Write down the extreme possible values for the true speed of the car.

11 The length of a section of pipe is stated as 4 m. Claudia carefully measures the pipe and finds the actual length to be 3.94 m.

  a Write down the size of the error in the stated length.

  b Five sections of pipe are joined together. Find the actual length of the joined pipes.

  c Write down the error for the joined pipes if the actual length of each pipe is rounded to the nearest metre.

  d Calculate the percentage error of the stated length against the actual length of joined pipes.

12 The first three terms of a sequence are -2, -9, and -16.

  a Write down the next two terms of the sequence.

  b Draw a mapping diagram of the first 5 terms.

  c Find a formula for the nth term of the sequence.

13 **a** Write down the first 3 terms of the sequence given by:
$$u_n = n(n+1)$$

  b Find the 15th term.

  c Which term of this sequence is 600?

14 The first three terms of an arithmetic sequence are -347, $k - 166$ and -185.

  a Find the value of k.

  b Find a formula for the nth term of the sequence.

  c Which is the first positive term of the sequence?

15 The sixth term of an arithmetic sequence is 49 and the fifteenth term is 130.

  a Find the common difference for this sequence.

  b Find the first term.

  c How many of the terms of this sequence have a value which is less than 300?

16 The sum of the first 7 terms of an arithmetic series is 329. The common difference is 14.

  a Find the value of the first term.

  b $69\,800$ is the sum of the first n terms of the sequence. Find n.

17 The first three terms of a geometric sequence are 0.75, 2.25 and 6.75.

  a Find the common ratio.

  b Write down a formula for the nth term.

  c Calculate the sum of the first 10 terms.

18 A rubber ball is dropped vertically from a height of 5 m. It bounces up to a height of 4.5 m on the first bounce, then to 4.05 m on the second bounce and so on.

  a Find the common ratio.

  b Calculate the height of the third bounce.

  c How far has it travelled vertically by the time it strikes the floor for the fourth time?

19 128 football clubs enter the first round of a knockout competition. In each round, half the participants are eliminated.

  a How many remain in the second and in the third rounds?

  b If there are n rounds, how many participants remain in the nth round?

  c Calculate the number of rounds needed in this competition to determine a winner.

20 The second term of a geometric sequence is 14.5 and the fifth term is 1.8125.

  a Determine the common ratio.

  b Find the value of the first term.

  c Find the sum of the first 5 terms.

21 The population of a small town increases by an average of 9% per annum. In 2000, the population was 1200.

  a Calculate the size of the population in 2005.

  b In which year will the population reach 2500?

  c Find the rate of increase that would result in the population reaching 3200 in 2010.

22 **a** Find the term that the sequences, $u_n = 178 - 4n$ and $u_n = 7n + 57$, have in common.

  b A firm's revenue function is $R = 25n$ and its cost function is $C = 21000 + 7.5n$, where n is the number of goods produced and sold. Find the value of n for the Cost to equal the Revenue for the firm.

  c The sum of the first n natural numbers is equal to $\dfrac{n(n+1)}{2}$. For what values of n does the sum exceed 435?

23 **a** Solve, using technology:

    i $12s + 17r = 277$
      $5s + 11r = 135$

    ii $u_1 + 27d = 162$
       $35d = 202 - u_1$

  b The cost of hiring a taxi includes a flat fee of $\$a$ plus $\$p$ per kilometre. A 12 kilometre taxi ride costs $20 and a 22 kilometre journey costs $34. Find the values of a and p.

24 The perimeter of a rectangle is 80 cm. The width is x cm.

  a Write down the value of the length, in terms of x.

  b Show that the area A of the rectangle is given by the function $A = 40x - x^2$.

  c The area of the rectangle is 375 cm^2. Find its length.

25 The approximate height above the ground (s) of a sky rocket at any time (t) seconds after firing is given by $s = ut - 5t^2$, where u represents the initial speed of the sky rocket. If the initial speed is 70 ms^{-1}, find:

  a the amount of time the rocket is in the air.

  b the time the rocket is above 30 m.

TOPIC 2 – NUMBER AND ALGEBRA (LONG QUESTIONS)

1 **a** Which of the following statements are false? Justify your answer.

    i $\{-2, -1, 0, 1, 2\} \subset \{x \in \mathbb{R} \mid x < 2\}$

    ii $\{0, 1, 2, 3, 4\} \subset \{x \in \mathbb{Z} \mid x \leqslant 5\}$

iii $\{x \in \mathbb{Z} \mid x^2 + x = 2\} = \{-1, 1, 2\}$

b $U = \{x \in \mathbb{N} \mid 14 \leqslant x < 30\}$

$A = \{\text{multiples of } 7\}, \quad B = \{\text{factors of } 56\},$
$C = \{\text{even numbers} \geqslant 20\}$

i List the members of each of the sets A, B and C contained in U.

ii Represent these sets of numbers on a 3-circle Venn diagram.

iii List the members of the following sets:

a $A \cap B \cap C$ **b** $(A \cap B) \cup C$
c $(A \cap B)' \cap C$ **d** $(A \cup C)' \cap B$

c p and q are different integers. Which of the following statements are false? Give an example to support your decision.

i $p + q = q + p$ **ii** $p - q = q - p$ **iii** $pq = qp$

2 a Draw a number line to represent $\{x \in \mathbb{R} \mid -5 \leqslant x \leqslant 5\}$. Represent the following on the number line using appropriate notation.

i $x \geqslant 4$ **ii** $1 \leqslant x < 3$
iii $-3 \leqslant x \leqslant 0$ **iv** $x < -4$

b Let $X = \{x \in \mathbb{Z} \mid -4 \leqslant x \leqslant 4\}$ and
$Y = \{y \in \mathbb{Z} \mid -4 \leqslant y \leqslant 4\}$.

On a set of coordinate axes, plot the points which represent:

i the set $W = \{(x, y) \mid \frac{y}{x} = -1, \ x \in X, \ y \in Y\}$

ii the set
$V = \{(x, y) \mid x \in X, y \in Y, x \geqslant 0, y \geqslant 0, y - x = 1\}$

c If $x, y \in \mathbb{Q}$ and $x > y$, write down an example which makes $x^2 < y^2$ true.

3 a Evaluate $25.32 \times \dfrac{6.057}{2.4 \times \sqrt{5.14}}$, giving your answer correct to:

i five significant figures
ii the nearest tenth
iii 1 significant figure.

b Three sections of fencing are erected. Each section has a stated length of 3.60 m, measured to the nearest centimetre. The actual length of each section is 3.63 m.

i Find the actual length covered by the three sections of fencing.

ii Calculate the percentage error between the actual length and stated length of the three sections of fencing.

c The three sections of fencing of part **b** form one side of a square enclosure. The enclosure will have a concrete floor 100 ± 5 mm thick. Concrete costs €47.50 per cubic metre.

i Write down the maximum and minimum possible values for the volume of concrete needed for the floor.

ii Calculate the difference in cost between the maximum possible volume of concrete and the planned volume based on the stated length.

iii Express this cost difference as a percentage of the planned cost.

4 a Write down the values of the first three terms of each of the following:

i $u_n = 120 + 3(n - 1)$ **ii** $u_{n+1} = u_n + 7, \ u_1 = 4$

b **i** Which term do the sequences listed in **a** have in common?

ii What is the value of that term?

c Which of the sequences has 151 as one of its terms?

d The sum of the first n terms of the sequences listed in **a** is the same. Find n.

e When will the difference between the sums of the sequences in **a** be 228?

5 The first 3 terms of a sequence are 56, 28 and 14.

a **i** Show that the sequence is geometric.
ii Find the 8th term of the sequence.
iii Find the sum of the first 8 terms.

b The third term of another geometric sequence is 24.5 and 5th term is 12.005 .

i Find the first term and the common ratio.
ii Write down the general formula for a term of this sequence.

c The first n terms of the sequence in **b** are larger than the corresponding terms for the sequence $u_n = 20 \times (0.8)^{n-1}$. Find n.

d For the sequence $u_n = 20 \times (0.8)^{n-1}$, find the sum of the first **i** 30 terms **ii** 50 terms **iii** 100 terms. Answer to 3 s.f. in each case. Comment on your results.

6 a Misha takes out a loan to purchase a generator for his business. He borrows \$20 000 at 12.5% per annum, compound interest. At the end of each year, Misha is required to pay \$k.

i If Misha does repay \$k each year, explain why the amount owing on the loan at the end of the first year is $\$(20\,000 \times 1.125) - k$.

ii Write down an expression, in terms of k, for the amount owing on the loan at the end of the second year.

iii At the end of the second year, the amount owing on the loan will be \$17 131.25. Find k.

b Misha paid a total of \$24 000 for the generator. Its value depreciated after purchase so that, at the end of the first year, it was only worth \$20 400. The value in each subsequent year would decline at the same rate.

i Find the percentage decrease in the value of the generator in the first year.

ii Calculate the value of the generator at the end of the second year.

iii Write down the formula for the value after n years.

iv Sketch the graph of the value of the generator for the first 6 years.

7 Tahlia borrows \$5000 from her bank. Her repayments each month are \$250 plus the interest for that month. Interest is charged at 1.2% each month.

a Determine the payments she must make at the end of the:
i first month **ii** second month **iii** third month.

These monthly payments form an arithmetic sequence.

b Find the first term and common difference for the sequence and hence write down the formula to find the value of the nth payment for this loan.

c Calculate the size of the payment at the end of the tenth month.

d Determine the number of payments required for Tahlia to pay off the loan.

e Calculate the total amount Tahlia will pay for this loan.

8 A radioactive material loses 10% of its weight per year. The weight of the material at the start of the first year was 200 g.

a **i** Write down the weight of the material at the start of the second and third years.

ii Write down the common ratio for the geometric sequence formed by the yearly weight of the material.

iii Find the weight of the material at the start of the 6th year.

iv Draw a sketch of the annual weight of the material for the first 6 years.

v At the start of which year will the weight of the material fall below 20 g?

b The weight of a second sample of radioactive material decreased from 120 g to 49.152 g after 6 years. Find the annual percentage rate of decrease.

SUMMARY

SETS

- A set is a collection of numbers or objects.
  For example, $A = \{\text{factors of } 16\}$

- The Universal set is the set of all things being considered.
  The symbol U is used to represent the universal set.

- $a \in A$ is read as a is a member (element) of the set A.

SUBSETS, INTERSECTION, UNION, COMPLEMENT

Given two sets, A and B:

- $A \subset B$ reads A is a **subset** of B and every element of A is also an element of B.

  $A \cap B$ represents the **intersection** and is the set made up of elements which are **in both** A and B.

- $A \cup B$ represents the **union** and is the set made up of elements which are **in A or B or both**.

- A' represents the **complement** of A and is the set made up of all elements which are in the Universal set and **not in** A.

Subsets, intersection, union and complement can be represented by shaded regions on a Venn diagram.

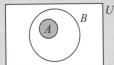 

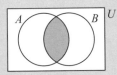 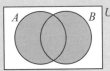

COUNTING IN A SET

$n(A)$ is used to represent the number of elements in a set.

For example, if $A = \{a, b, c, d, e\}$, then $n(A) = 5$.

Example:

For this Venn diagram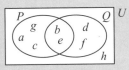

find **a** $n(P \cap Q)$ **b** $n(P \cup Q)$ **c** $n(Q')$

Solution:

   a $P \cap Q = \{b, e\}$ $\therefore$ $n(P \cap Q) = 2$
   b $P \cup Q = \{a, b, c, d, e, f, g\}$ $\therefore$ $n(P \cup Q) = 7$
   c $Q' = \{a, c, g, h\}$ $\therefore$ $n(Q') = 4$

PROBLEM SOLVING WITH VENN DIAGRAMS

Venn diagrams can be used to solve some problems.

Example:

A class of 30 pupils contains students who study French, students who study Spanish, students who study both French and Spanish and students who study neither. 16 students study French, 14 students study Spanish and 5 study neither.

How many students study both French and Spanish.

Solution:

Let x be the number of students who study both subjects.
Then $16 - x$ must study French only and $14 - x$ study Spanish only.

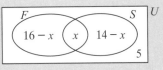

Now, $16 - x + x + 14 - x + 5 = 30$
             $\therefore \quad 35 - x = 30$
                  $\therefore \quad x = 5$

So, 5 students study both French and Spanish.

LOGIC

You must understand and be able to use:

- **Propositions**, symbolic notation, p, q, and r for propositions, compound propositions.

- **Conjunction:** $p \wedge q$, p and q relates to the region $P \cap Q$ on a Venn diagram.

- **Disjunction:** $p \vee q$, p or q relates to the region $P \cup Q$ on a Venn diagram.

- **Exclusive disjunction:** $p \underline{\vee} q$ relates to the region $P \cup Q$ but not $P \cap Q$ on a Venn diagram.

- **Negation:** $\neg p$ "not p" relates to the region P' on a Venn diagram.

- **Implication:** $p \Rightarrow q$ "If p then q."

- **Equivalence:** $p \Leftrightarrow q$ "p if and only if q."

- **Converse:** $q \Rightarrow p$ "If q then p."

- **Inverse:** $\neg p \Rightarrow \neg q$ "If not p then not q."

- **Contrapositive:** $\neg q \Rightarrow \neg p$ "If not q then not p."

TRUTH TABLES

p	q	$\neg p$	$\neg q$	$p \wedge q$	$p \vee q$	$p \underline{\vee} q$	$p \Rightarrow q$
T	T	F	F	T	T	F	T
T	F	F	T	F	T	T	F
F	T	T	F	F	T	T	T
F	F	T	T	F	F	F	T

Terms

- **Logical equivalence:** propositions having the same truth set.
- **Tautology:** propositions whose truth set is all true.
- **Contradiction:** propositions whose truth set is all false.

Example:

Let p be the proposition $x = 2$
and q be the proposition $3x^2 - 2x - 2 = 6$.
 a Write down the proposition $p \Rightarrow q$.
 b Is this proposition true of false?
 c Write down the converse of this compound proposition in words.
 d Is this proposition true or false? Give a reason for your answer.

Solution:

 a If $x = 2$, then $3x^2 - 2x - 2 = 6$.
 b True.
 c If $3x^2 - 2x - 2 = 6$, then $x = 2$.
 d False. $3x^2 - 2x - 2 = 6 \Rightarrow (3x + 4)(x - 2) = 0$
                             $\Rightarrow x = 2$ or $x = -\frac{4}{3}$.

Example:

 a Draw the truth tables for the compound propositions
    $(\neg p \vee q) \Rightarrow q$ and $p \wedge \neg q$.

 b Are the two compound propositions logically equivalent? Give a reason for your answer.

Solution:

a

p	q	$\neg p$	$\neg p \vee q$	$(\neg p \vee q) \Rightarrow q$
T	T	F	T	T
T	F	F	F	T
F	T	T	T	T
F	F	T	T	F

p	q	$\neg q$	$p \wedge \neg q$
T	T	F	F
T	F	T	T
F	T	F	F
F	F	T	F

b No, the final truth table columns are not the same.

PROBABILITY

- The probability of an event A occurring is given by $\mathrm{P}(A) = \dfrac{n(A)}{n(U)}$.
- The probability of the complement of an event A occurring is $\mathrm{P}(A') = 1 - \mathrm{P}(A)$.

LAWS OF PROBABILITY

- $\mathrm{P}(A \cup B) = \mathrm{P}(A) + \mathrm{P}(B) - \mathrm{P}(A \cap B)$.
- **Mutually exclusive events** are events that share no common outcomes. This means, $A \cap B = \varnothing$ and so $\mathrm{P}(A \cap B) = 0$ and $\mathrm{P}(A \cup B) = \mathrm{P}(A) + \mathrm{P}(B)$.
- **Conditional probability**. The probability of event A occurring given that event B has occurred is

$$\mathrm{P}(A|B) = \frac{\mathrm{P}(A \cap B)}{\mathrm{P}(B)}.$$

- **Independent events** are events where the occurrence of one of the events does not affect the occurrence of the other event. Consequently, $\mathrm{P}(A \cap B) = \mathrm{P}(A) \times \mathrm{P}(B)$.

USING DIAGRAMS TO FIND PROBABILITIES

Tree diagrams, Venn diagrams and lattices can be used to find probabilities.

Example:

The probability that it will snow tomorrow is 0.75. If it snows the probability that I will go skiing is 0.9. If it does not snow the probability that I will go skiing is 0.2.

a Draw a tree diagram to illustrate this information.

b Find the probability that I will go skiing tomorrow.

Solution:

a

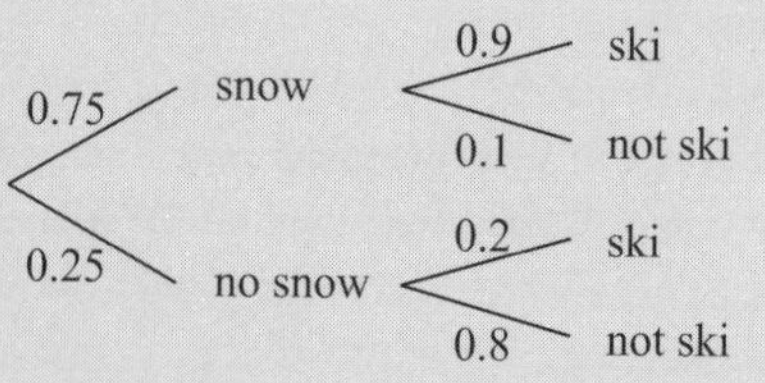

b $\mathrm{P}(\text{skiing}) = 0.75 \times 0.9 + 0.25 \times 0.2 = 0.725$

Example:

Two events are such that $\mathrm{P}(A) = 0.6$, $\mathrm{P}(B) = 0.5$ and $\mathrm{P}(A \cup B) = 0.85$.

a Find $\mathrm{P}(A \cap B)$.

b Are A and B mutually exclusive? Give a reason for your answer.

c Are A and B independent? Give a reason for your answer.

Solution:

a $\mathrm{P}(A \cup B) = \mathrm{P}(A) + \mathrm{P}(B) - \mathrm{P}(A \cap B)$

$\therefore \quad 0.85 = 0.6 + 0.5 - \mathrm{P}(A \cap B)$

$\therefore \quad \mathrm{P}(A \cap B) = 1.1 - 0.85 = 0.25$

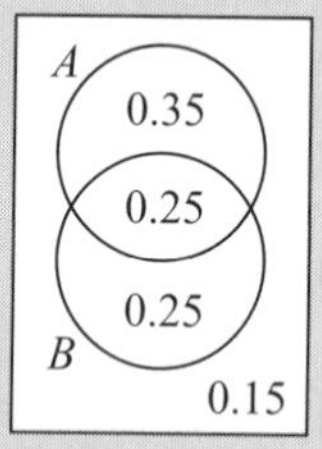

b $\mathrm{P}(A) + \mathrm{P}(B) = 1.1$ and $\mathrm{P}(A \cap B) = 0.85$
and as they are not equal, A and B are not mutually exclusive.

c $\mathrm{P}(A) \times \mathrm{P}(B) = 0.3$ and $\mathrm{P}(A \cap B) = 0.25$
and as they are not equal, A and B are not independent.

Example:

Two bags contain cards with numbers printed on them.
Bag 1 contains 5 cards with 0, 0, 1, 3 and 4 printed on them.
Bag 2 contains 4 cards with 0, 3, 4 and 5 on them.

a Draw a lattice diagram to illustrate this information.

b Find the probability that when one card is picked from each bag at random the total is an even number.

c Find the probability that given the total number is even it is less than 5.

Solution:

a

Bag 1 (columns), Bag 2 (rows)

Sum	0	0	1	3	4
0	0	0	1	3	4
3	3	3	4	6	7
4	4	4	5	7	8
5	5	5	6	8	9

b $\mathrm{P}(\text{even number}) = \frac{8}{20}$

c $\mathrm{P}(\text{less than } 5 \mid \text{total even}) = \frac{4}{8}$

TOPIC 3 – SETS, LOGIC AND PROBABILITY (SHORT QUESTIONS)

1 Set $A = \{\text{multiples of 4 greater than 0 and less than 20}\}$
Set $B = \{\text{even numbers greater than 0 and less than 10}\}$

a Find $A \cup B$.

b Find $A \cap B$.

c Set C contains 3 elements and is a subset of A. Write down one possible set C.

2 $\mathbb{N}$ is the set of natural numbers, $\mathbb{Z}$ is the set of integers and $\mathbb{Q}$ is the set of rational numbers.

a Write down an element that is in:

i $\mathbb{Z}$ **ii** $\mathbb{Z}'$ **iii** $\mathbb{N} \cap \mathbb{Q}$ **iv** $\mathbb{Q}' \cap \mathbb{Z}$

b Draw a Venn diagram to represent the sets $\mathbb{N}$, $\mathbb{Z}$, and $\mathbb{Q}$.

3 Let $U = \{\text{positive integers greater than 7 and less than 19}\}$
$A = \{\text{multiples of 3}\}$
$B = \{\text{factors of 36}\}$

a List the elements of $A \cap B$.

b List the elements of A'.

c Represent the relationship between sets A and B on a Venn diagram.

d Are the following statements true or false?

i $B \subset A$ **ii** $n(A' \cap B') = 7$ **iii** $A \cup B = A$

4 If $U = \{\text{positive integers less than 20}\}$
$P = \{\text{prime numbers less than 20}\}$
$F = \{\text{factors of 24}\}$.

Find:

a $n(F)$ **b** $P \cap F$ **c** $P \cup F$ **d** $P' \cap F$

5 Let $U = \{x \in \mathbb{Z} \mid 1 < x < 50\}$.

A, B, and C are subsets of U such that,

$A = \{$factors of $48\}$ $B = \{$multiples of $6\}$
$C = \{$multiples of $8\}$.

a List the elements in $A \cap B \cap C$.
b Find $n(B)$.
c List the elements in $A' \cap B$.

6 Given the information in the following Venn diagram:

$U = \{x \in \mathbb{N} \mid 1 < x < 10\}$
$P = \{$Prime Numbers$\}$

a Find the value of element b.
b Describe in words, the set $\mathbb{Q}$.
c Find the value of element a.

7 The following Venn diagram shows the sets U, A, B, and C

a State whether the following propositions are true or false for the information shown in the Venn diagram.

  i $A \cap B = \varnothing$ **ii** $A \cap C = C$
  iii $B \subset A'$ **iv** $C \subset (A \cap B)$

b Shade the region $A' \cap B$ on the Venn diagram above.

8 The Venn diagram below shows the number of members at a sports club who take part in various sporting activities where:

$S = \{$members who play soccer$\}$
$B = \{$members who play basketball$\}$
$G = \{$members who play golf$\}$.

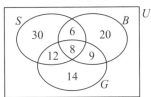

Find the number of members who:

a play all 3 sports
b play soccer or basketball but not both
c play only golf
d do not play basketball
e play more than one sport
f play soccer but do not play golf.

9 Let p and q be the propositions:

p: The sun is shining. q: I take the dog for a walk.

Write the following propositions using words only.

a $p \Rightarrow q$
b $\neg p \vee q$
c Write in words the converse of $p \Rightarrow q$
d Write the following proposition in symbolic form.
   "If I do not take the dog for a walk then the sun is not shining."
e Is the proposition in **d** the inverse, converse, or contrapositive of part **a**?

10 Consider each of the following propositions:

p: Peter has black hair. q: Peter plays baseball.
r: Peter is a student.

a Write each of the following arguments in symbols.
  i If Peter does not play baseball then he is not a student.
  ii If Peter does not have black hair then he is neither a student nor does he play baseball.

b Write the following argument in words: $\neg r \Rightarrow \neg(p \vee q)$.

11 Two propositions are given:

p: Wilson is an active dog. q: Wilson digs holes.

a Write the following propositions using words only.
  i $\neg p \wedge \neg q$ **ii** $p \veebar q$ **iii** $\neg p \Rightarrow q$

b By completing this truth table state whether the argument in **a iii** is a tautology, a contradiction or neither.

p	q	$\neg p$	$\neg p \Rightarrow q$
T	T	F	
T	F	F	
F	T	T	
F	F	T	

12 Given the two propositions:

p: I like the beach.
q: I live near the sea.

a Write the following in symbols and words:
  i the inverse   **ii** the contrapositive.

b Write in symbols the converse of the above propositions p and q.

13 Consider the two propositions p and q.

Complete the truth table below for the compound proposition $(p \Rightarrow \neg q) \vee (\neg p \Rightarrow q)$.

p	q	$\neg q$	$p \Rightarrow \neg q$	$\neg p$	$\neg p \Rightarrow q$	$(p \Rightarrow \neg q) \vee (\neg p \Rightarrow q)$
T	T	F		F		
T	F	T		F		
F	T	F		T		
F	F	T		T		

State whether the result above is a contradiction, a tautology or neither.

14 Three propositions are defined as follows:

p: The weather is hot. q: I have money.
r: I buy an ice cream.

a Write a sentence, in words only, for each of the following propositions:
  i $(\neg r \wedge \neg q) \vee p$ **ii** $(p \wedge q) \Rightarrow r$ **iii** $(\neg p \vee \neg q) \Rightarrow \neg r$
b Write in words the contrapositive for the proposition $p \Rightarrow r$

15
p: Molly has a DVD player.
q: Molly likes watching movies.

a Write the following proposition using words only: $\neg p \Rightarrow \neg q$

b Complete the following truth table for $p \Rightarrow q$

p	q	$p \Rightarrow q$
T	T	
T	F	
F	T	
F	F	

c Complete the following truth table for $\neg p \Rightarrow \neg q$.

p	q	$\neg p$	$\neg q$	$\neg p \Rightarrow \neg q$
T	T	F	F	
T	F	F	T	
F	T	T	F	
F	F	T	T	

d Are the two propositions $q \Rightarrow p$ and $p \Rightarrow q$ logically equivalent? Give a reason for your answer.

16 Consider the two propositions p and q.

a Complete the truth table for the compound proposition $(p \wedge q) \Rightarrow p$.

p	q	$p \wedge q$	$(p \wedge q) \Rightarrow p$
T	T	T	
T	F		
F	T		
F	F	F	

b Is the compound proposition $(p \wedge q) \Rightarrow p$ a contradiction, tautology, or neither?

17 Consider the two propositions p and q :

p: I eat an apple every day. q: I visit the doctor.

a State the negation of q.

b In words only, write the following propositions:
  i $\neg p \Rightarrow q$ **ii** $(\neg p \vee q) \Rightarrow q$.

c For the compound proposition $(\neg p \vee q) \Rightarrow q$, state whether it is a tautology, contradiction or neither.

p	q	$\neg p$	$\neg p \vee q$	$(\neg p \vee q) \Rightarrow q$
T	T	F	T	T
T	F	F		T
F	T	T	T	
F	F	T		

18 The probability of rain on any day in December is 0.2.

The partially completed tree diagram below shows the possible outcomes when the weather for two consecutive days is considered.

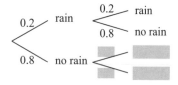

a Complete each of the boxes to finish the tree diagram.

b Use the tree diagram to determine the probability of:
  i raining two days in a row
  ii raining on one day only.

19 In the Venn diagram below sets A, B, and C are subsets of the Universal set $U = \{$Natural numbers less than 10$\}$.

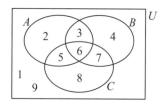

a **i** Find $n(A)$.   **ii** Find $n(A \cap B)$.

b List the elements in: **i** $A \cup B \cup C$ **ii** $(A' \cap B) \cup C$.

20 The Venn diagram below shows the number of students in a class who study various subjects.

$M = \{$students who study Music$\}$
$P = \{$students who study Physics$\}$
$D = \{$students who study Drama$\}$

Find the number of students who:

a study physics

b study Music or Drama but not both

c study Physics but not Music

d do not study Drama.

21 A die with 4 red faces and 2 green faces is rolled twice. Complete the following tree diagram to illustrate the possible outcomes.

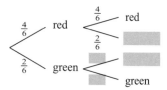

Use the tree diagram to determine the probability of rolling:

a two reds

b two greens

c one of each colour.

22 Events A and B have the following probabilities.

$P(A) = 0.35$ $P(B) = 0.7$ $P(A \cup B) = 0.8$

a Calculate $P(A \cap B)$.

b Represent this information on a Venn diagram.

c Find $P(A' \cap B')$.

d State, with a reason, whether events A and B are independent.

23 The following Venn Diagram shows the probabilities between two events A and B.

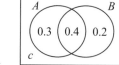

a Find the value of the probability c marked on the diagram.

b Use the Venn Diagram to determine:
  i $P(A \cup B)$ **ii** $P(A \cap B)$ **iii** $P(A' \cap B)$
  iv $P(A \mid B)$ **v** $P(B \mid A)$

24 The Venn Diagram below shows the number of students in a class that have dogs (D) and/or cats (C) for pets.

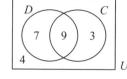

Determine the number of students:

a in the class

b who have both cats and dogs   **c** who only have dogs

d who have at least one of the pets   **e** who have no pets.

25 The table shows the number of different types of chocolates in a packet.

	soft	medium	hard
dark	10	24	15
light	18	14	9

a One chocolate is chosen at random. Find the probability that the chocolate is:
  i dark or hard   **ii** light, given that it is soft.

b If two chocolates had been chosen at random, find the probability that:
  i both are medium   **ii** at least one is soft and light.

TOPIC 3 – SETS, LOGIC AND PROBABILITY
(LONG QUESTIONS)

1 Let: $U = \{x \in \mathbb{N} \mid x \leqslant 10\}$ $P = \{$multiples of 2$\}$
$Q = \{$multiples of 3$\}$ $R = \{$factors of 12$\}$.

a List the elements of:
  i P **ii** Q **iii** R **iv** $P \cap Q \cap R$

b **i** Draw a Venn diagram to show the relationship between sets P, Q, and R.
  ii Write the elements of U in the appropriate place on the Venn diagram.

c Describe in words the sets:
  i $P \cup Q$ **ii** $P' \cap Q' \cap R'$

d Let p, q, and r be the statements: p: x is a multiple of 2
  q: x is a multiple of 3
  r: x is a factor of 12.

  i On your Venn diagram in **b i** shade the region corresponding to $p \veebar q$

  ii Use a truth table to find the values of $(p \wedge r) \Rightarrow (p \veebar q)$

  Begin by writing the first three columns of your truth table in the following format:

  iii Write down an element of U for which $(p \wedge r) \Rightarrow (p \veebar q)$ is true.

p	q	r
T	T	T
T	T	F
T	F	T
T	F	F
F	T	T
F	T	F
F	F	T
F	F	F

2 Consider the two propositions p and q and the compound proposition $\neg(p \wedge q) \Rightarrow \neg p \wedge \neg q$.

a **i** Copy the truth table below and complete the last four columns.

p	q	$\neg p$	$\neg q$	$p \vee q$	$\neg(p \vee q)$	$\neg p \wedge \neg q$	$\neg(p \wedge q) \Rightarrow \neg p \wedge \neg q$
T	T	F	F				
T	F	F	T				
F	T	T	F				
F	F	T	T				

ii Is the above result a tautology, a contradiction, or neither?

b Consider the two propositions: p: I work hard.
  q: I get a promotion.

i Write in words the conjunction of propositions p and q.

ii Write in words the inverse of $p \Rightarrow q$.

c At the TULCO telecommunications company the probability of a worker working hard is 0.8.

Consider two randomly selected workers. A partially completed tree diagram is shown below.

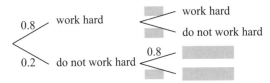

0.8 work hard
0.2 do not work hard
work hard
do not work hard
0.8
0.8

i Copy and complete the above tree diagram.

ii Use the tree diagram to find the probability that for two randomly selected workers:

  a they both work hard.
  b only one works hard.

3 Consider two sets P and Q. The Venn diagram shows the relationship between them.

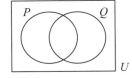

a On separate Venn Diagrams shade the regions corresponding to:

  i $p \veebar q$ **ii** $\neg(p \wedge q)$ **iii** $\neg p \vee \neg q$.

b By referring to **a ii** and **a iii** explain whether $\neg(p \wedge q)$ and $\neg p \vee \neg q$ are logically equivalent.

c Let: p: The bush has thorns.
  q: The bush is a rose bush.

Write a sentence using only words for the following proposition: $\neg(p \wedge q) \Rightarrow \neg q$

d Construct a truth table for the compound proposition in **c**. Begin by writing the first two columns of your truth table in the following format. Comment on your result.

p	q
T	T
T	F
F	T
F	F

4 The Venn diagram below shows the number of students out of a class of 30 senior students who like Rock music (R), Jazz music (J) and Classical music (C).

17 like Rock music,
9 like Jazz, and
7 like Classical music.

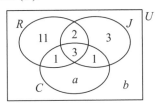

a **i** Find the number of students in the region labelled a.
 ii Describe in words the region containing 11 students.
 iii Find the number of students in the region labelled b.
 iv Describe region b in words.

b Draw a sketch of the Venn diagram and shade in the region $R' \cap J$.

c A student is chosen at random from this class. Determine the probability that this student:

 i likes all three types of music
 ii likes only Classical music
 iii likes Rock music given that the student likes Jazz music.

d Two students are randomly selected from this class. Determine the probability that:

 i both students like Rock music only
 ii one student likes Rock only and the other likes all three types.

5 80 students were asked what type of television programme they had watched the previous evening.

35 watched Sport (S)   42 watched News (N)
50 watched Drama (D)   10 watched all three types
7 watched Sport and News only
12 watched News and Drama only
14 watched Sport and Drama only.

a **i** Draw a Venn diagram to illustrate the relationship between the three types of television programme watched.
 ii On your Venn diagram indicate the number of students that belong to each region.
 iii Determine the number of students who watch neither Sport nor Drama nor News.

b A student is selected at random. Determine the probability that the student:

 i watched only Drama
 ii watched Sport given that the student watched News.

c Let p and q be the propositions:

  p: You watch sport on television.
  q: You like sport.

 i Write in words the following proposition: $p \Rightarrow q$.
 ii The converse of the proposition $p \Rightarrow q$ is $q \Rightarrow p$. Write this proposition in words.
 iii Consider the following proposition:

  "If you do not like sport then you do not watch sport on television."

  Express this statement using symbols only.
 iv Is the proposition in **c iii** the inverse, the converse or the contrapositive of the proposition **c i**?

6 The probability of rain falling on any day in Dunedin is 0.4. The tree diagram below shows the possible outcomes when two consecutive days are considered.

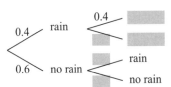

0.4 rain
0.6 no rain
0.4
rain
no rain

a Copy and complete the tree diagram by filling in the boxes.

b Use the tree diagram to determine the probability of:

 i rain on both days   **ii** no rain on one day.

c Find the probability of the weather being fine for five consecutive days.

d Consider the propositions:

  p: It is raining. q: I wear my raincoat.

Write the following propositions using words only.

 i $p \Rightarrow q$ **ii** $\neg q \Rightarrow \neg p$

e Consider the compound proposition $\neg(p \wedge q) \Rightarrow \neg p$.

 i Construct a truth table for this argument.
  Include headings of:
   p q $p \wedge q$ $\neg(p \wedge q)$ $\neg p$ $\neg(p \wedge q) \Rightarrow \neg p$.
 ii Give an example for when this argument is false.

7 a Two marbles are drawn from bag A containing 8 red and 5 blue marbles without replacement.

    i Draw a tree diagram to represent the sample space.

    ii Use the tree diagram to determine the probability of obtaining:

        a two marbles that are the same colour

        b at least one blue marble.

b A second bag B contains 7 red and 4 blue marbles. A five sided spinner with the numbers 1, 2, 3, 4, 5 on it is used to select from which bag the two marbles are taken. If an even number is spun then bag A is chosen and if an odd number is spun, bag B is selected. Draw a new tree diagram to represent all the possibilities and use the tree diagram to determine the probability of obtaining:

    i an even number on the spinner

    ii two blue marbles.

8 A box of chocolates contains 4 hard and 7 soft centres. One chocolate is selected randomly and eaten. A second chocolate is selected and eaten only if the first chocolate has a hard centre.

The tree diagram below represents the possible outcomes for this event.

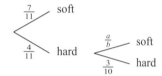

a   **i** Find the probability of choosing 2 chocolates.

    ii Find the values of a and b.

    iii Find the probability that both chocolates are hard centred.

    iv Find the probability of selecting one of each type.

b A second box of chocolates contains all soft centres flavoured either with strawberry or cherry. There are 5 strawberry and 7 cherry flavoured chocolates. One chocolate is selected at random, eaten, then another is selected.

    i Draw a tree diagram to represent all possible outcomes.

    ii Use the tree diagram from **b i** to determine the probability that:

        a both chocolates are strawberry

        b the second chocolate is strawberry.

    iii A child who does not like cherry flavoured chocolates randomly selects a chocolate from a new identical box, tries it and discards it if it is cherry flavoured. The child then selects another, repeating the process until a strawberry flavoured chocolate is found.

        Determine the probability that the child selects a total of 4 chocolates.

TOPIC 4   FUNCTIONS

SUMMARY

DOMAIN AND RANGE

- The **domain** of a function is the set of all possible values that x may take.

- The **range** of a function is the set of all possible values that y takes.

FUNCTIONS AS MAPPINGS

A function f maps elements x of its domain to elements $y = f(x)$ of its range. This is written as $f : x \mapsto f(x)$.

Example:

$f : x \mapsto 3 - 4x$ maps the number x to the number $y = 3 - 4x$.

As a particular case, $-2 \mapsto 3 - 4(-2) = 11$

Here f maps the value -2 in its domain to 11 in its range.

Note: The function f is often written as $y = f(x)$, so the function in the example could be written as $y = 3 - 4x$ or $f(x) = 3 - 4x$.

MAPPING DIAGRAMS

A mapping diagram is a useful way of showing how elements are mapped from the domain to the range.

Example

Draw a mapping diagram for the function $f : x \mapsto 5x - 1$ with domain $\{x \in \mathbb{Z} \mid -1 \leqslant x \leqslant 2\}$.

Solution:

$$f(-1) = 5(-1) - 1 = -6 \qquad f(0) = 5(0) - 1 = -1$$
$$f(1) = 5(1) - 1 = 4 \qquad f(2) = 5(2) - 1 = 9$$

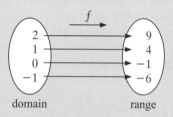

In this case, elements of the domain $\{-1, 0, 1, 2\}$ are mapped to elements of the range $\{-6, -1, 4, 9\}$.

FUNCTION TYPES

▶ **Linear**

A **linear function** is a function of the form $f : x \mapsto mx + c$ or $f(x) = mx + c$, where both m and c are constants.

The graph of a linear function $f(x) = mx + c$ is a straight line with gradient m and y-intercept c.

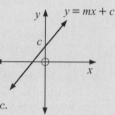

Example

Find the equation of the line passing through the points A$(1, 5)$ and B$(3, -3)$.

Solution:

$$\text{Gradient,} \quad m = \frac{5 - -3}{1 - 3} = -4$$

Substituting $(1, 5)$ in $y = mx + c$
$$\text{gives} \quad 5 = -4 \times 1 + c$$
$$\therefore \quad 5 = -4 + c \quad \text{and so} \quad c = 9$$
$$\text{Equation is} \quad y = -4x + 9 \quad \{\text{gradient-intercept form}\}$$
$$or, \quad \text{using} \quad Ax + By = Ax_1 + By_1$$
$$4x + y = 4(1) + (5)$$
$$\therefore \quad 4x + y = 9$$
$$\therefore \quad 4x + y - 9 = 0 \quad \{\text{general form}\}$$

▶ **Quadratic**

- A **quadratic function** has form $f : x \mapsto ax^2 + bx + c$ or $f(x) = ax^2 + bx + c$ where $a \neq 0$, and a, b and c are constants.

- The graph of a quadratic function is **parabolic** in shape.

- For $a > 0$, the graph opens upwards.

  For $a < 0$, the graph opens downwards.

- Quadratic graphs have a vertical **axis of symmetry**, $x = \dfrac{-b}{2a}$.

  Note: The axis of symmetry is midway between the x-intercepts.

- The **vertex (turning point)** has coordinates $\left(\dfrac{-b}{2a}, f\left(\dfrac{-b}{2a}\right)\right)$.

  Note: The y-coordinate of the vertex of a parabola is either the maximum or minimum value of the function.

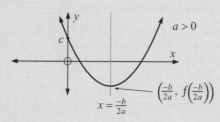

Example:

A quadratic function is given by $f : x \to 2x^2 - x - 1$.

a Find: **i** the y-intercept
       ii the x-intercepts
       iii the equation of the axis of symmetry
       iv the maximum or minimum value of $f(x)$.

b Sketch the graph of the function.

Solution:

a **i** The y-intercept occurs when $x = 0$.
Since $f(0) = 2(0)^2 - 0 - 1 = -1$ the y-intercept is -1.

ii The x-intercepts occur when $y = 0$.
$$\therefore \quad 2x^2 - x - 1 = 0$$
$$\therefore \quad (2x+1)(x-1) = 0 \quad \{\text{factorising}\}$$
$$\therefore \quad x = -\tfrac{1}{2} \text{ or } 1$$

So, the x-intercepts are $-\tfrac{1}{2}$ and 1.

iii The equation of the axis of symmetry is $x = \dfrac{-b}{2a}$.

Since $\dfrac{-b}{2a} = \dfrac{-(-1)}{2 \times 2} = \tfrac{1}{4}$, the axis is $x = \tfrac{1}{4}$.

or The average of the zeros is $\dfrac{-\frac{1}{2} + 1}{2} = \dfrac{\frac{1}{2}}{2} = \tfrac{1}{4}$, etc

iv Since a is positive, the parabola opens upwards:

$\therefore$ we have a minimum turning point at $x = \tfrac{1}{4}$,

and as $f(\tfrac{1}{4}) = 2(\tfrac{1}{4})^2 - (\tfrac{1}{4}) - 1 = \tfrac{1}{8} - \tfrac{1}{4} - 1 = -1\tfrac{1}{8}$

the minimum value of $f(x)$ is $-1\tfrac{1}{8}$, occuring at $x = \tfrac{1}{4}$.

b

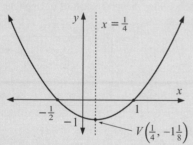

▶ Exponential

- An **exponential function** has form $f(x) = ka^{\lambda x} + c$ where k, λ and c are constants.

- The graph of an exponential function is either **always increasing** or **always decreasing** and doing so at either an increasing or decreasing rate as shown.

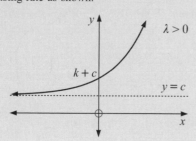

- $y = c$ is the equation of the **horizontal asymptote** such that c determines the vertical position of the graph.

$f(x) = 2^x + 5$ is 5 units vertically above $f(x) = 2^x$.

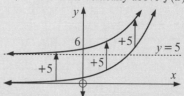

- a and λ influence the steepness of the graph.

Example:

For the function $f(x) = 3 \times 2^x + 4$

a find the y-intercept
b write down the equation of the horizontal asymptote
c sketch the graph.

Solution:

a The y-intercept occurs when $x = 0$.
$$\therefore \quad y = 3 \times 2^0 + 4 = 3 \times 1 + 4 = 7$$

b The horizontal asymptote is $y = 4$.

c

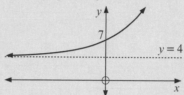

▶ Sine and cosine

- A **sine function** has the form $\quad f(x) = a\sin bx + c \quad$ or $\quad f : x \mapsto a\sin bx + c$

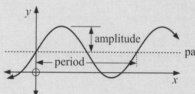

A **cosine function** has the form $\quad f(x) = a\cos bx + c \quad$ or $\quad f : x \mapsto a\cos bx + c$

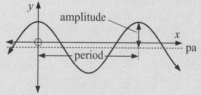

Both functions are periodic and fluctuate regularly between maximum and minimum values.

- For both functions,
  a is the **amplitude**
  b affects the **period** of the function and period $= \dfrac{360^\circ}{b}$
  c is the **principal axis** (also called the **median line**).

Example:

For the function $y = 2\sin 3x + 1$:

a find the amplitude
b determine the period
c find the equation of the principle axis
d sketch its graph.

Solution:

a Amplitude $= a = 2$.

b Period $= \dfrac{360^\circ}{3} = 120^\circ$.

c The principle axis has equation $y = c$, i.e., $y = 1$.

d The graph of $y = 2\sin 3x + 1$:

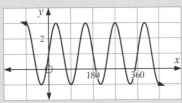

Example:

For the function $y = 3\cos 2x - 1$:

a find the amplitude

b determine the period

c find the equation of the principle axis

d sketch its graph.

Solution:

a Amplitude $= a = 3$.

b Period $= \dfrac{360°}{2} = 180°$.

c The principle axis has equation $y = c$, i.e., $y = -1$.

d The graph of $y = 3\cos 2x - 1$:

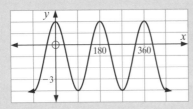

NOTE ON AXIS INTERCEPTS

For all functions $y = f(x)$, the x-intercept values can be found by making $y = 0$ (i.e., by solving $f(x) = 0$).

y-intercept values can be found by making $x = 0$.

Example:

For the function $y = \dfrac{2}{x+4} + 2$, find the y and x-intercepts.

Solution:

The y-intercept occurs when $x = 0$

$\therefore \quad y = \dfrac{2}{0+4} + 2 = \frac{1}{2} + 2 = 2\frac{1}{2}$. So, the y-intercept is $2\frac{1}{2}$.

The x-intercept occurs when $y = 0$, $\therefore \quad \dfrac{2}{x+4} + 2 = 0$

$\therefore \quad x = -5 \quad \{\text{gdc}\}$ So, the x-intercept is -5.

NOTE ON ASYMPTOTES

- Certain graphs of functions approach certain lines on the Cartesian Plane. The asymptote for an exponential function has been described above.

- Students should be able to recognise vertical and horizontal asymptotes from a careful study of graphs, using their gdc.

Example:

Find the vertical and horizontal asymptotes for the graph of

$y = \dfrac{2}{x+4} + 2.$

Solution:

Using a graphics calculator, a graph is drawn.

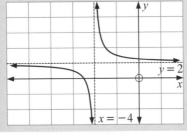

Based on this graph, it can be seen that:

the horizontal asymptote occurs at $y = 2$, and

the vertical asymptote occurs at $x = -4$.

GRAPHS OF OTHER FUNCTIONS

Any function which does not fit into the category of linear, quadratic, exponential or trigonometric is regarded as an 'unfamiliar' function and should be analysed with the assistance of a graphics calculator.

Example:

a Sketch the graph of $y = \dfrac{x}{x-3}$ for $-5 \leqslant x \leqslant 10$.

Indicate clearly the x and y-intercepts.

b Write down the equation of the vertical asymptote.

c Write down the equation of the horizontal asymptote.

d On the same axes sketch the graph of $y = 2^x$.

e Hence, solve $\dfrac{x}{x-3} = 2^x$.

Solution:

a

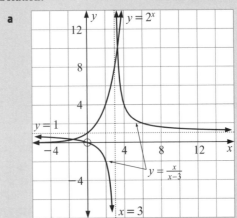

b $x = 3$

c $y = 1$

d Drawn on the graph above.

e Using a graphics calculator, the points of intersection of the two graphs are $(-1.55, 0.341)$ and $(3.33, 10.1)$.

TOPIC 4 – FUNCTIONS (SHORT QUESTIONS)

1 The graph below shows the cost of a telephone call $\$C$ which lasts t minutes.

a Find the equation of the line $C(t)$.

b Using your equation, calculate the cost for a call lasting 23 minutes.

c Determine the length of a phone call which costs $\$18.31$. Round your answer to the nearest minute.

2 A function $h(t) = 1 - 2t^2$ is defined for $t \in \{-2, -1, 0, 1, 2, 3\}$.

a Represent $h(t) = 1 - 2t^2$ using a mapping diagram.

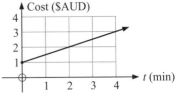

b List the elements of the domain of $h(t)$.

c List the elements of the range of $h(t)$.

3 The graph below shows the percentage P of radioactive Carbon-14 remaining in an organism t thousands of years after it dies.

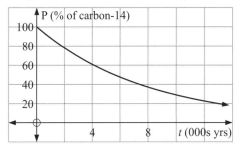

Using the graph only:

a Write down the percentage of Carbon-14 remaining after 4 thousand years.

b Determine the number of years for the percentage of Carbon-14 to reach 50%.

c The equation of the graph for all positive t is given by $P = 100 \times 2^{-\left(\frac{5t}{28}\right)}$.

   Calculate the percentage remaining after 19 thousand years.

d Write down the equation of the asymptote to the curve.

4 Two functions, f and g are defined as follows:
$f : x \mapsto 15 - 2x, \qquad g(x) = 2^x + 1$

a Calculate $f(2)$.

b Calculate $g(-2)$.

c Find the value of x for which $g(x) = f(x)$.

5 The number of people N on a small island, t years after settlement, seems to increase according to the formula
$$N = 120 \times (1.04)^t.$$

Use this formula to calculate:

a the number of people present at the start of the settlement

b the number of people present after 4 years (round your answer to the nearest integer)

c the number of years it would take for the population to double.

6 A graph of the quadratic $y = ax^2 + bx + c$ is shown below. The vertex V is shown, as is the y-intercept.

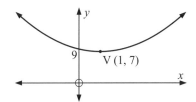

a Determine the value of c.

b Given that the axis of symmetry for a quadratic in the form $y = ax^2 + bx + c$ is $x = \dfrac{-b}{2a}$, write an equation involving a and b.

c Using the point $(1, 7)$, write another equation involving a and b.

d Find a and b.

7 A function f maps x onto $x^3 - 3x^2 - x + 3$. The domain of f is the set of real numbers from -2 to 3 (both inclusive).

a Sketch the graph of f.

b Determine the range of f.

8 An object thrown vertically upwards in the air has height (relative to the ground) given by $H(t) = 19.6t - 4.9t^2$ for the time, t, when the object is in the air. H is measured in metres and t in seconds.

a Determine $H(0)$ and interpret its meaning.

b Find the time when the object is at ground level other than at $t = 0$.

c The function $H(t) = 19.6t - 4.9t^2$ is an accurate model for the motion of the object only when it is in the air. Write down the domain of $H(t)$ using interval notation.

d Determine the maximum height reached by the object.

9 A part of the graph of the function $f(x) = x^2 + 3x - 28$ is shown below.

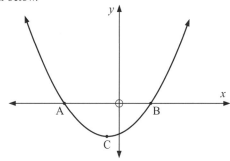

a Factorise the expression $x^2 + 3x - 28$.

b Find the coordinates of A and B.

c Determine the equation of the axis of symmetry.

d Write down the coordinates of C, the vertex of the parabola.

10 Consider the function $f(x) = 2\sin(\frac{1}{2}x) - 3$.

a Determine the   **i** amplitude   **ii** period.

b Sketch the graph of $y = f(x)$ on the grid below.

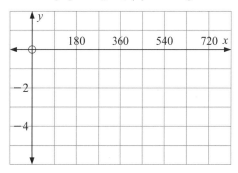

11 Consider the function $f(x) = 8x - 2x^2$.

a Factorise fully $f(x)$.

b Determine the x-intercepts for the graph of $y = f(x)$.

c Write down the equation of the axis of symmetry.

d Determine the coordinates of the vertex.

12 The diagram below shows a function f, mapping members of the set A onto members of set B.

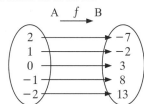

a   **i** Using set notation, write down all members of the:
      a domain of f **b** range of f.

   ii Determine the equation of the function f.

b The function $g(x) = 4 \times 2^{3x} - 3$ is defined for all $x \in \mathbb{R}$. Write down the range of g.

13 The number of ants, N (in thousands), in a colony is given by $N(t) = 30 - 3^{3-t}$ where t is the time (in months) after the beginning of the colony. ($t \geqslant 0$)

a Calculate the initial number of ants at the start of the colony.

b Calculate the number of ants present after 2 months.

c Find the time taken for the colony to reach 20 000 ants.

d Determine the equation of the horizontal asymptote of $N(t)$.

e According to the function $N(t)$, what is the smallest number of ants the colony will *never* reach?

14 Find the equations of the trigonometric functions shown in the diagrams below.

a

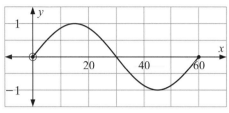

b

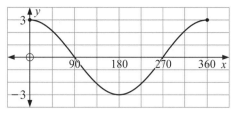

15 Consider the function $f(x) = \dfrac{2^x}{x-1}$.

   a Find the y-intercept.

   b Determine the minimum value of $f(x)$ for $x > 1$.

   c Write down the equation of the vertical asymptote.

   d Calculate the value of $f(5)$.

   e Sketch the graph of $y = f(x)$ for $-4 \leqslant x \leqslant 7$ showing all the features found above.

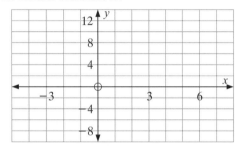

16 Consider the graph of $y = 3 + \dfrac{1}{x-2}$.

   a Sketch the graph on the grid below.

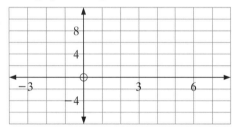

   b Write down the equations of the vertical and horizontal asymptotes.

17 A refrigerator has an internal temperature of $27\,^{\circ}\text{C}$ before being turned on. The temperature reaches 6°C, 3 hours after being turned on.

It is known that the internal temperature T (in $^{\circ}\text{C}$) is given by the function $T(t) = A \times B^{-t} + 3$, where A and B are constants and t is measured in hours.

   a Given that $T(0) = 27$, determine the value of A.

   b Hence determine the value of B.

   c Find the internal temperature of the refrigerator, 5 hours after being turned on.

   d Write down the minimum temperature that the refrigerator could be expected to reach.

18 A quadratic function has the form $f(x) = ax^2 + bx + 7$. It is known that $f(2) = 7$ and $f(4) = 23$.

   a Using appropriate substitutions, form a set of simultaneous equations which allow a and b to be found.

   b Find a and b.

   c Hence calculate $f(-1)$.

19 The daily profit P (in Euros) made by a business depends on the number of workers employed. The daily profit is modelled by the function $P(x) = -50x^2 + 1000x - 2000$, where x is the number of workers employed on any given day.

   a Using the axes provided below, sketch the graph of
$$P(x) = -50x^2 + 1000x - 2000.$$

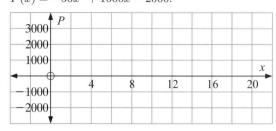

   b Determine the number of workers required to maximise the profit.

   c Find the maximum possible profit.

   d A flu virus prevents all but 1 worker attending work. Calculate the maximum amount of money the business loses on that day.

20 The diagrams below are sketches of four out of the following five functions:

   a $y = a^x$ **b** $y = \sin x - a$ **c** $y = \cos x - a$
   d $y = x^2 - a$ **e** $y = x - a$

A

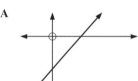

B

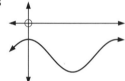

C

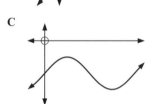

D

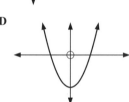

Complete the table given to match each sketch with the correct function.

Graph	Function
A	
B	
C	
D	

21 Identify the diagrams which best represent the graph of each of the functions $f(x)$, $g(x)$ and $h(x)$.

   a $f(x) = x^2 - 3x$ **b** $g(x) = x^2 + 3x$ **c** $h(x) = x^2 - 9$

A   **B**

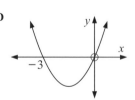

C   **D**

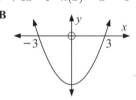

E

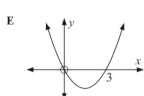

Complete the table given to match each sketch with the correct function.

Graph	Function
$f(x)$	
$g(x)$	
$h(x)$	

22 Consider the graph of $y = f(x)$, where
$f(x) = x^3(x-2)(x-3)$.

a Use your graphics calculator to find:
  i all x-intercepts
  ii the coordinates of any local maximum or minimum points.

b Sketch the graph of $y = f(x)$ using the grid provided. Show all the features found above.

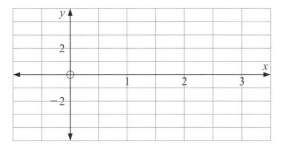

23 A function $p : x \mapsto x^2 + x - 2$ is defined for
$x \in \{-2, -1, 0, 1, 2\}$.

a Represent $p : x \mapsto x^2 + x - 2$ using the mapping diagram below.

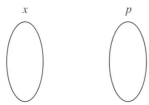

b List the elements of the domain of p.

c List the elements of the range of p.

24 The graph of the form $y = a(x-b)(x-c)^2$ is shown in the diagram below.

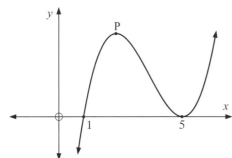

a Determine the values of b and c using the graph above.

b Given that the y-intercept is -50, calculate the value of a.

c The point P is located at a local maximum of this graph on $0 \leqslant x \leqslant 5$. Find the coordinates of P.

25 a Sketch the function $y = x^4 - 2x^3 - 3x^2 + 8x - 4$ for $-3 \leqslant x \leqslant 3$ and $-15 \leqslant y \leqslant 5$.

b Write down the coordinates of any local maximum or local minimum values.

c Write down the value(s) of x for which
$x^4 - 2x^3 - 3x^2 + 8x - 4 = 0$

TOPIC 4 – FUNCTIONS (LONG QUESTIONS)

1 A company manufactures and sells CD-players.

If x CD-players are made and sold each week, the weekly cost $\$C$ to the company is $C(x) = x^2 + 400$.

The weekly income $\$I$ obtained by selling x CD-players is $I(x) = 50x$.

a Find:
  i the weekly cost for producing 20 CD-players
  ii the weekly income when 20 CD-players are sold
  iii the profit/loss incurred when 20 CD-players are made and sold.

b Determine an expression for the weekly profit $P(x)$ given $P(x) = I(x) - C(x)$ if x CD-players are produced and sold. Do not attempt to simplify or factorise your answer.

c The maximum weekly profit occurs at the vertex of the function $P(x)$.

Determine the number of CD-players which must be made and sold each week to gain the maximum profit.

d Calculate the profit made on *each* CD-player if the company does maximise the profit.

e Given that $P(x)$ can be written as
$P(x) = (x-10)(40-x)$, find the largest number of CD-players the company could produce each week in order to make a positive profit.

2 Consider the graph of $y = f(x)$ where $y = 2 + \dfrac{4}{x+1}$.

Using your graphics calculator:

a Find the x-intercept.

b Find the y-intercept.

c Calculate $f(-2)$.

d Determine the equation of the:
  i horizontal asymptote
  ii vertical asymptote.

e Sketch the graph of $y = 2 + \dfrac{4}{x+1}$ for $-5 \leqslant x \leqslant 3$.

Label the axes intercepts and asymptotes clearly.

3 The graph of $y = \dfrac{4}{2x-3}$ is shown below.

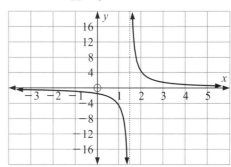

a Write down the equation of the:
  i vertical asymptote
  ii horizontal asymptote.

b A graph of $y = a^x$ is to be drawn on the axes above for $a > 0$.

Determine the y-intercept for $y = a^x$.

c Determine the equation of the horizontal asymptote for $y = a^x$.

d If $y = a^x$ intersects $y = \dfrac{4}{2x-3}$ at $x = 2$, determine the value of a.

e For your value of a, calculated in part **d**, sketch the graph of $y = a^x$ on the axes above.

4 A cardboard box is to have a fixed volume of 36 cm³.

The width W (in cm), of the box is defined by the function

$$W(x) = \frac{x + 6}{x}.$$

A graph of $y = W(x)$ is shown below for $0 < x \leqslant 7$.

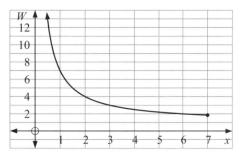

a Use the graph to complete the table below for the width function $W(x) = \dfrac{x + 6}{x}$.

x	1	2	3	4	5	6
$W(x)$	7	4			2.2	2

b The length L (in cm), of the box is defined by the function $L(x) = x$.

Draw the graph of $y = L(x)$ accurately on the axes provided above.

c Using your graph to assist, determine the value of x which produces a square base for the cardboard box.

d Show that the height H (in cm) of the cardboard box (no longer a square base) is given by the function

$$H(x) = \frac{36}{x + 6}.$$

e Hence, show that the total amount of cardboard (in cm²) required to produce a *closed* box is

$$A = 2x + 12 + \frac{72x}{x + 6} + \frac{72}{x}$$

f Use your graphics calculator to graph A and hence determine the smallest amount of cardboard required to create this cardboard box.

5 The cost $\$C$ of producing x bicycles in a factory is given by $C(x) = 6000 + 40x$. The revenue $\$R$ earned from the sale of these bicycles is given by $R(x) = 100x$.

a Graph each function on the axes provided.

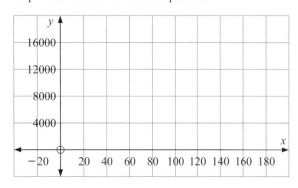

b Determine the initial setup cost before any bicycles are made or produced.

c Calculate the number of bicycles which must be made and sold in order for the factory to break even (revenue = cost).

d Calculate the revenue earned *per* bicycle.

e Write down the profit function $P(x)$ for all $x \geqslant 0$.

f Find the amount of profit from the sale of 400 bicycles.

6 The temperature (in °C) over a 24 hour period in a city can be modelled by the function $C(t) = 21 - 9\sin(15t)$ where t represents the number of hours from midnight.

a Sketch a graph of C for $0 \leqslant t \leqslant 24$.

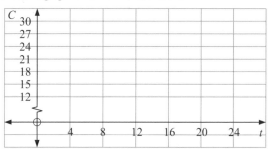

b Determine the temperature at 1:30 pm.

c Determine the maximum temperature and the time that this occurs.

d Find the range of temperatures between 10:00 am and 7:30 pm.

e Find the time when the temperature was rising most rapidly. Explain your reasoning clearly.

7 Consider the function $f : x \mapsto \dfrac{x^3}{2^x}$.

Use your graphics calculator to find:

a the y-intercept

b the maximum value of $f(x)$ for $-2 \leqslant x \leqslant 12$

c $f(2)$ and $f(-1)$.

d Sketch the graph of $y = f(x)$ for $-2 \leqslant x \leqslant 12$ on the axes below showing all features found above.

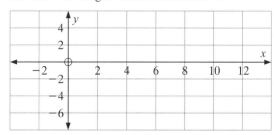

e On the same axes above, sketch the function $g(x) = (x - 5)^2 - 7$.

Clearly show the coordinates of the minimum for $g(x)$ and any intersection points with $f(x)$.

f Hence, or otherwise, find all solutions to: $\dfrac{x^3}{2^x} + 7 = (x - 5)^2$.

8 The centre of a large wind turbine lies 12 metres above the ground. The blades have a length of 3 metres and rotate 5 times per second. To start with, the tip of the blade (Point P) is located at the highest possible point.

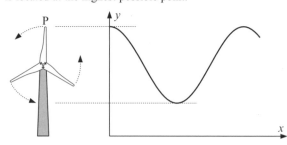

a Find the time taken for one full revolution.

b Determine the equation of the height of point P (in metres) from the ground in the form $P(t) = a\cos(bt) + c$.

Point R is located on a smaller wind turbine. The height of point R (also located at the tip of the turbine) is modelled by $R(t) = 11 - \cos(720t)$.

c Find the time taken for R to complete one full revolution.

d Find the first time it takes for P and R to be situated the same distance above the ground.

e Assuming both P and R begin at the same time ($t = 0$), determine the time it takes before both P and R are located at their *minimum* positions at the same time.

SUMMARY

THE NUMBER PLANE

- Also referred to as xy-coordinate axes or the Cartesian Plane.
  Point P has an ordered pair of coordinates (x, y).

- Axes are always labelled. An arrow in the positive direction on each axis is standard.

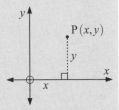

DISTANCE BETWEEN TWO POINTS

Uses Pythagoras' Theorem
$$d^2 = (x_2 - x_1)^2 + (y_2 - y_1)^2$$

So, $d = \sqrt{(x_2 - x_1)^2 + (y_2 - y_1)^2}$

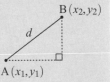

MIDPOINT

- The midpoint, M, is half way between two points.

- For $A(x_1, y_1)$ and $B(x_2, y_2)$ the midpoint is $M\left(\dfrac{x_1 + x_2}{2}, \dfrac{y_1 + y_2}{2}\right)$.

GRADIENT

- The **gradient** of a line is a measure of its steepness.

- The gradient (or slope) is the vertical difference between two points relative to the horizontal difference.
  So, $\text{gradient} = \dfrac{\text{rise}}{\text{run}}$.

- For $A(x_1, y_1)$ and $B(x_2, y_2)$, the gradient of a line AB can be found using $m = \dfrac{y_2 - y_1}{x_2 - x_1}$.

- **Note:**   A horizontal line has zero gradient.
  A vertical line has undefined gradient.

- The gradient is a number. It does not have units.

- Parallel lines have the same gradient, i.e., $m_1 = m_2$.

- Two lines are perpendicular if the product of their gradients is -1,
  i.e., $m_1 \times m_2 = -1$ and hence $m_1 = \dfrac{-1}{m_2}$
  i.e., the gradients are negative reciprocals.

EQUATION OF A LINE

- **Gradient-intercept form:** $y = mx + c$, where m is the gradient of a line and c is the y-intercept.

- General form: $ax + by + d = 0$

INTERSECTING LINES

- Two lines meet at their simultaneous solution.

- The solution is an ordered pair (x, y) and is found by:
  - **graphing** on coordinate axes and finding the coordinates of the **point of intersection**
  - the method of **substitution**
  - the method of **elimination**
  - equating of ys
  - using a gdc.

Example:

Find the point of intersection of the lines with equations
$$2x + y = 7$$
$$3x + 2y = 11$$

Solution:

Using a graphics calculator, $x = 3, \; y = 1$.

So, they meet at $(3, 1)$.

THE PERPENDICULAR BISECTOR OF A LINE SEGMENT

The line passing through the midpoint of the line joining $A(x_1, y_1)$ and $B(x_2, y_2)$ and perpendicular to the line AB is known as the **perpendicular bisector** of AB.

To find the perpendicular bisector of A and B we proceed as follows:
- Find the midpoint of AB.
- Find the gradient of AB.
- Find the negative reciprocal of the gradient of AB.
- Determine the equation of the perpendicular bisector.

Example:

For points $A(-1, 4)$ and $B(4, 3)$:

a Find the distance AB.

b Find the midpoint of AB.

c Find the equation of the perpendicular bisector of the line AB.

Solution:

a $AB = \sqrt{(x_2 - x_1)^2 + (y_2 - y_1)^2}$
  $= \sqrt{(4 - -1)^2 + (3 - 4)^2}$
  $= \sqrt{26}$ units
  which is approximately 5.10 units.

b   Midpoint, M is $\left(\dfrac{x_1 + x_2}{2}, \dfrac{y_1 + y_2}{2}\right)$ i.e., $(1.5, 3.5)$.

c   Gradient of AB $= \dfrac{\text{rise}}{\text{run}} = \dfrac{3 - 4}{4 - -1} = -\dfrac{1}{5}$

$\therefore$ gradient of perpendicular $= 5$
{remember that for perpendicular lines $m_1 \times m_2 = -1$}
Now, as the line passes through the point $(1.5, 3.5)$, and the equation is $y = mx + c$
then $3.5 = 5 \times 1.5 + c$
$\therefore \; c = -4$

$\therefore$ the equation of the perpendicular bisector is $y = 5x - 4$.

RIGHT ANGLED TRIANGLE TRIGONOMETRY

- Pythagoras' Theorem: $a^2 + b^2 = c^2$

- To solve right angled triangles for missing sides and angles we use the three trigonometric ratios:

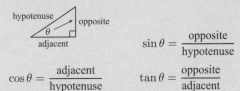

$$\sin\theta = \frac{\text{opposite}}{\text{hypotenuse}}$$

$$\cos\theta = \frac{\text{adjacent}}{\text{hypotenuse}} \qquad \tan\theta = \frac{\text{opposite}}{\text{adjacent}}$$

Example:

A boy sees a plane 3000 m directly above his head. He knows he is 10 km away from the airport on the same level.

a Calculate the distance of the plane from the airport. (A diagram is always useful in these questions.)

b Determine the angle the plane makes with the top of the airport tower which is 100 m tall.

Solution:

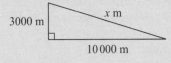

a $x = \sqrt{3000^2 + 10\,000^2} \approx 10\,400$ m

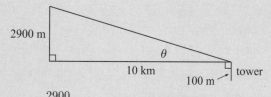

b $\tan\theta = \dfrac{2900}{10\,000}$ $\quad\therefore\quad \theta = \tan^{-1}\left(\dfrac{2900}{10\,000}\right)$
$\qquad\qquad\qquad\qquad\therefore\quad \theta \approx 16.2^\circ$

NON-RIGHT ANGLED TRIANGLES

- For non-right angled triangles, we can solve for missing sides and angles using the Sine Rule and Cosine Rule.

Sine Rule: $\quad \dfrac{\sin A}{a} = \dfrac{\sin B}{b} = \dfrac{\sin C}{c}$

Use when given *two angles and one side* or *two sides and an angle not included* between the two sides.

Cosine Rule: $\quad a^2 = b^2 + c^2 - 2bc\cos A \quad$ or

$$\cos A = \dfrac{b^2 + c^2 - a^2}{2bc}$$

Use when given *three sides* or *two sides and the included angle*.

- We can find the area of a non-right angled triangle by using Area $= \frac{1}{2}ab\sin C$.

- You must be able to construct fully labelled diagrams from verbal statements.

Example:

A children's playground ABCD is in the form of a quadrilateral with the dimensions shown. A path cuts diagonally across the playground from A to C. Find the area of the playground.

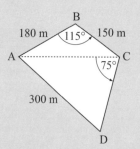

Solution:

We need to find the distance AC. We use the Cosine Rule because we know two sides and the included angle.

Now, $\qquad AC^2 = 180^2 + 150^2 - 2 \times 180 \times 150\cos 115^\circ$
$\quad\therefore\quad AC = 278.79$
$\quad\therefore\quad AC \approx 279$ m

We can now use the Sine rule as we have two sides and a non-included angle.

Now, $\quad \dfrac{\sin\theta}{278.79} = \dfrac{\sin 75}{300}$

$\quad\therefore\quad \sin\theta = \dfrac{\sin 75}{300} \times 278.79$

$\quad\therefore\quad \sin\theta = 0.89763$
$\qquad\therefore\quad \theta = 63.8^\circ$

So, angle ADC is 63.8°

The area of the playground is
$= \frac{1}{2} \times 180 \times 150 \times \sin 115^\circ + \frac{1}{2} \times 300 \times 278.79 \times \sin 41.2^\circ$
$= 39\,800$ m^2

GEOMETRY OF 3-DIMENSIONAL SHAPES

You must be able to

- calculate surface area and volume
- find lengths of lines joining vertices
- find midpoints of line segments
- find angles between lines and planes.

Example:

A sand building competition was held on a beach. The winner made the pyramid drawn alongside with a square base of length 6 m and a vertical height of 9 m. VX is the vertical height and M is the midpoint of AB.

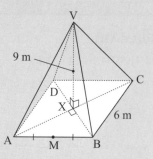

Calculate

a the slant height of the pyramid, VA
b the angle the face VAB makes with the base of the pyramid
c the volume of sand contained in the pyramid
d the cost of plastic used to cover the pyramid to protect it from rain given that the plastic costs £8.50 per 10 m^2.

Solution:

a First we find the length of VA.

Now $\quad AC = \sqrt{6^2 + 6^2} \quad$ {Pythagoras}
$\quad\therefore\quad AC = \sqrt{72}$
$\quad\therefore\quad XA = \frac{1}{2}\sqrt{72} \approx 4.242\,64$
$\quad\therefore\quad VA \approx \sqrt{9^2 + 4.242\,64^2}$
$\qquad\qquad\approx 9.95$ m

b The angle is VMX where M is the midpoint of AB.

$XM = 3$ m
$\tan\angle VMX = \frac{9}{3}$
$\therefore\quad \angle VMX = \tan^{-1}(3)$
$\qquad\qquad\approx 71.6^\circ$

c Volume $= \frac{1}{3} \times$ area of base $\times$ height
$\qquad\quad = \frac{1}{3} \times 6 \times 6 \times 9$
$\qquad\quad = 108$ m^3

d The height of triangle ABV $= \sqrt{9.95^2 - 3^2} \approx 9.49$ m

Area of triangle ABV $\approx \frac{1}{2} \times 6 \times 9.487 = 28.46$ m^2

Surface area $=$ area of base $+$ area of four triangles
$\qquad\qquad\approx 6 \times 6 + 4 \times 28.46$
$\qquad\qquad\approx 149.884$
$\qquad\qquad\approx 150$ m^2

Cost of plastic $= \dfrac{150}{10} \times £8.50 = £127.50$

TOPIC 5 – GEOMETRY AND TRIGONOMETRY ▰▰▰▰▰
(SHORT QUESTIONS)

1 **a** Plot the points S(2, 1) and T(-4, -2) on coordinate axes.
  b Find the length of the line segment from S(2, 1) to T(-4, -2).
  c Find the value of b ($b > 0$) given that R(b, 4) is 5 units from S(2, 1).

2 **a** Calculate the gradient of the line passing through G(3, 1) and H(-3, 3).
  b Find the midpoint of GH.
  c Determine the equation of the perpendicular bisector of GH.

3 Given straight line L_1: $\ 4x - 3y = 7$ and straight line L_2: $\ 2x + ky = 5$:
  a Find the gradient of L_1.
  b For the line L_2, find k if the two lines L_1 and L_2 are
    i parallel   **ii** perpendicular.

4 A triangle ABC has vertices A(−2, 2), B(4, 4) and C(5, 1).

 a Plot the points, A, B and C, on coordinate axes.

 b Using gradients, show that the triangle is right angled at B.

 c Determine the length of side AC.

5 Two parallel lines are shown in the diagram.

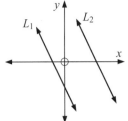

 a L_1 has equation $7x + 3y = 12$. Find the gradient of L_2.

 b Determine the equation of the line, perpendicular to L_2, which passes through $(7, 1)$.

6 **a** The straight line $2x - 4y = 7$ meets the x-axis at the point $(k, 0)$. Find the value of k.

 b The straight line $ax + by + d = 0$ passes through the points $(3, 2)$ and $(-6, 0)$. Find the integer values of a, b, and d.

7 In the diagram below the two straight lines L_1 and L_2 are shown.

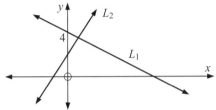

 a L_1 has a gradient of $-\frac{1}{2}$. It passes through the point $(0, 4)$. Find the equation of L_1, expressing your answer in the form $ax + by + d = 0$, where $a, b, d \in \mathbb{Z}$.

 b L_2 passes through $(-2, -1)$ and $(4, 8)$. Find the point of intersection of L_1 and L_2.

8 **a** Find k if $kx + 3y = 7$ has an x-intercept of 4.

 b The two straight lines $ax - y = 4h$ and $ax + 2y = h$ intersect at the point $(1, -1)$. Find the values of a and h.

9 Shown is part of the graphs of $y = \dfrac{24}{x}$ and $y = 3x - 1$.

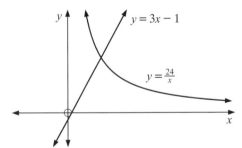

 a Find the coordinates of the point where the graphs intersect.

 b Find the equation of the line perpendicular to $y = 3x - 1$ passing through the point of intersection found in **a**.

10 A triangle is drawn inside a semi circle as shown. The semi circle has a radius of 5 cm. Side AB has length 8 cm and side BC has length 6 cm.

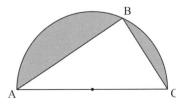

 a Use the theorem of Pythagoras to show that triangle ABC is right angled at B.

 b Find the size of the shaded area.

11 In the following diagram $AD = DC = BD = 4$ cm and angle $BDC = 64°$.

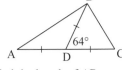

 a Show that $\angle ABC$ is a right angle.

 b If BC has length 4.24 cm, find the length of AB.

 c Find the area of $\triangle ABC$.

12 Lin is going to calculate the height of a mobile phone tower. He measures the angle of elevation from point A to the top of the tower, then moves 60 m closer to point B and takes a second reading. The information is given in the diagram below.

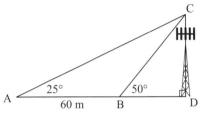

 a Calculate the measure of angle ACB.

 b Determine the height of the mobile phone tower.

13 Consider the quadrilateral ABCD as shown below.

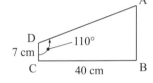

 a Show that AB has length 21.56 cm correct to two decimal places.

 b Find the length AD.

 c Find the area of quadrilateral ABCD.

14 An equilateral triangle ABC has sides of 50 cm. Perpendicular lines are drawn from B to AC and from A to BC. These two lines meet at point D. DM is perpendicular to AB. This information is shown on the diagram.

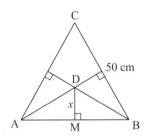

 a Write down the measure of $\angle ABC$.

 b Calculate the shortest distance, x, from AB to D.

15 A 6 metre flagpole is supported by three guy wires. Each wire is fixed to the ground 3.2 metres from the base of the flagpole and attached $\frac{2}{3}$ of the way up the pole.

 a Draw a diagram to show this information.

 b Find the angle each wire makes with the ground.

 c Find the total length of all three wires.

16 The area of the triangle DEF is 120 cm^2.

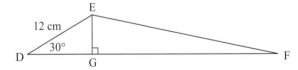

 a Show that the length of DF is 40 cm.

 b Find the length of the perpendicular from E to DF.

17 Triangle ABC has AB $= 8$ cm and AC $= 13$ cm. Angle ABC $= 70°$.

 a Draw a neat diagram to illustrate this information.

 b Find the measure of angle BCA.

 c Calculate the area of triangle ABC.

18 A landmark X is observed from B and C, which are 330 m apart. Angle XBC is 63° and angle BCX is 75°.

  a Draw a neat, labelled diagram to illustrate this information.

  b Find the distance of the landmark from B.

19 The 5th hole at the Flagstaff golf course has a layout as shown. From T to A on the fairway, the distance is 240 m and from A to F the distance is 135 m.

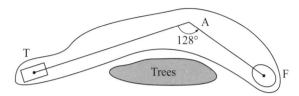

  a Find the straight-line distance from T to F.

  b Find angle ATF.

20 Triangle ABC has side AB = 8 cm, side BC = 10 cm and side AC = 12 cm.

  a Draw a carefully labelled diagram to illustrate this information.

  b Find the smallest angle in triangle ABC.

  c Find the area of triangle ABC.

21 Quadrilateral PQRS has measurements as shown.

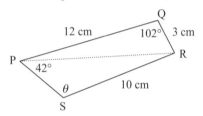

  a Find the length of PR.

  b Determine the measure of the angle marked θ.

22 A rectangular prism has a height of 7 cm and length twice as long as its width. Its volume is 350 cm³.

  a Show that its dimensions are 5 cm by 10 cm by 7 cm.

  b Find the length of the longest pencil that will fit into the box.

23 Triangle ABC has AB = 17 cm, AC = 19 cm, and an area of 120 cm².

  a Draw a clearly labelled diagram representing this information.

  b Determine the measure of ∠BAC.

  c Determine the length of the remaining side.

  d Find the volume of a triangular prism with a cross section the same as triangle ABC and length of 13.5 cm.

24 A square-based, right pyramid has a side length of 50 m and vertical height of 7 m.

  a Draw a diagram of the pyramid.

  b Calculate the length of a slanting edge.

  c Find the measure of the angle between the slanting edge and the diagonal of the base.

  d Find the surface area of a triangular face of the pyramid.

25 The quadrilateral ABCD shown alongside has ∠ABC = ∠ADC = 90°. Side AD = 10 cm, side DC = 6 cm, and side BC = 9 cm.

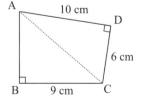

  a Find the length of AB.

  b Determine the area of quadrilateral ABCD.

  c If this quadrilateral was the cross section of a solid prism with volume 484 cm³, find the length of the prism.

TOPIC 5 – GEOMETRY AND TRIGONOMETRY (LONG QUESTIONS)

1 The vertices of triangle ABC are A(7, 1), B(−3, −5) and C(−1, 3).

  a Plot the points A, B, and C on a set of xy-coordinate axes. Use a scale of 1 cm to represent 1 unit on each axis.

  b **i** Find the length of AC.

    ii Show that the length of BC is equal to the length of AC.

    iii The gradient of line BC is 4. Find the gradient of the line through A and C.

    iv Show that ∠ACB = 90°.

    v Find the area of triangle ABC.

  c **i** Determine the equation of the line through A and B. Express your answer in the form $ax + by = d$ where $a, b, d \in \mathbb{Z}$.

    ii D is the midpoint of AB. Find the equation of the line through D and C.

2 **a** Plot the points A(−5, −2), B(3, 4), and C(5, −4) on a set of xy-coordinate axes. Use a scale of 1 cm to represent 1 unit for both axes.

  b **i** Find M, the midpoint of AB.

    ii Find N, the midpoint of BC.

  c **i** Find the gradient of the straight line through M and N.

    ii Hence find the equation of the straight line through M and N. Express your answer in the form $ax + by = d$ where $a, b, d \in \mathbb{Z}$.

  d Show that AC is parallel to MN.

  e The length of MN is $\sqrt{26}$ units long. Show that AC is twice this length.

  f **i** AB is 10 units long and BC is $\sqrt{68}$ units long. Find the measure of angle ABC.

    ii Show that the area of triangle ABC is 38 units².

    iii The area of triangle BMN is 9.5 units². Find the perpendicular distance between the parallel sides of quadrilateral AMNC.

3 The vertices of the triangle ABC as shown in the diagram below are A(−4, 4), B(10, 2), and C(2, −4).

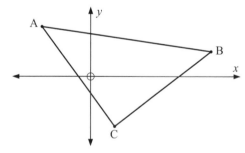

  a **i** Find the lengths of AC and BC.

    ii Show that triangle ABC is isosceles.

    iii Find the coordinates of the midpoint, M, of the line AB.

    iv State the value of the angle AMC.

  b **i** The gradient of the line through A and C is $-\frac{4}{3}$. Find the gradient of the line BC and hence show that angle ACB = 90°.

    ii Find the size of angle CBA.

  c **i** Find the equation of the line joining the points B and C. Express your answer in the form $ax + by = d$ where $a, b, d \in \mathbb{Z}$.

    ii Write down the equation of a line that is

      a parallel to the line through B and C

      b perpendicular to the line through B and C.

4 The shape of Clifton Park forms quadrilateral ABCD as shown below. A diagonal path crosses the park from A to C.

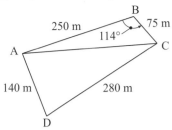

a **i** Calculate the length of the diagonal AC.
  ii Find the measure of angle ADC.
  iii Find the area of triangle ADC.
  iv Determine the area of the whole park.

b Inside the park are two identical towers in the shape of right circular cones as shown.
Each conical tower has a vertical height of 7.3 m and base diameter of 3 m.

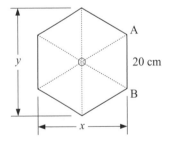

  i Find the slant height of each structure.
  ii Find the angle between the base and the slant height.
  iii Find the total volume of the two conical towers.

c The curved surface of each cone is to be painted. One litre of paint will cover 15 m². Calculate the number of litres of paint required to paint both conical towers.

5 **a** Three footballers form a triangle and kick a ball between them. Juan is 35 metres from Lee and 40 metres from Kim. Kim is 50 metres from Lee.

  i Draw a clearly labelled diagram representing this information.
  ii Through what angle must Kim turn after receiving the ball from Juan to kick it to Lee?

b An archaeologist has located some ancient treasure (T) in a desert. To mark the location he uses his theodolite to measure the direction of the treasure from two points 60 metres apart. From point A the treasure is located at an angle of 43° to T and from B at an angle of 36° to T. This information is shown below.

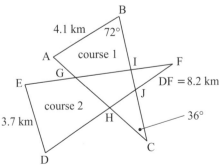

  i Find angle ATB.
  ii Find the distance from A to T.
  iii Find the vertical distance from the line AB to the treasure T.

c The triangle marked by A, T, and B is considered a sensitive area. How large is the sensitive area?

6 The diagram below shows the routes of two triangular orienteering courses ABC and DEF.

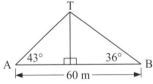

a **i** The length from E to F is 20% longer than the length from A to C. Show that the length EF is 7.96 km.
  ii Find the measure of angle DEF.
  iii Find the total area covered by course 2.

b **i** Find the length of course 1.
  ii Wael is able to run at an average of 14 kmh⁻¹ on course 1. Course 2 is hillier and he is only able to average 10 kmh⁻¹. Calculate the additional time it will take him to complete course 2 compared to course 1. Give your answer to the nearest 10 minutes.

7 A large artificial icecream is to be made in the shape of a hemisphere on top of an inverted cone as shown, for a shop front display.

The overall height of the giant icecream is 7 m while the cone itself is 4 m in height.

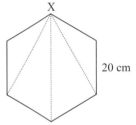

a **i** Show that the radius of the cone is 3 m.
  ii Calculate the total volume of the icecream.

b **i** Find the angle between the slant height of the cone and the base of the hemisphere.
  ii Find the slant height of the cone.
  iii Find the total surface area of the icecream.

c **i** The icecream is to be made from lightweight aluminium with each square metre of material weighing 1.23 kilograms. Calculate the overall weight of the icecream.

8 A street sign is to be made in the shape of a regular hexagon with equal sides of 20 cm. From the vertex labelled X, three diagonals can be drawn, thus dividing the shape into four triangles as shown.

a Show that each interior angle of the sign is 120°.

b From the centre O, of the sign, line segments are drawn to the vertices. Each line bisects each vertex as illustrated below.

  i Consider ΔAOB. Given that OA = OB, show that ∠AOB = 60°.
  ii State the nature of triangle OAB.
  iii Find the total area of the sign.

c The sign will be made from a rectangular piece of metal and the remainder will be discarded. For manufacturing purposes the overall height (y) and width (x) of the sign need to be known.

  i Calculate the height, y, of the sign.
  ii Calculate the width, x, of the sign.
  iii Find the area of the rectangular piece of metal the sign will be cut from.
  iv Each square centimetre of metal costs €0.35. Calculate the cost of the metal that is wasted from the cutting process.

SUMMARY

TYPES OF QUANTITATIVE (NUMERICAL) DATA

- **Discrete data**, that takes exact number values, and is usually a result of counting.

  e.g., 1, 2, 3, 4, ...

  For example, the number of houses in a street.

- **Continuous data**, that takes number values within a certain range, and is usually a result of measurement.

  e.g., 5, 5.5, 5.55

  For example, the height of plants.

ORGANISING DATA

▶ **Ungrouped data**

- *Raw data:* 12, 21, 32, 15, 23, 34, 27
- *Ordered data:* 12, 15, 21, 23, 27, 32, 34

- Stem and leaf plot   Back to back stem and leaf plot

```
1 | 2 5              1 | 5 | 3 5
2 | 1 3 7        5 3 1 | 6 | 2 4 6
3 | 2 4          4 2 | 7 | 1 5 9
                      3 | 8 | 0
```

        Note: 2 | 3   represents 23

- Frequency table

number	frequency
5	2
6	3
7	3
8	1

▶ **Grouped data**

-    Frequency table   Cumulative frequency table

height (cm)	freq
0 - 4	5
5 - 9	9
10 - 14	15
15 - 19	6

height (cm)	cumulative freq
0 - 4	5
5 - 9	14
10 - 14	29
15 - 19	35

- Class intervals are equal width.
- Mid-interval values (class midpoints)

  $\dfrac{0+4}{2} = 2$, $\dfrac{5+9}{2} = 7$ etc.

- Lower and upper boundaries of the class interval:

  5 - 9   has boundaries   4.5 - 9.5

REPRESENTING DATA

All graphs require **labelled axes** and a **marked scale**.

- **Histograms**

Height of plants

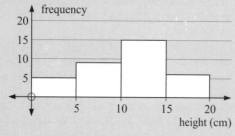

- ▶ Frequency is on the vertical axis.
- ▶ Bars are equal width.
- ▶ Bars are joined.

- **Frequency Polygons**

Height of plants

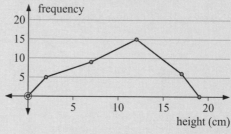

- ▶ Frequency is plotted against midpoint of class interval.
- ▶ Graph returns to the horizontal axes at the start of the first class and the end of the final class.

- **Cumulative frequency graphs**

Height of plants

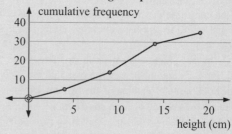

- ▶ Cumulative frequencies plotted against the end points of the class interval.
- ▶ Curve begins at the horizontal axis.

MEASURES OF CENTRAL TENDENCY

Ungrouped discrete data: data such as   5, 6, 7, 2, 5

- The **mean**, $\overline{x}$, is the arithmetic average of the scores.

  For the given data, $\overline{x} = \dfrac{5+6+7+2+5}{5} = 5$

- The **median** is the middle value of an *ordered* set of data.

  The middle value is found at $\dfrac{n+1}{2}$

  where n is the number of terms in the data set.

  Since $n = 5$, $\dfrac{n+1}{2} = \dfrac{6}{2} = 3$ and as the ordered

  data set is: 2, 5, 5, 6, 7,   the median $= 5$

- The **mode** is the most frequently occurring value
  ∴   mode $= 5$.

Grouped discrete data:

This is data with a frequency table such as:

Number	frequency
5	2
6	3
7	3
8	1
Total	9

The mean is calculated by adding an fx column to the table.

Number (x)	frequency (f)	fx
5	2	10
6	3	18
7	3	21
8	1	8
Total	9	57

mean $= \dfrac{\sum fx}{\sum f}$

$= \dfrac{57}{9}$

≈ 6.33

As $\dfrac{n+1}{2} = \dfrac{9+1}{2} = 5$ the median is the 5th value

∴   median $= 6$.

The data is **bimodal** with modes of 6 and 7.

Grouped data

Frequency table

height (cm)	midpoint (x)	freq (f)	fx
0 - 4	2	5	10
5 - 9	7	9	63
10 - 14	12	15	180
15 - 19	17	6	102
	Total	35	355

The mean, $\bar{x} = \dfrac{\sum fx}{\sum f} = \dfrac{355}{35} \approx 10.1$

We use a **cumulative frequency polygon** to find the median.

The modal class is 10 - 14.

QUARTILES

Ungrouped discrete data e.g., 2, 5, 8, 9, 12, 15, 18, 19, 21

- As $n = 9$, the lower quartile Q_1 is found at

  $\dfrac{n+1}{4} = \dfrac{10}{4} = 2.5,$

  i.e., half way between the 2nd and 3rd values

  $\therefore \quad Q_1 = \dfrac{5+8}{2} = 6.5$

- The second quartile, Q_2, (median) is found at

  $\dfrac{n+1}{2} = \dfrac{10}{2} = 5,$

  i.e., the 5th score. $\therefore \quad Q_2 = 12$

- The upper quartile Q_3 is found at the $3 \times 2.5 = 7.5$ position.
  i.e. half way between the 7th and 8th values

  $\therefore \quad Q_3 = \dfrac{18+19}{2} = 18.5$

Grouped data

Quartiles (and **percentiles**) are found from a **Cumulative frequency graph**. (A percentile scale may be added to the graph.)

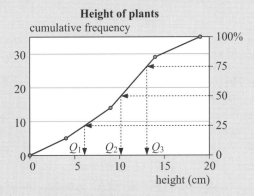

Height of plants

Notice that

- $Q_1 = $ 25th percentile, $Q_2 = $ 50th percentile,
  $Q_3 = $ 75th percentile
- We draw lines on the graph to show the method.
- Percentile values can be easily read using the percentage scale.

MEASURES OF DISPERSION

For the **ungrouped discrete data**: 2, 5, 8, 9, 12, 15, 18, 19, 21

- **Range** = highest value − lowest value = $21 - 2 = 19$
- **Interquartile range (IQR)** = $Q_3 - Q_1 = 18.5 - 6.5 = 12$
- **Standard deviation**

  We use graphics calculators to find the standard deviation in examinations. Always use the value for the population standard deviation in examinations (x_{σ_n} for Casio or σ_x for TI).

OUTLIERS

Outliers are values outside the limits of $Q_1 - 1.5 \times$ IQR and $Q_3 + 1.5 \times$ IQR.

For our example,

$6.5 - 1.5 \times 12 = -11.5$ and $18.5 + 1.5 \times 12 = 36.5$, and as no data values lie outside the interval $-11.5 < x < 36.5$, there are no outliers in this data set.

DISPLAYING THE SPREAD OF DATA

We use a **box and whisker plot**.

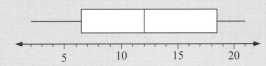

- A scale must be used.
- Label appropriately.
- The five-figure summary (min, Q_1, Q_2, Q_3, max) can be obtained from the box plot drawn on gdc (use trace).

BIVARIATE DATA (TWO VARIABLES)

We use a **scatter diagram** (or **scatter plot**).

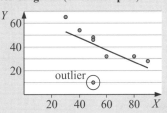

Note that:

- Straight **line of best fit** (drawn by eye) must pass through $(\bar{x}, \bar{y})$.
- **Outliers** are often omitted from data and statistics recalculated.
- **Correlation** describes the nature and direction of any relationship.
- Correlation does not imply any causal relationship.

CORRELATION

To find the strength of the relationship between two variables we use **Pearson's product-moment correlation coefficient**, r.

- The calculated value (r) describes the strength of any relationship, $-1 \leqslant r \leqslant 1$.
- r close to ± 1 very strong relationship
  $r > 0.8$ or < -0.8 strong
  $r > 0.6$ or < -0.6 moderate
  r between -0.6 and 0.6 weak
- In the example above, the relationship would be weak/moderate ($r \approx 0.6$) with the outlier included, and strong ($r > 0.9$) with the outlier removed.
- In examination questions where a calculation for r is required, the value of the covariance s_{xy} will be given.
- Students are expected to find s_x and s_y using a gdc.
- If use of formula is not stipulated, students are expected to find the value for r using a gdc.

REGRESSION LINE FOR y ON x

You need to be able to find the regression line for y on x.

Note that:

- For calculation by formula, s_{xy} will be given in examination questions.
- If use of formula is not stipulated, students are expected to determine the equation of the regression line using a gcd.
- The regression equation is used for estimating values. It is usually reliable when **interpolating**. It can be unreliable when **extrapolating**.

CHI-SQUARED (χ^2) TEST FOR INDEPENDENCE

Notes:

- Write down null and alternate hypotheses.
- Calculation of χ^2 expected values by hand can be asked for.
- Calculation of the χ^2 statistic by formula is required.
- Use of tables χ^2 and the calculation of degrees of freedom.
- If calculation by formula and use of tables is not stipulated it is expected that students will determine values from a gdc.
- Knowledge and use of probability value (p-value) from a gdc.
- Examination questions will focus on the upper tail test.
- Expected values less than 5 result in an unreliable χ^2 test. We combine cells to overcome this problem.

TOPIC 6 – STATISTICS (SHORT QUESTIONS)

1 The number of customers entering a shop each hour on a particular day is listed below.

   14, 23, 26, 34, 24, 18, 26, 16, 25

a Is the data discrete or continuous?

b Determine the mean, median, mode and the range for this data.

c Find the total income for the shop if the mean amount spent per customer is $14.20

2 The number of houses in certain streets of a council area is presented in the following frequency table.

no. of houses	frequency
0 - 9	5
10 - 19	12
20 - 29	14
30 - 39	18
40 - 49	8
Total	57

a Is the data discrete or continuous?

b Construct the histogram for this data.

c On the same diagram, draw the frequency polygon for this data.

d What is the modal class for this data?

3 The stem plot below lists the number of birds present in a park on 22 days last month.

```
0 | 3, 5, 7
1 | 3, 4, 7, 7, 8
2 | 0, 2, 2, 2, 5, 7
3 | 1, 4, 5, 6, 9
4 | 0, 2, 9        scale:   1 | 3   represents 13 birds
```

a Determine the median and quartile values.

b Test for any outliers in this data.

c Find the probability that, on any day, the number of birds present is more than the upper quartile.

4 The height of 50 plants was measured (to the nearest cm) and the results are given in the table shown.

Height (cm)	frequency
0 - 9	2
10 - 19	15
20 - 29	21
30 - 39	7
40 - 49	5
Total	50

a Is the data discrete or continuous?

b List the mid-interval values for each class.

c Write down the lower and upper boundaries for the second class.

d Find the approximate mean height of the plants.

5 a Write down the cumulative frequencies for the height of plants in question **4**.

b Draw the cumulative frequency graph.

c Use your graph to determine the 80th percentile.

d How many plants are taller than the 80th percentile?

6 The Cumulative frequency curve below represents the finishing time (minutes) of 30 competitors in a recent orienteering contest.

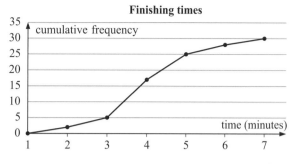

Finishing times

Use the graph above to find:

a the median finishing time (Answer to 1 decimal place.)

b the time required for a runner to finish in the 1st Quartile.

c How many runners finished in a time between 2 and 5 minutes?

7 a The mean of 7 integers is 14. The integers, in ascending order, are: 9, 10, a, 13, b, 16, 21.
   Find the values of a and b.

b Six integers, in ascending order, are: 1, 5, 9, 11, 16, p.
   If the mean of the six numbers has the same value as the median, find p.

8 The statistics below represent a sample of 30 employees' wages ($'000) at two firms.

Data set 1:   mean = 38,   median = 35,
standard deviation = 7

Data set 2:   mean = 38,   median = 41,
standard deviation = 11.5

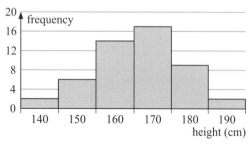

a The diagram above is a frequency polygon for data set 1. On the same diagram, sketch an approximate frequency polygon for data set 2.

b Which of the data sets has the greater dispersion in the wages paid to their employees?

c Which of the data sets is likely to have the smaller inter quartile range?

d Which of the data sets is likely to have more people earning higher wages?

9 A survey of the heights of Year 12 students at an international school gave the following results. All measurements have been rounded to the nearest 10 cm.

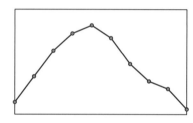

a What are the boundaries for the 170 cm class?

b Find the approximate mean and standard deviation of the students' height in this survey.

c How many students were taller than 2 standard deviations above the mean?

10 The list below shows the amount of weekly rent, in dollars, for houses in a certain city.

a Find the mean and standard deviation for weekly rents.

b What is the probability that the rent for a randomly chosen house will be greater than $140?

c Determine the percentage of houses that have rents greater than one standard deviation above the mean.

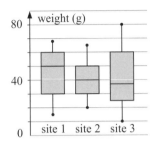

Weekly rent ($)	Frequency
80 - 99	3
100 - 119	15
120 - 139	26
140 - 159	30
160 - 179	14
180 - 199	1

11 The box plots show the weights of particular species of fungus collected from 3 different sites in a forest.

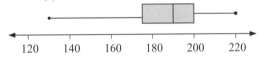

a Which site has the greatest range of weights?

b At which site are the weights of fungi least spread?

c Which site has the highest median weight?

d At which site were the heaviest fungi found?

e Which site has the highest proportion of weights above 40 grams?

f Which site has the lowest proportion of weights above the upper quartile?

12 For the boxplot shown below:

a write down the values of the lower quartile, median and upper quartile

b find the range

c calculate the value of the interquartile range

d determine whether the minimum value is an outlier.

13 The following marks were obtained by students in a Mathematics Examination.

| 67 | 62 | 75 | 78 | 78 | 49 | 57 | 59 | 61 | 72 |
| 75 | 25 | 82 | 68 | 85 | 81 | 48 | 70 | 76 | 87 |

a Find the five-number summary.

b Represent this information as a box and whisker plot.

c Test for any outliers. Suggest a possible reason for any outlying value.

14 The numbers of spelling errors made by year 9 students in an essay are displayed on the cumulative frequency diagram.

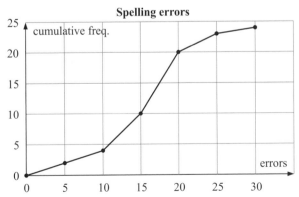

a Use the cumulative frequency graph to find the five-number summary for the numbers of errors students made in the essay.

b Draw the box and whisker plot for student spelling errors.

15 The following prices ($'000) for houses sold last month in a certain suburb were:

240, 260, 262, 280, 310, 325, 330, 340, 760

a Find the median price for these sales.

b Determine the interquartile range.

c Omit any outliers from the data and recalculate the median.

d What is the percentage change in the median price with the outlier omitted?

16 Given: $s_x = 17.4$, $s_y = 25.6$, $s_{xy} = 405$, $\overline{x} = 63$, $\overline{y} = 110$:

a Calculate the coefficient of correlation (r).

b Describe the relationship between the two variables, x and y.

c Determine the equation of linear regression for y on x.

d Find the value of y when x is 70.

17 The table shows the exchange rate for Argentine pesos (against USD) and interest rates in Argentina over a period of time.

Exchange rate	2.85	2.95	2.90	2.75	2.65
Interest rate	7.40	7.50	7.55	7.25	7.25
Exchange rate	2.80	3.05	2.98	2.95	
Interest rate	7.35	7.65	7.75	7.60	

a Draw the scatter diagram for the given data.

b Write down the value of the correlation coefficient for this data.

c Describe the nature and strength of the relationship that appears to exist between the exchange rate and interest rates over this period of time.

18 Consider the following data on farm production.

Monthly rainfall (mm)	5	10	15	20	25	30
Yield (tonnes)	14	21	29	31	30	28

a Determine the coefficient of correlation (r). What does the value of r suggest about the nature and strength of the relationship between monthly rainfall and crop yield?

b Draw the scatter diagram for the farm data.

c Explain why the coefficient of correlation may not be an appropriate measure for this data.

19 Consider the following contingency table.

	Y_1	Y_2
X_1	32	14
X_2	25	19

a Show that the expected values (whole numbers) are:

	Y_1	Y_2
X_1	29	17
X_2	28	16

b Show that the chi-squared statistic for this data is 1.72

20 A nursery has developed a new hybrid plant. They claim that this particular hybrid will grow equally well under any light conditions. They have provided the following data to support their belief.

	Height < 60 cm	Height $\geqslant 60$ cm
Sunlight	37	43
Shade	22	18
Dark	25	19

a Write suitable null and alternate hypotheses for a chi-square test.

b Write down the χ^2 statistic for the plant data.

c Write down the critical value at the 5% level of significance.

d Is there evidence to support the nursery's claim?

21 a Test the independence of the following factors at the 5% level of significance.

	Factor Y_a	Factor Y_b	Factor Y_c
Factor X_a	6	3	7
Factor X_b	21	35	28
Factor X_c	16	11	22

If expected values are less than 5, the reliability of the chi-square test is reduced.

b Identify the row/column containing the low expected value.

c Combine the first two rows and retest for independence.

d Comment on the result.

22 The number and weight of potatoes in a sample of 2.5 kg bags is listed.

Number in bag	89	97	105	110
Median weight (g)	28	26	25	23

Number in bag	125	140	145	150
Median weight (g)	21	18	18	16

a Determine the equation of linear regression for this information.

b Use your equation to find the number of potatoes in a bag if the median weight is:
   i 100 grams   **ii** 200 grams

c Which of the answers in **b** is likely to be more reliable? Give a reason for your answer.

23

X	30	50	80	60	50	90	40	50
Y	65	12	28	42	46	26	54	48

a Write down the equation of linear regression and the coefficient of correlation.

b Remove the outlier from the data and recalculate the equation of the regression line and the correlation coefficient.

c Comment on the change in the slope of the line and the strength of the relationship.

24 9 students sat a mathematics examination. The results that they obtained and the number of hours that each of them studied are shown in the table.

Study time (hrs)	7	6	3	16	15	11	18	32	20
Result (%)	56	42	25	80	65	60	85	96	90

a Write down the equation of the straight line of best fit.

b Tony's score in the examination was 70%. According to the result of the line of best fit, for how long did he study?

c In terms of the marks obtained in the examination, explain the meaning of the y-intercept and the gradient of the equation of the line of best fit.

25 A government agency believes that the evidence submitted by a chemical firm in support of the claim that their product is safe has possibly been manipulated. The agency asks you to conduct a chi-squared test.

	Minimal effect	Negligible effect	no effect
Plants without disease	101	109	115
Plants with disease	205	221	229

H_0: the deviation from expected values is due to random chance.

a Determine the chi-squared probability value for this data.

b Test the p-value against the 1% and 0.5% levels of significance (lower tail test).

c What conclusion can you draw from the chemical company's data?

TOPIC 6 – STATISTICS (LONG QUESTIONS)

1 The prices ($) for 25 similar printers are displayed in a stem and leaf diagram below:

```
27 | 1 2 4 9
28 | 0 1 5 7 8
29 | 0 0 2 3 4 7 8 9 9 9
30 | 3 4 7 9
31 | 1 6          Scale   28 | 5   represents $285
```

The mean of this data is 293 and the standard deviation 12.0

a **i** Calculate the median, range, lower and upper quartiles.

   ii Display these statistics on a horizontal box and whisker plot. Use a scale of 1 cm to represent $10.

b Three months later the prices for the same printers were recorded:

The prices ranged between 269 and 329 dollars with a mean of 295 dollars and standard deviation of 11 dollars. The lower and upper quartiles were 280 and 305 respectively and the median was 295. Show this data as a box and whisker plot using the same scale as in **a**.

c **i** Describe the main difference between the box and whisker plots.

   ii Explain whether or not this information shows that the price of printers has increased. Give a clear reason for your answer.

d Find the percentage increase in the mean price of printers over the 3 month period.

2 The following data was obtained in a statistical experiment which involved measuring the distance travelled by two toy cars. Each car was rolled down a slope 40 times. The measurements were rounded to the nearest tenth of a metre.

Red car	3.6	4.6	5.6	6.4	4.2	5.3	6.1	4.5
	5.4	4.6	3.9	6.2	5.8	4.5	5.4	6.1
	4.5	5.6	5.7	4.8	3.9	5.6	6.1	5.9
	4.1	5.3	4.2	6.2	7.4	5.4	5.8	4.5
	3.9	5.4	5.7	4.8	5.4	5.7	6.1	6.4

Blue car	
number of rolls	40
Mean distance	4.9 m
Median distance	4.8 m
Shortest distance	3.2 m
Longest distance	6.7 m
First quartile	4.1 m
Third quartile	5.4 m
Standard deviation	0.8 m

a Determine the mean and standard deviation for the distance travelled by the red car.

b Complete the table of cumulative frequencies for the red car data.

Distance (m)	Cumulative frequency
3.5 - < 4.0	
4.0 - < 4.5	
4.5 - < 5.0	
5.0 - < 5.5	
5.5 - < 6.0	
6.0 - < 6.5	
6.5 - < 7.0	
7.0 - < 7.5	

c Draw the Cumulative frequency graph for the distance travelled by the **red car**. Use a scale of 1 cm to represent 1 m on the horizontal axis and 1 cm to represent 10 units on the vertical scale.

d Use the graph to find the following statistics for the **red car**:   **i** median distance
   ii lower quartile
   iii upper quartile.

e Draw the box and whisker plots for both cars *on the same axis*.

f Compare the statistics for distance travelled by the two toy cars. Is it reasonable to assume that the same machine manufactured these two toys? Give reasons for your answer.

3 A manufacturer states that each box of a certain cereal contains 320 g, on average. Each box of a random sample of 24 boxes was weighed with the following results recorded, in grams.

312	320	326	330	306	322	326	330
312	308	307	316	315	328	334	309
308	325	320	332	316	321	314	324

a Calculate the mean weight and the range of weights for the boxes.

b Organise the data into a frequency table with the first class as 305 - 309.

c Use the information in your table to draw the frequency polygon for the cereal data.

d Comment on the manufacturer's stated average weight. Six months later, another randomly selected 24 boxes were weighed with the following results.

Ave. weight	Frequency
310 - 314	3
315 - 319	5
320 - 324	8
325 - 329	6
330 - 334	2

e Calculate the mean weight for the new data.

f Draw the frequency polygon for the new data on the same graph as above.

g Does the evidence suggest that the manufacturer has improved the production process in the six months?

4 A large store employs 100 sales staff. The employees' total sales for last year are listed in the table below.

Sales ($ '000)	Number of Staff
60 to less than 70	3
70 to less than 80	8
80 to less than 90	11
90 to less than 100	23
100 to less than 110	27
110 to less than 120	20
120 to less than 130	8

a Represent this information as a histogram.

b Write down the minimum and maximum sales required for a staff member to be in the highest class.

c Calculate the mean and the standard deviation of the sales per staff for the year using 65, 75, etc., as the midpoints of each class. Give your answers to the nearest hundred dollars.

d The store had an incentive scheme last year that offered a $900 bonus to all staff with sales exceeding +2 standard deviations from the mean.
   i What was the minimum amount of sales ($) required for a staff member to qualify for this bonus?
   ii Approximately how much money did the store pay in bonuses?

e If the top 8 sales staff were to get the bonus, how many standard deviations above the mean would the limit need to be set?

f At the end of the year the store's manager decided to reduce the number of sales staff. Every staff member whose sales were less than 1.385 standard deviations from the mean would be removed from the team. How many staff would go?

5 A jeweller measured the volume and mass of some samples of silver which he had purchased. He suspected that one of the samples might be a fake. The results are listed in the table.

Sample	A	B	C	D	E	F
Volume (cm^3)	3	6	4	7	16	8
Mass (g)	40	95	50	160	285	130
Sample	G	H	I	J	K	L
Volume (cm^3)	5	12	9	6	10	11
Mass (g)	65	210	155	90	170	190

a Draw the scatter plot for this data. Use 1 cm to represent 20 g on the horizontal axis and 1 cm to represent 1 cm^3 on the vertical scale.

b   **i** Calculate the mean for both volume ($\bar{x}$) and mass ($\bar{y}$).
   ii Draw the straight line of best fit for the data. The line should pass through the point ($\bar{x}$, $\bar{y}$).

c Describe the relationship which appears to exist between the volume and mass of the samples of silver.

d Write down the value of the (linear) coefficient of correlation.

e   **i** Remove the suspect value from the data and then write down the equation of the linear regression line for this data.
   ii Use your equation to find the expected mass of the sample of silver with the same volume as the suspect sample.
   iii Calculate the percentage error between the given and expected masses of the suspect sample based on the expected mass.

6 The scatter diagram shows the age and annual income for 10 randomly chosen individuals.

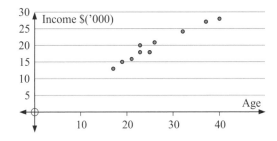

The following statistics have been calculated for this data.

Age		Income	
Mean	26.3	Mean	20
Median	24	Median	19
Mode	23	Mode	18
Standard Deviation	7.25	Standard Deviation	4.78

The covariance for age and income is 33.9.

a   **i** Determine the value of the correlation coefficient (r).
   ii Describe the relationship between the age and annual income for these individuals.

b Determine the equation of the linear regression line for age and income.

c Use the equation in **b** to estimate:
   i the annual income for someone aged 30 years
   ii the annual income for someone who is 60 years of age.

d Comment on the reliability of both answers in **c**.

7 Fifty words were randomly selected from story A and another fifty words were randomly selected from story B. The number of letters from each word were recorded and the results are summarized in the frequency table below.

Number of letters in a word	Frequency of words in story A	Frequency of words in story B
2	5	7
3	13	9
4	6	10
5	8	6
6	5	6
7	5	8
8	2	2
9	4	1
10	2	1

a Draw frequency polygons for both stories on the same axes.

b Determine the five-number summary of word length for both stories and display the statistics as side-by-side box and whisker plots.

c Write down the mean and standard deviation of word length for both stories.

d Construct a 2×2 contingency table by adding the number of words with less than 5 letters and the number of words with 5 or more letters for each story.

e Test for independence at the 10% significance level for the chi-square distribution.

f What conclusion can be drawn from the test?

g Is there any evidence to support the claim that the two stories were written by different authors?

8 Jack believes that students' choice of breakfast cereal is related to gender. He conducts a survey at his school and records the following information. He plans to use a chi-squared test to discover if his belief is correct.

	Muesli	Rolled Oats	Corn Flakes	Weetbix
Female	2	7	24	12
Male	4	15	13	13

a Write a suitable null hypothesis for a chi-squared test.

b Write down the expected values for this data.

c Jack observes the expected values and realises that the results of a chi-square test may not be reliable because there are expected values which are less than 5. He decides to combine the first two columns of data in the contingency table.

Write down the contingency table for the combined data.

d Show that the chi-squared statistic for the combined table is 6.88.

e Test the calculated chi-squared statistic at the 5% level of significance.

f What conclusion can Jack draw from the test?

g If Jack had chosen to use the original contingency table, would he have drawn the same conclusion? Justify your answer.

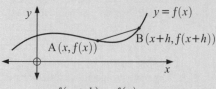

SUMMARY

NOTATION

- If $f(x)$ is a function, then $f'(x)$ is its derivative.
- If y is the graph of a function, then $\dfrac{dy}{dx}$ is its gradient function.

APPROXIMATING THE GRADIENT OF A TANGENT TO $y = f(x)$

For the graph of a function $y = f(x)$, consider two points A and B on $y = f(x)$, such that their coordinates are $A(x, f(x))$ and $B(x + h, f(x + h))$.

The gradient between A and B is $\dfrac{f(x + h) - f(x)}{h}$.

The gradient between A and B can be used as an approximation to the gradient of the tangent to $y = f(x)$ at the point A. As the point A is brought closer to the point B, the approximation improves.

FUNCTIONS OF THE FORM $y = ax^n$

For functions of the form $f(x) = ax^n$, where a is a constant, the **derivative** or **gradient function** is

$$f'(x) = anx^{n-1}.$$

Example:

Given $f(x) = x^3 - \dfrac{4}{x} + 5$, find $f'(x)$.

Solution:
$$f(x) = x^3 - \frac{4}{x} + 5$$
$$\therefore \quad f(x) = x^3 - 4x^{-1} + 5$$
$$\therefore \quad f'(x) = 3x^2 - 4(-1)x^{-2} + 0$$
$$\therefore \quad f'(x) = 3x^2 + \frac{4}{x^2}$$

GRADIENT AT A POINT

The gradient of $y = f(x)$ at a point $x = k$ is found by evaluating the derivative of $f(x)$ at $x = k$, i.e., by finding $f'(k)$.

Example:

Given $f(x) = 3x^2 - 2x + 1$, find the gradient of the function at the point where $x = 3$.

Solution:

Differentiating $f(x)$, we have $f'(x) = 6x - 2$.

At $x = 3$, $f'(3) = 6(3) - 2 = 16$.

Hence the gradient at $x = 3$ is 16.

TANGENTS TO CURVES

To find the equation of the tangent to the curve $y = f(x)$ at $x = k$ we:

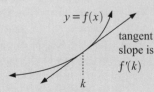

- Find the coordinates of the *point of contact*.

  At $x = k$, the point of contact is $(k, f(k))$.

- Find the *gradient function* $\dfrac{dy}{dx}$ (or $f'(x)$) and evaluate the gradient function at $x = k$.

- Determine the *equation of the line* using the point of contact $(k, f(k))$ and the gradient found at $x = k$.

Example:

Find the equation of the tangent to the curve $y = 6 - 3x - 4x^2$ where $x = -2$.

Solution:

$$\frac{dy}{dx} = -3 - 8x$$

When $x = -2$, $\frac{dy}{dx} = -3 - 8(-2) = -3 + 16 = 13$

$\therefore$ gradient of the tangent $= 13$

When $x = -2$, $y = 6 - 3(-2) - 4(-2)^2 = -4$

$\therefore$ point of contact is $(-2, -4)$

The equation of a straight line is $y = mx + c$.

For $m = 13$ and at $(-2, -4)$ $\quad -4 = 13(-2) + c$
$$\therefore \quad c = 22$$

Hence, the equation of the tangent is $y = 13x + 22$.

THE SECOND DERIVATIVE

- If $f(x)$ is a function, then $f''(x)$ is its **second derivative**.

- If $y = f(x)$ is the graph of a function, $\frac{d^2y}{dx^2}$ is the derivative of the derivative.

- A second derivative can be found by finding the derivative of the gradient function, i.e., by finding the derivative of the derivative function.

For example, given $\quad f(x) = 4x^3 - 3x^2 + 5x - 2$
then $f'(x) = 12x^2 - 6x + 5$
and $f''(x) = 24x - 6$

CURVE SHAPE

For a given interval, if the graph of $y = f(x)$ is such that:

- $f'(x) > 0$, then $y = f(x)$ is **increasing** on the interval.

- $f'(x) < 0$, then $y = f(x)$ is **decreasing** on the interval.

- If $f'(x) = 0$ at the point $x = k$, then $y = f(x)$ is **stationary** (neither increasing or decreasing) at $x = k$.

For example, for the graph of $y = f(x)$ alongside:

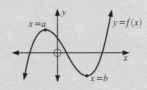

- the function is increasing for $x < a$ and $x > b$
- the function is decreasing for $a < x < b$
- the function is stationary at $x = a$ and $x = b$.

LOCAL MAXIMA AND MINIMA

- If $f'(x) = 0$ at $x = k$, then the point $(k, f(k))$ is either a **local maximum** point, a **local minimum point** or a **horizontal inflection** point.

  Note: Horizontal points of inflection are not part of the syllabus.

- If $f(x)$ is increasing for $x < k$ and decreasing for $x > k$, then $(k, f(k))$ is a **local maximum**.

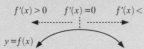

- If $f(x)$ is decreasing for $x < k$ and increasing for $x > k$, then $(k, f(k))$ is a **local minimum**.

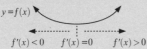

PROBLEMS IN CONTEXT

Problems will also be set in context such that calculus techniques are required to find a maximum or minimum value. The following steps should be used:

- Draw a diagram of the situation.
- Find an equation with the variable to be maximised/minimised as the subject of the formula and one other variable.
- Find the first derivative and the values of x when the first derivative is zero.
- Check that the answer gives a maximum or minimum value which is within an acceptable domain.

Example:

A closed rectangular box has a square base of side x cm and a height of h cm. The internal surface area of the box is 400 cm^2.

Show that the volume, V cm^3, of the box is
$$V = 100x - \frac{x^3}{2}.$$

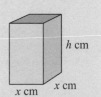

Hence, calculate the value of x to give the box a maximum volume.

Solution:

Surface area of the box is $\quad A = 2x^2 + 4xh$
$$\therefore \quad 400 = 2x^2 + 4xh$$
$$\therefore \quad 4xh = 400 - 2x^2$$
$$\therefore \quad h = \frac{400 - 2x^2}{4x}$$

If V is the volume of the box then $\quad V = x^2h$
$$\therefore \quad V = x^2\left(\frac{400 - 2x^2}{4x}\right)$$
$$\therefore \quad V = \frac{400x^2}{4x} - \frac{2x^4}{4x}$$
$$\therefore \quad V = 100x - \frac{x^3}{2}.$$
$$\therefore \quad \frac{dV}{dx} = 100 - \frac{3x^2}{2}$$

For a turning point $\frac{dV}{dx} = 0$ and so $100 - \frac{3x^2}{2} = 0$

This equation has solution $x = \sqrt{\frac{200}{3}} \approx 8.16$

So, for maximum volume, $x \approx 8.16$ cm.

We check that this case provides a maximum by using a graphics calculator and a sketch of the graph.

TOPIC 7 – CALCULUS (SHORT QUESTIONS)

1 Consider the function $y = x^3 - 4.5x^2 - 6x + 13$.

  a Find $\frac{dy}{dx}$.

  b Calculate the x-coordinates of the points on $y = x^3 - 4.5x^2 - 6x + 13$ where the tangent has a gradient of 6.

2 Consider the graph of $y = ax^2 + bx + c$ where a, b and $c \in \mathbb{R}$ and $a \neq 0$.

  a Find $\frac{dy}{dx}$ in terms of a, b and c.

  b When $x = k$, $\frac{dy}{dx} = 0$. Find the value of k in terms of a, b and c.

  c It is known that for $x < k$, $\frac{dy}{dx} < 0$.

   Write down if y is increasing or decreasing when $x < k$.

d It is also known that for $x > k$, $\dfrac{dy}{dx} > 0$.

Write down if $x = k$ corresponds to a local maximum or local minimum point.

3 a Write $y = \dfrac{7}{x^3}$ in the form $y = 7x^k$, where $k \in \mathbb{Z}$.

b Hence, differentiate $y = \dfrac{7}{x^3}$, giving your answer in the form $y = \dfrac{a}{x^b}$, where $b \in \mathbb{N}$.

4 Consider the graph of $y = \dfrac{2x^4 - 4x^2 - 3}{x}$.

a Write the equation as three separate terms in the form ax^k, $k \in \mathbb{Z}$.

b Differentiate y with respect to x.

c Find the gradient of y at $x = -1$.

5 For the function $f(x) = 3x^2 - \dfrac{4}{x} + 7$,

a Find $f'(x)$.

b Hence, find $f''(x)$.

6 The graph of $y = f(x)$ is shown. At $x = 2$, the tangent to $f(x)$ is horizontal.

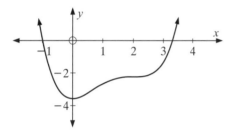

a State the values of x for which $y = f(x)$ is
i increasing **ii** decreasing.

b Without finding the function $f(x)$, find x when $f'(x) = 0$.

c On the diagram given, draw the tangent to $y = f(x)$ at $x = 3$.

7 Consider the function $f(x) = x^4 - 6x^2 - x + 3$.

a Find $f'(x)$.

b Find $f''(x)$.

c Hence or otherwise, find the x-coordinates of any maximum or minimum values of $f'(x)$.

8 A function $g(x) = \left(3x - \dfrac{1}{x}\right)^2$.

a Fully expand and simplify $g(x)$.

b Hence, find $g'(x)$.

c Find the gradient of $y = g(x)$ at $x = -1$.

9 a Differentiate the function $y = 2x^3 - 3x^2 - 264x + 13$.

b Hence, find the x-coordinates of the points where the gradient of $y = 2x^3 - 3x^2 - 264x + 13$ is equal to -12.

10 A function is defined as $f : x \mapsto ax^2 + bx + c$, where a, b and c are integers.

a Find an expression for $f'(x)$.

b Given that $f'(x) = 2x - 6$, find the values of a and b.

c The minimum value of f is 2.
i Determine the x-coordinate of the minimum value of f.
ii Hence, find the value of c.

11 The velocity of an object (in km/h) is modelled by the function $v(t) = 7t - t^2$ for $0 \leqslant t \leqslant 7$.

a Find the velocity at $t = 1$.

b At what other time on $0 \leqslant t \leqslant 7$ is the velocity the same as at $t = 1$?

c Find $v'(t)$.

d Hence, find the maximum velocity of the object.

12 The tangent to the curve $y = x^2 - kx + 11$, $k \in \mathbb{Z}$, is known to pass through two points A(6, 7) and B(0, −5).

a Find the gradient of the tangent which passes through A and B.

b Find $\dfrac{dy}{dx}$ in terms of k.

c Given that C is the point of contact where the tangent meets the curve, find the value of k if C has an x-coordinate of 4.

13 Consider the function $f(x) = x^2$.

a Find $f(2)$.

b Find $f(2 + h)$.

c Given that $m = \dfrac{f(2 + h) - f(2)}{h}$, find m in terms of h, in simplest form.

14 a Differentiate the function $y = \dfrac{4}{x} + x$ with respect to x.

b Calculate the values of x for which $\dfrac{dy}{dx} = 0$.

c Hence, find the coordinates of any local maximum or minimum values.

15 The height H of a small toy aeroplane t seconds after it is thrown from the top of a building is given by the function $H(t) = 80 - 5t^2$ where $t \geqslant 0$.

a Find the initial height of the toy aeroplane.

b Determine the time it takes for the toy aeroplane to hit the ground.

c Find $H'(t)$.

d Find $H'(2)$ and interpret a meaning for this value.

16 a Write the expression $\dfrac{4 - 3x + x^2}{x^2}$ as three separate fractions.

b Find $\dfrac{d}{dx}\left(\dfrac{4 - 3x + x^2}{x^2}\right)$

c Solve $\dfrac{d}{dx}\left(\dfrac{4 - 3x + x^2}{x^2}\right) = 0$

17 Consider the equation of the curve $y = \dfrac{a}{x} - x^2 + 1$ where a is a real number.

a Find the value of a if the gradient of the curve is -5 when $x = 2$.

b Using this result, find the point on the curve where $x = 2$.

c Hence, determine the equation of the tangent to the curve at $x = 2$.

18 The distance s (in kilometres) of a group of hikers from their base camp t hours after starting out is given by
$s = 2t^3 - 18t^2 + 54t$ for $0 \leqslant t \leqslant 5$.

a Calculate the average speed of the hikers in the first 4 hours.

b Find $\dfrac{ds}{dt}$.

c Find the values of t for which $\dfrac{ds}{dt} = 0$ and hence determine the distance travelled by the hikers before they stop momentarily within the first 4 hours.

19 The function $f(x) = x^3 - 3x^2 - 24x + 26$.

a Find $f'(x)$.

b Find the values of x such that $f'(x) = 0$.

c Find $f''(x)$.

d Find the value of x such that $f''(x) = 0$.

20 The graph below shows the function $y = k^x$, where $k > 0$ and $x \in \mathbb{R}$.

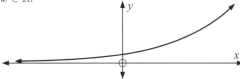

a Determine where $y = k^x$ is increasing.

b Find the y-intercept

c Given that the gradient of $y = k^x$ is $m = 1$ at $x = 0$, find the equation of the tangent at $x = 0$.

21 a By first calculating $\dfrac{dy}{dx}$, determine the gradient of the tangent to the curve $y = x^3 - x + 2$ at the point where $x = -1$.

b Another tangent to the curve $y = x^3 - x + 2$ exists at $x = k$. The tangent at $x = k$ is parallel to the tangent at $x = -1$. Find k.

22 Consider the function $f(x) = \dfrac{6}{x} - \dfrac{2}{x^3}$.

a Find $f'(x)$.

b Find the value of x for which $f'(x) = 0$.

c Find the equations of the tangents to $y = f(x)$ at the points where $f'(x) = 0$.

23 The distance s (in kilometres) travelled by a truck after t hours is given by $s(t) = t^4 - 12t^3 + 48t^2 + 4t$.

a Find $s'(t)$ and evaluate at $t = 3$ hours.

b Find $\dfrac{s(3) - s(0)}{3 - 0}$.

c Give an interpretation to the meaning of the answer to **b**.

24 Consider the function $f(x) = \frac{1}{3}x^3 - x^2 - 15x + 15\frac{2}{3}$.

a Differentiate $f(x)$ with respect to x.

b Calculate the values of x where $f'(x) = 0$.

c The corresponding y-coordinates for the maximum and minimum values of $f(x)$ are $42\frac{2}{3}$ and $-42\frac{2}{3}$ respectively and the y-intercept is $15\frac{2}{3}$.

Using this information, sketch the graph of $f(x)$ indicating clearly the local maximum, local minimum and y-intercept.

25 Consider the function $y = x^3 - 3x + 2$.

a Find $\dfrac{dy}{dx}$.

b Hence, find the position of the local maximum and local minimum points.

c Sketch the graph of $y = x^3 - 3x + 2$ clearly showing the maximum and minimum points and the y-intercept.

TOPIC 7 – CALCULUS (LONG QUESTIONS)

1 Consider the function $f(x) = 4x^2 - 3x - \dfrac{2}{x}$.

a Calculate $f(-1)$.

b Differentiate $f(x)$ with respect to x.

c Calculate the gradient of $y = f(x)$ at $x = -1$.

d Hence, determine the equation of the tangent to $y = f(x)$ at $x = -1$.

e Use your graphic display calculator to find the coordinates of the other point where the tangent to $y = f(x)$ at $x = -1$ meets the curve.

2 The cost C (in dollars) of producing x bracelets is modelled by the function $C(x) = -0.2x^2 + 4x + 10$ for $0 \leqslant x \leqslant 10$.

a Calculate $C(5)$ and explain what this represents.

b Differentiate C with respect to x (i.e., find $C'(x)$).

c State the units that $C'(x)$ would be measured in.

d Find $C'(5)$.

e Is C increasing or decreasing at $x = 5$?

f Determine the maximum value of C on $0 \leqslant x \leqslant 10$.

3 Consider the cubic function $y = x^3 + ax^2 + bx + 3$, where a and b are integers.

a The point $(1, 8)$ is known to exist on $y = x^3 + ax^2 + bx + 3$. Using substitution, find an equation containing only a and b.

b Determine $\dfrac{dy}{dx}$ in terms of a and b.

c A tangent with equation $y = 2x + 6$ exists at $(1, 8)$.

  i Determine the gradient of the tangent at $x = 1$.

  ii Write down a second equation containing only a and b using this information.

d Hence, determine the values of a and b.

4 A tank is being filled with water in such a way that the volume of water, V litres, in the tank after a time t minutes is given by $V(t) = 10t^2 - \frac{1}{3}t^3$, for $0 \leqslant t \leqslant 30$.

a Find $V(5)$ and explain what this represents.

b Calculate $V'(t)$ and express your answer in fully factorised form.

c Write down the units that $V'(t)$ is expressed in.

d Find t when $V'(t) = 0$.

e Find $V'(5)$ and $V'(25)$.

f Determine the range of values for which $V(t)$ is increasing.

g Determine the maximum value of $V'(t)$.

5 A function $f(x) = Ax + \dfrac{B}{x}$ is known to have a tangent with equation $y = 3x + 2$ at $x = 1$. A and B are integers.

a Find the coordinates of the point where the tangent touches $f(x)$.

b Using this result, form an equation involving A and B.

c Find $f'(x)$ in terms of A and B.

d Calculate the gradient at $x = 1$.

e Using the results from **d** and **e**, form another equation involving A and B.

f Find the values of A and B.

6 A rectangular dog enclosure is to be constructed against a wall using fence material (as shown in the diagram).

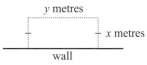

a Given that 30 metres of fence is available, show that $y = 30 - 2x$.

b Hence, find an expression for the area of the enclosure $A(x)$ in terms of x only.

c If the area of the enclosure is to be 100 m^2, determine the dimensions of the enclosure.

d Using differential calculus, find the *dimensions* of the largest possible area that can be created with the 30 metres of fence.

e Find the largest possible area.

7 Consider the graph of $y = f(x)$ where $f(x) = x^3$.

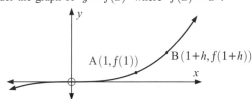

a Point A is located on $y = f(x)$ at $x = 1$. Find the coordinates of A.

b The point B is located at $x = 1 + h$. Find the coordinates of B if: **i** $h = 1$ **ii** $h = 0.1$ **iii** $h = 0.01$

c Hence, find the gradient of AB if:
  i $h = 1$ **ii** $h = 0.1$ **iii** $h = 0.01$

d Which value of h would provide a better approximation to the gradient of the tangent to $y = f(x)$ at $x = 1$?

e By finding the derivative of $f(x) = x^3$, find the actual gradient of the tangent to $y = f(x)$ at $x = 1$.

8 A rectangular box with an *open* top (no lid) is to be constructed using a piece of cardboard as shown. The maximum amount of material available is 1200 cm².

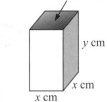
open top

y cm

x cm

x cm

a Find an expression for the total surface area of the box.

b Hence, show that $y = \dfrac{1200 - x^2}{4x}$.

c Find an expression for the volume V in terms of x only.

d Find $V'(x)$.

e Using this result, find the dimensions which produce the maximum volume.

f Determine the maximum volume.

TOPIC 8   **FINANCE**

SUMMARY

CURRENCY CONVERSION

- Given a **ratio**, for example, USD : GBP = 1 : 0.5623

  1 USD can be exchanged for 1×0.5623 GBP

  1 GBP can be exchanged for $\dfrac{1}{0.5623}$ USD.

- Given **buying** and **selling** values

  ▶ **Selling:**

  Foreign currency bought = other currency sold × *selling* rate

  Cost in other currency = $\dfrac{\text{foreign currency bought}}{\text{selling rate}}$

  ▶ **Buying:**

  Foreign currency sold = your currency bought × *buying* rate

  Your currency bought = $\dfrac{\text{foreign currency sold}}{\text{buying rate}}$

- **Commission**

  ▶ Deducted as a fixed percentage per transaction *or*

  ▶ Calculated by difference between *buying* and *selling* rates.

Example:

Stefan plans to travel from France to Hawaii for a week's holiday. He converts 2000 Euro to USD to cover his expenses. The exchange rate from Euro to USD is 1 : 1.191. His bank charges a commission of 1% on each transaction.

a Calculate the amount of USD he will receive.

b At the last moment, Stefan has to cancel his holiday due to illness and he converts the USD back to Euro. How many Euros will he get?

Solution:

a He receives $2000 \times 1.191 \times 0.99 = 2358.18$ USD.

{for 1% commission, multiply by 0.99}

b He gets $\dfrac{2358.18}{1.191} \times 0.99 = 1960.20$ Euro.

SIMPLE INTEREST

Simple Interest is calculated using $I = \dfrac{Crn}{100}$ where

     C is the capital, the amount invested or borrowed

     n is the time in years

     r is the annual interest rate

     I is the interest earned or charged.

     (See also topic 2 on arithmetic sequences.)

- Repayments for loans = $\dfrac{\text{capital} + \text{interest}}{\text{number of repayments}} = \dfrac{C + I}{N}$

- Use of gdc solver to find C, r and n.

Example:

A loan of $6000 at 6% p.a. simple interest is taken over 5 years.

a Calculate the amount that needs to be repaid.

b Determine the monthly repayment.

Solution:

a $I = \dfrac{Crn}{100} = \dfrac{6000 \times 6 \times 5}{100} = \$1800$

     ∴ the amount to be repaid is $C + I = \$7800$.

b Monthly repayment = $\dfrac{\$7800}{5 \times 12 \text{ months}} = \$130.00$

COMPOUND INTEREST

Compound interest is calculated using $I = C\left(1 + \dfrac{r}{100}\right)^n - C$

where

C is the capital, the amount invested or borrowed

n is the time in years

r is the annual (nominal) interest rate

I is the interest earned or charged.

(See also topic 2 on geometic sequences.)

- For finding the amount use: $F_v = C\left(1 + \dfrac{r}{100}\right)^n$

  Note: $I = F_v - C$

- Periodic Compounds

Half-yearly;	use $\frac{r}{200}$	and $n \times 2$
Quarterly;	use $\frac{r}{400}$	and $n \times 4$
Monthly;	use $\frac{r}{1200}$	and $n \times 12$
Daily;	use $\frac{r}{36500}$	and $n \times 365$

- Repayments for loans $= \dfrac{\text{capital} + \text{interest}}{\text{number of repayments}}$

  $\qquad = \dfrac{C + I}{N}$

  $\qquad = \dfrac{F_v}{N}$

- Use of gdc (**TVM** or **solver**) to find C, r and n.

Example:

A loan of £6000, at a nominal rate of 6% p.a. compounding quarterly over 5 years, is to be repaid.

a Find the amount required to be repaid.

b Determine the quarterly repayment.

c Find the nominal rate of interest which will result in a quarterly repayment of £480 when £6000 is borrowed over 5 years with quarterly compounds.

Solution:

a $F_v = C\left(1 + \dfrac{r}{100}\right)^n = 6000 \times \left(1 + \dfrac{6}{400}\right)^{5 \times 4}$

$\qquad\qquad = 6000 \times \left(1 + \dfrac{6}{400}\right)^{20}$

$\qquad\qquad = £8081.13$

b Quarterly repayment = $\dfrac{£8081.13}{20} = £404.06$

c Total repayment = £480 × 20 = £9600

So, we need to solve for r in

$9600 = 6000\left(1 + \dfrac{r}{400}\right)^{5 \times 4}$

∴ the rate is 9.51% per annum. {using a gdc}

DEPRECIATION

For calculating a **future value** being **depreciated** at a **fixed rate** of r% p.a. we use

$$F_v = C\left(1 - \dfrac{r}{100}\right)^n$$

- **Depreciation** is the **reduction** in the value of an asset over time.
- The formula calculates annual compounds only.
- F_v is also known as B_v, the **Book value** of an asset.

INFLATION

- **Inflation** is the increase in the value of money over time.
- We are concerned only with inflation for a **fixed** percentage rate with **annual** compounds only.

   Real increase
   = current value − indexed value (indexed for inflation)

Example:

An old piece of furniture was valued recently at 25 000 JPY. The furniture was purchased for 18 000 JPY five years ago. The average annual rate of inflation has been 4.75% for the past 5 years.

The real increase in value is defined as
the current value − the original value, indexed for inflation.
Find the real increase in the value of the piece of furniture.

Solution:

$$\text{Cost, indexed for inflation} = 18\,000 \times (1.0475)^5$$
$$= 22\,701 \text{ JPY}$$

$$\text{Real increase in value} = 25000 - 22700.88$$
$$= 2299 \text{ JPY}$$

Note:

- Can you read depreciation and inflation **tables**?
- Read the question carefully as
  ▶ many loan / repayment tables are per \$1000
  ▶ many tables round off final values.
- Note carefully compounding rates and periods.
- **multipliers** are $\left(1 + \frac{r}{100}\right)$ or $\left(1 - \frac{r}{100}\right)$
- Can you prepare Depreciation Schedules?

TOPIC 8 – FINANCE (SHORT QUESTIONS)

1 The exchange rate from United States Dollars (USD) to British Pounds (GBP) is 1 : 0.5768.
  a Determine the exchange rate from GBP to USD.
  b How many British pounds will I receive when I change USD 365?
  c How much USD will I receive for GBP 500?

2 A bank's exchange rate for 1 Euro is 141.9 Japanese Yen. The bank charges 1% commission on each transaction.
  a Calculate the amount of Yen that would be received if 1000 Euro were exchanged.
  b How much Euro would be received if 46 000 Yen were exchanged?

3 Given that   CNY : PHP = 1 : 6.684   and
          PHP : INR = 1 : 0.8559,
  a find the number of Indian Rupees (INR) that would be received when 2000 Chinese Yuan (CNY) is exchanged.
  b Find the amount of CNY that 5000 INR would convert to.

4 A bank in Scotland offers the following rates for changing 1 British Pound (GBP) to Canadian Dollars (CAD), 'buy at 2.0113', 'sell at 1.9854'.
  a Convert GBP 300 to CAD.   **b**   Convert CAD 300 to GBP.

5 A currency exchange service changes USD to CHF using 'buy at 1.311', 'sell at 1.286'.
  Shelley wants to exchange 400 dollars (USD) to Swiss Francs (CHF).
  a How much will she receive?

b If Shelley changes the Francs back to USD immediately, how many dollars will she get?
  c How much has the exchange of currencies cost Shelley?

6 The exchange rate from Japanese Yen (JPY) to Australian Dollars (AUD) is 1 : 0.01106
  A commission of 1.5% is charged per transaction.
  a Determine the amount of commission (in AUD) charged for changing 60 000 Yen to Australian dollars.
  b How many dollars would be received?
  c If the dollars were converted back to Yen immediately, how many Yen would there be?

7 Annie and Dave won a prize of \$5000. They spent half the money and placed the remainder in an investment account, which paid simple interest at 6.5% per annum.
  How much would be in their account after $3\frac{1}{2}$ years?

8 An investment of 12 500 Philippine Pesos (PHP) has grown to 15 500 pesos after 4 years.
  a Calculate the annual rate of simple interest that would have applied to this investment.
  b If the annual rate had been 1% higher, how long would it have taken to earn the same amount of interest?

9 a How long will it take for CHF 4000 to earn CHF 1800 interest at 7.5% simple interest?
  b Determine the additional time required for the total amount to be CHF 6700.

10 An investment is valued at \$6000 after 5 years at an annual simple interest rate of 10%. Find the original value of the investment.

11 Jana takes out a loan to buy a car. She borrows \$5600 at 8.8% per annum, simple interest, to be repaid in equal monthly instalments over 3 years.
  a Determine the amount of interest to be paid.
  b Calculate the total amount that Jana has to repay.
  c Calculate the amount of the monthly repayment.

12 a Find the interest earned over 6 years if 30 000 rupees is invested in an account that pays 9% annual interest, compounded annually.
  b Determine the equivalent simple interest rate for this investment.

13 a Determine the value after 4 years and 3 months if \$4750 is invested at a nominal rate of 6.7%, compounded monthly.
  b How much interest has been earned?
  c How much less interest would have been earned if the interest rate had been compounded annually?

14 Which of the following provides the best return:
  a a nominal rate of 6%, compounded annually
  b a nominal rate of 5.94%, compounded quarterly
  c a nominal rate of 5.9%, with monthly compounds.

15 a Charles and Linda want to have one million dollars in 25 years time. How much would they need to place in an investment account, paying an annual rate of 9.5% compounding monthly, to reach their goal?
  b If they had invested the same amount at 9.5% annual simple interest, how much less would they have earned?

16 a How long will it take for \$6500 to earn at least \$2000 interest at a nominal rate of 8%, compounded quarterly?
  b Calculate the rate of interest, compounded annually, which would earn the same amount of interest over the same period of time.

Mathematical Studies SL – Exam Preparation & Practice Guide

17 Sanjay borrows INR 120 000 from a bank to purchase equipment for his business. Interest of 9.75%, compounding monthly, is charged. The terms of the loan require Sanjay to repay the total amount over 3 years, by quarterly instalments.

a Find the total amount that Sanjay must repay.

b Calculate the amount that he will have to repay each quarter.

c How much less would each quarterly payment be if the interest was compounded half-yearly?

18 CNY 20 000 is borrowed at a compound interest rate of 12% per annum, adjusted quarterly. The loan will be repaid at CNY900 per quarter.

The table below analyses the repayment of this loan for the first two quarters.

Quarter	Capital	Interest	Repayment	Amount Outstanding
1	20 000	600	900	19 700
2	19 700	591	900	19 391
3	19 391		900	
4			900	

a Complete the table for the third and fourth quarters.

b Draw a graph of the amount outstanding each year for the first 6 quarters.

19 Some furniture, purchased for €6000, is valued at €1200 after 5 years.

a Calculate the average annual depreciation per year.

b If the furniture depreciated by a set percentage each year, what would that rate be?

c List the annual book value at the end of each of the 5 years, if the furniture did depreciate by the rate found in **b**.

20 The value of a delivery van, purchased by a business for $20 000, will depreciate by 20% per annum.

The depreciation schedule below shows the value of the van at the start of each year, the depreciation for that year and the value of the van at the end of each year.

Year	Start Value	Depreciation (20% p.a.)	End Value
1	20 000	4000	16 000
2	16 000	3200	12 800
3	12 800		
4			

a Complete the table for years 3 and 4.

b In which year will the value of the van first fall below $5000?

21 **a** Find the book value of a computer after 3 years, if it was purchased for CAD 4500 and depreciated at a rate of 22.5% per annum.

b **i** What was the original cost of a tractor whose book value after 5 years was GBP 29 000 if the depreciation occurred at a rate of 17.5% per annum? Give your answer to the nearest dollar.

ii Determine the amount of depreciation for the 5 years and then find the constant amount per year, which would need to be taken from the original cost to achieve the same end book value.

22 Lin purchased a home in Adelaide in 1995 for $187 000. Real Estate values in Adelaide have increased by an average annual rate of 6% since that time.

a What would be the value of her home in 2005?

b If Lin sold her home in 2005 for $360 000, find the average annual rate of increase returned on her investment.

23 Mr and Mrs Gevers bought a meat pie at a football match and each paid $2. Mr Gevers commented that he could remember when the cost of a pie was only 40 cents.

a How long ago would this have been if the annual inflation rate had averaged 5% over this time?

b If the rate of inflation remains the same, how many years will it take for the price of a pie to reach $2.50?

24 The table below shows the inflation multiplier, for various rates of inflation and time periods.

Rate (r%) year (n)	2.5	3	3.5	4	4.5
1	1.025	1.03	1.035	1.04	1.045
2	1.0506	1.0609	1.0712	1.0816	1.0920
3	1.0769	1.0927	1.1087	1.1249	1.1412
4					
5	1.1314	1.1593	1.1877	1.2167	1.2462

a Complete the details for year 4.

b Use the values in the table to find:

i the price of an article in 3 years' time if the current cost is $250 and the average rate of inflation is 4%

ii how long ago (to the nearest year) the price of a packet of biscuits was $1.45, if the current price is $1.68 and inflation has averaged 3% per year

iii the rate of inflation which would apply if the price of goods increased from $560 to $611.52 over 2 years.

25 Marika is paid a salary of SAR25 000 per year. Her salary is expected to increase by 3% per year. Marika's expenditure is SAR 22 500 each year. The rate of inflation averages 5% per year.

a Write an equation that calculates the value of her salary (S) in n years' time.

b Write an equation to calculate the amount of her expenditure (E) in n years' time.

c How many years will it take for Marika's spending to be greater than her earnings?

TOPIC 8 – FINANCE (LONG QUESTIONS)

1 Hogie wants to buy a fishing boat for $27 000. He could pay for it either by:

Option 1: Paying 15% deposit to the boat dealer and $157.60 a week for 48 months. (Assume there are 4 weeks in a month.)

Option 2: Borrowing the full amount from the bank and repaying the loan at $578.70 a month for 5 years.

a For option 1:

i Calculate the amount of the deposit Hogie will need to pay.

ii How much will he have to borrow?

iii Calculate the amount of interest charged for this option.

iv Determine the total amount that Hogie will pay for the boat.

b How much will Hogie have to repay if he chooses option 2?

A third option would require Hogie to borrow the full amount at an annual simple interest rate of 6%.

He would have to repay the loan in equal monthly instalments over $4\frac{1}{2}$ years.

c **i** Find the total cost of the boat if he chose this option.

ii Determine the amount that Hogie would have to repay each month.

d How much will he save if he chooses the cheapest of the three options?

2 Marilia obtains a personal loan of $30 000 to renovate her home. The loan is to be repaid monthly over 5 years and the interest rate is 8.25% p.a.

a **i** Use the table below to determine the amount of each monthly repayment Marilia will have to make.

Table of monthly repayments per $1000

Term of Loan	7.00%	7.25%	7.50%	7.75%
5 years	19.7953	19.9155	20.0357	20.1559
10 years	11.6108	11.7413	11.8718	12.0023
15 years	8.9883	9.1288	9.2693	9.4098

Term of Loan	8.00%	8.25%	8.50%	8.75%
5 years	20.2761	20.3963	20.5165	20.6367
10 years	12.1328	12.2633	12.3938	12.5243
15 years	9.5503	9.6908	9.8313	9.9718

(**Note:** The resulting monthly instalments are rounded off to the next 10 cents.)

ii Calculate the total amount that Marilia will have to repay.

iii Determine the amount of interest that Marilia will pay.

iv Calculate the equivalent rate of simple interest charged on this loan for the 5 years.

b Marilia could borrow the money for the renovations from another lender. The nominal interest rate charged is 5%, compounding monthly. The loan would be repaid in equal monthly instalments over 4 years.

i Calculate the total amount to be repaid.

ii Determine the size of each monthly payment.

c What advice would you give Marilia? Justify your answer.

d List one disadvantage for Marilia if she chose the loan offered by the lender in part **b**.

3 Beryl deposited $1000 in an investment account on the first of January in 2001. The account pays 7.2% interest, compounded annually. The interest is added to the account on the last day of each year.

a How much was the investment worth at the end of 2001?

b Beryl invested an additional $1000 into the account on the first day of each of the years, 2002, 2003 and 2004.

Write down the value of her investment at the end of each of the years 2002, 2003 and 2004.

c Draw a bar graph of the value of Beryl's investment against time. Use 2 cm to represent 1 year on the horizontal axis and 1 cm to represent $500 on the vertical axis.

d If Beryl had chosen to make a single lump sum investment at the beginning of 2001, what amount would she have needed to invest, to end up with the same value at the end of 2004?

e If she had invested $4000 as a lump sum for the 4 years, what rate of simple interest would have earned the same amount of interest as her investment account?

4 In the compound interest formula, $I = C\left(1 + \frac{r}{100}\right)^n - C$, the term $\left(1 + \frac{r}{100}\right)$ is often called 'the multiplier'.
The table below shows the value of the multiplier for various rates and compounding periods.

Compound period	6%	7.5%	10%	12.5%
annual	1.06	1.075	1.10	c
quarterly	1.015	a	1.025	1.031 25
monthly	1.005	1.006 25	b	1.010 417

a Write down the values of a, b and c.

b Using the values from the table,

i show that the value of an investment of CHF 4000 will grow to CHF 5813.18 over 5 years at a nominal rate of 7.5%, compounded monthly

ii how long will it take for this investment to be greater than CHF 5000 at 10%, compounding quarterly?

c Determine the amount needed to be invested now, at 12.5%, compounding monthly, if the future value of the investment is to be CHF 10 000 after 7 years.

d The exchange rate for USD to Swiss francs (CHF) is 1 : 1.2778. A bank charges 1.5% commission for each transaction.

USD 6700 is changed to Swiss Francs. The money is then placed in a savings account that pays a nominal rate of 6%, compounding quarterly.

i Calculate the number of Swiss Francs to be invested.

ii Find the amount in the account after 9 months.

e If the Francs are changed back to US dollars after 9 months, how much USD will there be?

f What assumption are you making in part **e**?

5 Eddie wants to have £5500 in 3 years' time to travel overseas. He already has £1800 saved in an account paying 5.6% annual interest, compounding quarterly.

a **i** Calculate the value of his savings after 3 years.

ii Find the additional amount required to reach his target.

b Eddie's father has offered to add enough money to the original savings so that the final amount will be £5500. Find how much Eddie's father will need to add to the account.

c Eddie's friend Thomas is planning to travel overseas with him. Thomas is planning to borrow the whole amount and repay it by equal monthly instalments over the following 2 years. The bank will charge a nominal rate of 9%, compounding monthly on the loan.

i Find the total amount that Thomas will need to repay.

ii Determine the amount of each monthly payment.

d How much extra will Thomas pay for the trip compared to Eddie and his father?

6 Ali and Sam invest €5000 at 6.8% annual interest, compounded half-yearly.

a **i** Calculate the value of the investment after 4 years.

ii Determine the interest earned on the investment.

b At the end of the four years, 25% tax is required to be paid on the interest.

How much money do they have after the tax is paid?

c Ali and Sam could have invested the money at 6.5%, compounding quarterly.

Calculate the difference in the after tax amount if they had chosen this investment.

d A third option would have returned an after tax amount of €430 after 3 years.

i Calculate the amount of interest earned, before tax was paid.

ii Find the annual rate of interest, compounding monthly, which applied to this option.

7 Vitus deposited SAR 20 000 in a bank account which paid a nominal rate of 6.5% per year, compounding quarterly.

a **i** Show that the amount in the account after 1 year was SAR 21 332.03.

ii Determine the number of years it would take for the amount to reach SAR 25 884.45.

b At the end of the first year, Vitus thought about closing the account and placing the available funds in some company debentures, which paid 9.5% simple interest.

i If Vitus chose the debentures, calculate the value of the investment after 3 years.

ii How much extra could Vitus earn by investing in the company debentures?

c Vitus was concerned about the additional risk of investing in a company so he decided to keep part of the SAR 21 332.03 in the bank account and invested the other part in the com-

Mathematical Studies SL – Exam Preparation & Practice Guide

pany debentures. If the total value of the two investments was SAR 26 779.35 after 3 years, calculate the amount of money he left in the bank account.

8 Margarita bought a second-hand MGB sports car, in 1990, for $9500. From the time of purchase, the value of the car depreciated at an average annual rate of 17.5%.

a Copy and complete the table below, showing the book value of Margarita's car at the beginning and end of each of the first three years, and the amount of depreciation for each of those years.

Year	Book Value at start	Depreciation	Book Value at end
1	9500	1662.50	7837.50
2	7837.50		
3			

For the next two years, the value of the car depreciated by 10% per year.

b Write down the value of the car at the end of each of these two years.

c **i** Calculate the total amount of depreciation over the five years.

ii Find the compounding, annual depreciation rate for the whole of the five years.

d At the end of 1995, Margarita's MGB was 25 years old. It had become a 'classic'. Classic cars are much sought after by car enthusiasts and the price tends to rise over time.

If the average appreciation rate for Margarita's classic MGB was 8% per year after 1995, determine the value of her car at the end of 2005.

e Calculate the percentage change in the value of the MGB from the day of purchase.

Paper 1

1 The following list of numbers is given:
$$\sqrt{3}, \tfrac{1}{3}, 5, \pi, -5, \sqrt{16}, 0.\dot{6}.$$

a Write down the numbers from the list which belong to the set of integers.

b Write down the numbers from the list which belong to the set of rational numbers.

c Write down the numbers from the list which belong to the set of natural numbers.

2 A function $f : x \mapsto 2x^2 + x - 3$ is defined for
$$x \in \{-2, -1, 0, 1, 2\}$$

a Represent f using the given mapping diagram.

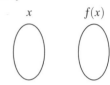

b **i** Express the elements of the domain of f using interval notation.

ii List the elements of the range of f.

3 The exact measurements of the length and width of a rectangular swimming pool are 9.85 m and 5.90 m respectively.

a Calculate the area of the surface of the swimming pool.

b Jonty rounds these measurements to the nearest whole number before he calculates the area.

Determine the percentage error in Jonty's calculation.

4 30 students were asked the type of milk drinks they liked. 8 students said they liked plain milk only, 13 liked chocolate milk only and 4 students did not like either.

a Find the number of students who liked both plain and chocolate milk.

b Represent the information above on a Venn diagram.

c Determine the probability of a student, chosen at random from this group, liking only one type of milk.

5 The frequency table below shows the price of tickets for attending various events at the Festival of Arts.

Cost ($)	Number of events
20 - 39	12
40 - 59	15
60 - 79	11
80 - 99	7
100 - 119	5

a Find the probability of a ticket for a randomly chosen event at the festival costing more than $60.

b Find the mean and standard deviation for the price of tickets.

c Find the percentage of events whose ticket price is less than 0.722 standard deviations above the mean.

6 Andy travels from New York to London. He can buy 1.00 USD for 0.80 GBP and can sell 1.00 USD for 0.75 GBP. Andy converts 2000 USD into GBP.

a How many GBP does he receive?

b He spends 1200 GBP whilst in London and then converts the remaining GBP back into USD.

Find how many GBP he has remaining?

c Calculate how many USD he receives.

7 The seventh term of a geometric sequence is 320 and the eleventh term is 5120. Find

a the common ratio

b the first term

c the twentieth term.

8 James and Lesley invested \$20 000 in a fund which paid 6.8% per annum nominal interest, compounded monthly.

   a Find the value of their investment after 48 months.

   b The average rate of inflation during these 4 years was 3.2% per annum.

     Increase the value of the original investment to account for inflation over the four years.

   c The real increase for an investment is defined as the actual increase − the original value, indexed for inflation.

     Calculate the real increase in the value of James and Lesley's investment.

9

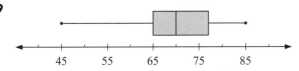

For the box plot shown above:

   a Find the values of the upper and lower quartiles.

   b Calculate the value of the interquartile range.

   c Determine whether the minimum value is an outlier.

10 A company produces plastic boxes. The company sells the boxes for \$12.50 each. The company estimates the cost of producing x boxes as $\$(9.5x + 45)$. Calculate:

   a the profit made when 100 boxes are produced and sold

   b the number of boxes which must be produced and sold for the firm to 'break-even' (Revenue = Cost)

   c the number of boxes needed to be produced and sold to make a profit of \$1000.

11 The truth table below shows some truth-values for the statement $(p \veebar q) \Rightarrow \neg(p \wedge q) \vee q$

$p \wedge q$	$\neg(p \wedge q)$	$p \veebar q$	$\neg(p \wedge q) \vee q$	$(p \veebar q)$ $\Rightarrow \neg(p \wedge q) \vee q$
T	F	F		
F	T	T	T	T
F	T	T	T	T
F	T			T

   a Fill in the missing truth-values on the table.

   b Write down the contrapositive of the statement:

     If Bozo is a clown then Bozo has a red nose.

12 a Find the equation of the line joining the points A$(-2, -3)$ and B$(1, 3)$, giving your answer in the form $ax+by+d = 0$ where a, b, $d \in \mathbb{Z}$.

   b Find the equation of the perpendicular bisector of AB.

13 A function is defined as $f(x) = ax^2 + bx + d$, where a, b and d are integers.

   a Find an expression for $f'(x)$.

   b If $f'(x) = 5x - 10$, find the values of a and b.

   c The minimum value of $f(x)$ is -4.

     Determine the x-coordinate of the minimum value of $f(x)$ and hence find the value of d.

14 A megaphone in the shape of a cone has vertical angle $60°$ and a slant height of 45 cm as shown in the diagram below.

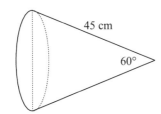

   a Determine the diameter of the megaphone.

   b Determine the volume of the megaphone.

15 The diagram shows part of the graph of a cosine function.

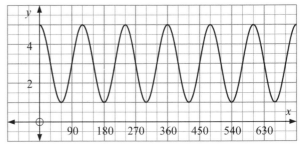

   a Using the graph:

     i write down the amplitude

     ii find the period.

   b If the graph has equation $y = a\cos(bx) + c$ state the values of a, b and c.

Paper 2

1 The coordinates of the vertices of a parallelogram are A$(-2, 1)$, B$(6, 3)$, C$(3, -1)$, and D$(-5, d)$. AC is a diagonal of the parallelogram.

   a Using a scale of 1 cm to represent 1 unit on both axes, plot the points A, B and C. (2 marks)

   b **i** Find the gradient of the line through B and C.

     ii Explain why the gradient of AD is the same as the gradient of BC.

     iii Find the value of d. (5 marks)

   c The length of AC is $\sqrt{27}$ units and BC is 5 units long.

     i Find the length of AB.

     ii Find the value of angle ABC. (6 marks)

   d Find the area of the parallelogram ABCD. (3 marks)

2 A sports locker at school contains 6 basketballs, 9 footballs and 5 volleyballs. During a sports lesson, a teacher chooses two balls from the locker at random, without replacement.

   a Draw a tree diagram showing all the possible outcomes. Write the probabilities for each branch on the diagram. (4 marks)

   b Find the probability that the teacher chooses:

     i two basketballs

     ii one basketball and one football

     iii both balls the same. (8 marks)

   c The two balls are replaced at the end of the lesson. During the next lesson, another teacher chooses a ball at random from the locker, replaces it, and then chooses a second ball. Determine the probability that the balls chosen are:

     i two volleyballs

     ii both basketballs, given that the two balls are the same. (6 marks)

3 The temperature of a cup of coffee in a plastic cup, t minutes after it is poured, is modelled by $T_P(t) = 61 \times (0.95)^t + 18$.

   a **i** Calculate the values of a and b in the table below.

Time t (min)	0	5	10	15	20	25	30
Temp. (°C)	a	65.2	54.5	46.3	39.9	34.9	b

     ii Find the time it will take for the temperature to reach $25°$. (4 marks)

   b On graph paper using 1 cm for every two minutes on the horizontal axis and 1 cm for every $10°C$ on the vertical axis, draw and label a graph representing this information. (4 marks)

Mathematical Studies SL – Exam Preparation & Practice Guide

c A china cup is used for a new cup of coffee. The temperature of coffee in the china cup T_F, t minutes after it is poured, is given by
$T_F(t) = 53 \times (0.98)^t + 18$

i Determine the initial temperature of the new cup of coffee.

ii Comment on the rate of heat loss of the china cup compared to the original plastic cup.

iii Using your graphic display calculator, determine the time it takes for the temperature within each cup to be equal.
Give your answer correct to the nearest tenth of a minute. (6 marks)

d In the longer term, what temperature will each cup of coffee approach? (2 marks)

4 a The following table shows the number of people using a public swimming pool in a particular month. The maximum daily temperatures vary from $18°$ to $35°$.

Max. temperature	°C	Daily attendance	
Mean	29.9	Mean	87.3
Standard Deviation	4.78	Standard Deviation	21.4

The covariance for temperature and attendance is 93.7.

i a Determine the value of the coefficient of correlation (r) for this data.

b Describe the nature of the relationship between the maximum temperature and attendance at the swimming pool. (5 marks)

ii Find the equation of the linear regression line for attendance as a function of temperature. (4 marks)

iii Use the equation of linear regression to estimate the number of people attending the pool on a day when the maximum temperature is:

a i $20°$ **ii** $40°$.

b Which of the estimates in **iii a** is the more reliable? Give a reason for your answer. (5 marks)

iv The manager of the pool plans to use the forecast temperature to determine the number of staff to be employed each day. Does the manager's plan seem sensible? Justify your answer. (2 marks)

b The manager of the pool records the gender of the swimmers attending the pool each day. She believes that the maximum temperature on any day causes a different attendance pattern for males and females.

Given the following information about average daily attendance and temperature, conduct a chi-squared test at the 5% significance level to determine if the manager is right.

	Temp. < 30	Temp. $\geqslant 30$
Male	36	47
Female	51	40

i Write down a suitable hypothesis for the chi-squared test. (1 mark)

ii Find the p-value of the chi-squared statistic for this data. (2 marks)

iii What conclusion can be drawn from the test? Justify your answer. (2 marks)

5 a For the function $f(x) = 3x^3 - 4x + 5$:

i Find $f(1)$. (2 marks)

ii Calculate $f'(x)$. (2 marks)

iii Find the gradient of the tangent at $x = 1$. (2 marks)

iv Determine, algebraically, the equation of the tangent to the curve given by $f(x) = 3x^3 - 4x + 5$ at the point where $x = 1$. (2 marks)

v The tangent to the curve at $x = 1$ intersects $f(x)$ at one other point.
Using your graphic display calculator, find the coordinates of this point of intersection. (2 marks)

b A rectangular box has a square base as shown.

i Write down an expression for the volume V of the box. (2 marks)

ii Given $y = \dfrac{30\,000 - x^2}{2x}$, write the volume in terms of x only. (2 marks)

iii Find $\dfrac{dV}{dx}$. (2 marks)

iv Hence, find the value of x which maximises the volume of the box. (3 marks)

SPECIMEN EXAMINATION B

Paper 1

1 The number 0.051762 is rounded to 0.0518

a State which *two* of the following are accurate descriptions of the rounding.

A Correct to 3 decimal places.

B Correct to 4 significant figures.

C Correct to 3 significant figures.

D Correct to the nearest ten-thousandth.

b Write 0.0518 in the form $a \times 10^k$ where $0 \leqslant a < 10$, $k \in \mathbb{Z}$.

c Calculate the percentage error in the rounding.

2 The histogram shows the weight of sheep (to nearest 10 kg).

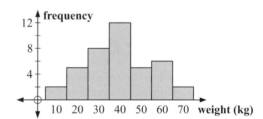

a Find the number of sheep that were weighed.

b Calculate the mean weight for these sheep.

c The farmer sends all sheep whose weight is more than 50% above the mean, to the market.

Determine the percentage of these sheep that will be delivered to the market.

3 Triangle ABC is shown in the figure with $AC = 10$ cm and $AB = 8.5$ cm. Angle $CDA = 90°$ and angle $ACD = 38°$.

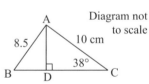

Calculate the length of: **a** DC **b** BD

4 The cost, in Euros, of producing x pairs of jeans is $C(x) = 15.6x + 245$. Each pair of jeans can be sold for €42.50. Find:

a the total revenue obtained by selling 22 pairs of jeans

b the cost of producing 22 pairs of jeans

c the profit made by producing and selling 22 pairs of jeans

d the profit per pair of jeans.

5 P and Q are subsets of a universal set U such that:

$U = \{1 \leqslant x \leqslant 13, \ x \in \mathbb{Z}\}$,

$P = \{$prime numbers between 1 and 13 inclusive$\}$,

$Q = \{$factors of 24$\}$

List the members of sets **a** P **b** Q **c** $(P \cup Q)'$

6 A box contains 10 wooden shapes. There are 5 triangles, 4 rectangles and 1 rhombus. 2 shapes are chosen at random from the box without replacement.

Calculate the probability that:

a both are triangles

b one of the chosen shapes is the rhombus

c the first chosen is a rectangle, given that the second is a rectangle.

7 The diagram shows a function $f(x)$, mapping members of the set A to members of set B.

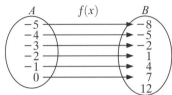

a Write down an inequality for x describing the domain.

b Using **set notation**, write down all members of the range of $f(x)$.

c Write down the equation of the function $f(x)$ in the form $y = mx + c$.

8 Jacinta won a prize of \$5000. She spent half the money and placed the remainder in an investment account which paid simple interest of 7.5% per annum.

a Calculate the amount that would be in the account after $3\frac{1}{2}$ years.

b Find the rate of simple interest that would have returned an amount of \$3400 in the account after $3\frac{1}{2}$ years.

9 a Differentiate the function $y = 2x^3 - 3x^2 - 264x + 13$.

b Hence, find the x-coordinates of the points where the gradient is equal to -12.

10 Eddie purchases 4 reams of paper and 3 pens for a total cost of £19.

Let the price of a ream of paper be £r and the price of a pen be £p.

a Write an equation in r and p that represents Eddie's purchase.

b If the cost of 2 pens was deducted from the cost of 3 reams of paper, the total amount would be £10.

Write a second equation in r and p that represents this information.

c Solve the two equations you have written simultaneously and hence determine the cost of purchasing 5 reams of paper and 5 pens.

11 The table below shows the different activities chosen by a class of final year students at their end of year expedition.

	Climbing	Swimming	Mountain Biking
Female	9	18	8
Male	15	16	24

It is decided to see if the activities chosen are independent of gender for this class. A χ^2 test is conducted at the 5% level of significance.

a Write down the table of expected values.

b Write down the χ^2 calculated test statistic.

c Find the p-value for the test.

d Write down the conclusion this test gives you. Give a clear reason for your answer.

12 Twenty numbers are in an arithmetic sequence. The sum of the numbers is 560 and the last number is 66. Find

a the first term

b the common difference.

13 a On axes like those below, sketch the graph of $y = \sin(2x) - 1$ for $0° \leqslant x \leqslant 360°$.

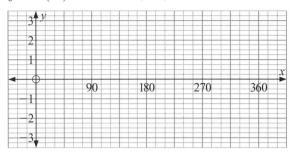

b Find the coordinates of the points where $y = \sin(2x) - 1$ meets the line $y = -\frac{1}{2}$ in the interval, $0° \leqslant x \leqslant 90°$.

14 Consider the function $y = \dfrac{2^x}{x-2}$.

If necessary, use your graphics display calculator to:

a find the value of y when $x = 3$

b find the y-intercept

c determine the minimum value of the function for $x \geqslant 2$

d write down the equation of the vertical asymptote.

15 A trapezium, ABCD has equal non-parallel sides AB and DC. The shorter parallel side is a cm, and the other parallel side is $2a$ cm. The height of the trapezium is 7 cm and its area is 42 cm^2.

a Draw a neat, labelled diagram to illustrate this information.

b Find the lengths of the parallel sides of trapezium ABCD.

Paper 2

1 Jaime invests in a savings scheme. She puts 500 USD into the bank on the 1st January each year from 2005 to 2015 inclusive. Interest is paid on the 31st December of each year at the rate of 2.5% per annum compounded annually.

a Calculate the amount Jaime will have in the bank on the 2nd January 2006. (3 marks)

b Calculate the amount she will have in the bank on the 2nd January 2007. (4 marks)

c i Write down a formula for a geometric series that represents the amount of money in Jaime's account after n years at midnight December 31st.

ii Find the amount that she will have in the bank at midnight on December 31st 2015. (5 marks)

d i Determine the total amount that Jaime invested over all these years.

ii Calculate the amount of interest earned on her total investment. (2 marks)

2 The following list shows the results of an examination that 30 students in an IB class took at the end of the first year of the course.

40, 55, 45, 70, 60, 65, 45, 48, 80, 75, 78, 85, 45, 38, 54, 75, 32, 75, 58, 65, 60, 75, 78, 45, 68, 85, 88, 45, 55, 68

a Draw an ordered stem and leaf diagram to show this information. (4 marks)

b Calculate the mean mark. (2 marks)

c Write down the:

i median **ii** lower quartile

iii upper quartile. (3 marks)

d Draw a box and whisker diagram to illustrate this information. (4 marks)

e Represent the examination results as a frequency table. Group the data with intervals of: 30 - 39, 40 - 49, 50 - 59, 60 - 69, 70 - 79, 80 - 89. (2 marks)

f Write down the modal group. (1 mark)

g Calculate an estimate of the mean from your frequency table. (2 marks)

h Determine the error in your estimated mean. (1 mark)

3 Consider the two parallel lines L_1: $y = 5 - 2x$ and L_2: $y = kx + c$.

a Draw the line L_1 for $-3 \leqslant x \leqslant 6, -3 \leqslant y \leqslant 6$. Use a scale of 1 cm to represent 1 unit on both axes. (4 marks)

b **i** Given that L_2 passes through $(2, -3)$ find the values of k and c.

ii On your graph, draw L_2. (5 marks)

c **i** Show that $(3, -1)$ lies on L_1.

ii Through the point $(3, -1)$ draw a line perpendicular to both L_1 and L_2. Label this line L_3. (4 marks)

d **i** Find the equation of L_3. Express your answer in the form $ax + by + d = 0$, where $a, b, d \in \mathbb{Z}$.

ii Determine the point of intersection of L_3 and L_2. (6 marks)

4 In a class of 40 students, 8 students like all three subjects: History, Science, and Music. 11 of the students like History and Science, 10 students like History and Music, and 13 students like Science and Music. In total 26 students like History, 21 like Science, and 16 like Music.

a Display this information on a Venn diagram. (4 marks)

b Find the probability that a randomly selected student

i likes History only

ii does not like Music

iii likes Music or Science but not History

iv likes at least one of the three subjects. (6 marks)

c Find

i P(Science ∩ Music)

ii P(History ∩ Science ∩ Music)′

iii P(History′ ∩ Science′) (5 marks)

d Find the probability that a student chosen at random likes History, given that they like Music. (2 marks)

e Find the probability that 2 students, chosen at random, both like History and Science. (3 marks)

5 a The diagram below shows the graphs of two functions: $y = 8 - x^2$ and $y = 2^{-x}$.

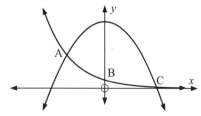

i Write down the coordinates of B, the y-intercept of the graph of $y = 2^{-x}$. (2 marks)

ii Find the coordinates of the two points of intersection, A and C. (3 marks)

iii Determine the values of x for which $2^{-x} > 8 - x^2$. (2 marks)

b Consider the graph of $y = \sin\left(\frac{x}{2}\right)$ for $0 \leqslant x \leqslant 720$.

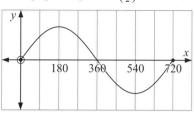

i Determine the interval of the domain for which $y = \sin\left(\frac{x}{2}\right)$ is

a increasing

b decreasing. (6 marks)

ii Find the values of x in the domain for which

a $\frac{dy}{dx} = 0$

b the gradient of the graph is the steepest. (5 marks)

SPECIMEN EXAMINATION C

Paper 1

1 Let $M = 6 \times 10^4$, $E = 1.5 \times 10^8$, $I = 8 \times 10^2$

a Calculate $\frac{M}{EI}$, giving your answer in the form $a \times 10^k$ where $1 \leqslant a < 10$, $k \in \mathbb{Z}$.

b Find the value of $\sqrt[3]{\dfrac{34.5^2 - 103}{50.5 + 19}}$ giving your answer

i correct to 4 significant figures

ii correct to the nearest whole number.

2 The temperature (in $^\circ$C) is measured at midday in Perth over a period of 10 days.

The results are: 18, 15, 20, 22, 18, 19, 15, 25, 24, 26

a Calculate the mean temperature.

b Find the median temperature.

c A newspaper publishes the mean temperature rounded to the nearest whole number.

Find the percentage error in rounding the mean temperature to the nearest whole number.

3 p and q are two propositions.

p: x is a prime number

q: x is a factor of 12

a Write down $p \Rightarrow \neg q$ in words.

b Find a value of x for which $p \Rightarrow \neg q$ is false.

c Write down, in words, the inverse of $p \Rightarrow \neg q$.

d State whether the inverse is true for all values of x giving a clear reason for your answer.

4 a Find the equation of the line passing through the points $(-2, 2)$ and $(1, 5)$.

b The equation of a second line is $x + y = 3$. Find the point of intersection of the two lines.

5 The cube shown has edges of length 20 cm.

The midpoint of AP is M. Calculate the length of:

a AC **b** CM

and find **c** angle CMR.

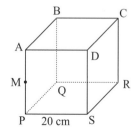

6 A series is given by $85 + 78 + 71 + \dots - 48$.

a Calculate the number of terms in the series.

b Find the sum of the terms in the series.

7 A bag contains 40 beads; some are green and some are yellow. The probability of a bead drawn at random being green is $\frac{1}{5}$.

a Find the number of green beads in the bag.

b Calculate the probability that two beads drawn at random from the bag are both yellow.

c Find the number of green beads that should be added to the bag to change the probability of drawing a green bead to $\frac{1}{2}$.

8 A function is given as $f(x) = x^2 + ax + b$. The zeros of $f(x)$ are $x = -1$ and $x = 3$.

a Find the values of a and b.

b Find $f'(x)$.

c Find the coordinates of the minimum point on the graph of $f(x)$.

9 The tables below show the number of pupils in three different groups who scored 0, 1, 2, 3, or 4 marks in a test question.

a

Marks	0	1	2	3	4
Number of pupils	5	9	x	6	8

Write down a possible value for x if the modal class is 2 marks.

b

Marks	0	1	2	3	4
Number of pupils	2	1	3	1	y

Write down a value for y if the median is 3 marks.

c

Marks	0	1	2	3	4
Number of pupils	z	4	3	2	1

Calculate z if the mean is 1 mark.

10 The points XZYW are on level ground. A surveyor knows that XY is 5 km and requires knowing the distances XZ and XW.

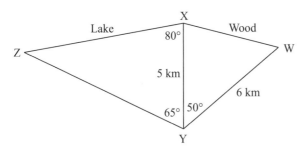

The distance XZ cannot be measured directly because of a large lake between X and Z. By measurement he finds that angle ZYX is $65°$ and angle ZXY is $80°$.

a Calculate XZ.

b A wood obstructs his view of W from X. He finds by measurement that YW is 6 km and angle XYW is $50°$. Calculate XW.

11 **a** Factorise $x^2 - 49$.

b Solve the equation $2 + 7x - 2x^2 = 4(1 + x^2)$.

12 Two variables x and y are such that:

$\overline{x} = 15.5$, $s_x = 2.58$, $\overline{y} = 24.0$, $s_y = 4.35$, $s_{xy} = 10.6$

a Calculate the correlation coefficient, r.

b Comment on your result for r.

c Find the equation of the regression line of y on x.

13 Complete the following truth tables:

a $p \vee \neg q$

p	q	$\neg q$	$p \vee \neg q$
T	T		
T	F		
F	T		
F	F		

b $(p \wedge q) \vee \neg q$

p	q	$\neg q$	$p \wedge q$	$(p \wedge q) \vee \neg q$
T	T	F		
T	F	T		
F	T	F		
F	F	T		

c State whether $p \vee \neg q$ and $(p \wedge q) \vee \neg q$ are logically equivalent. Give a clear reason for your answer.

14 Given the function $f(x) = \dfrac{10}{x} - x^2$:

a Find $\dfrac{dy}{dx}$.

b Determine the gradient of the tangent to the function $f(x)$ at the point where $x = -2$.

15 Water flows through a cylindrical pipe of radius 4 cm at a rate of 50 cms^{-1}.

a Find the volume of water, in litres, that passes through the pipe in 1 hour.

b The water is used to fill a swimming pool of dimensions 10 m $\times$ 4.50 m $\times$ 1.50 m.

Calculate how long it will take to fill the swimming pool.

Paper 2

1 **a** The 150 IB students at Russell High School can be members of the Performing Arts club (P), the Choir club (C) or the Sports club (S). It is given that:

$n(P) = 70$ $n(P \cap C) = 25$ $n(P \cap C \cap S) = 5$
$n(C) = 50$ $n(P \cap S) = 15$
$n(S) = 70$ $n(C \cap S) = 20$

i Draw a Venn diagram to illustrate this information. (4 marks)

ii Write down the number of students who are not members of any of the three clubs. (1 mark)

iii Find the probability that a student chosen at random belongs to the Performing Arts club. (2 marks)

iv Find the probability that a student chosen at random belongs to the Performing Arts club or the Choir club but not both. (2 marks)

v It is known that a student belongs to the Choir club. Calculate the probability that the student also belongs to the Sports club. (2 marks)

b At MacKenzie High School the students can only belong to one of the clubs: Performing Arts, Choir or Sports. The data is given in the table below.

	Performing Arts	Choir	Sports
Males	40	30	80
Females	20	50	30

A student believes that gender is a determining factor in belonging to a club. She decides to test this by conducting a χ^2 test at the 5% level of significance.

i Write down a suitable null hypothesis. (1 mark)

ii *Show that* the expected value for females belonging to the Sports club is 44. (2 marks)

iii Write down the χ^2 test statistic for this data. (2 marks)

iv State what the student's conclusion should be. Give a clear reason for your answer. (2 marks)

2 The population affected by a virus grows at a rate of 20% per day. Initially there are 10 people affected.

  a Find the number of people affected after 1 day. (2 marks)

  b Find the number of people affected after 1 week. Give your answer correct to the nearest whole number. (3 marks)

  c Let the number of people affected after t days be given by $f(t) = Na^t$.
State the value of **i** N **ii** a. (3 marks)

  d Using the graphical display calculator sketch the graph of $f(t)$ for $0 \leqslant t \leqslant 20$, showing clearly the value of the y-intercept. (4 marks)

  e Write down the range of $f(t)$ for the given domain. Give your answer correct to the nearest whole number. (3 marks)

  f Write down the equation of the horizontal asymptote of the graph of $y = 10(1.2)^t$. (2 marks)

3 The box and whisker plots below show the maximum daily temperatures of two cities during the month of September.

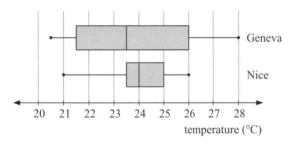

  a Write down the median temperature for Nice. (1 mark)

  b Write down the lower quartile for Nice. (1 mark)

  c Calculate the range and interquartile range for Nice. (3 marks)

  d The temperature range for Geneva is 7.5^oC and the interquartile range is 4.5^oC. Write down which city was hotter on average. (1 mark)

  e Explain the significance of the different lengths of the two boxes. (2 marks)

  f Find

    i the smallest possible number of days Geneva was hotter than Nice (3 marks)

    ii the largest possible number of days Geneva was hotter than Nice. (2 marks)

4 The United Bank of Australia offers compound interest of 3.5% per annum on its deposit account. Niki deposits 10 000 AUD in an account at this bank.

  a **Show that** at the end of 5 years the total amount will be approximately 11 900 AUD. (3 marks)

  b Calculate the number of complete years required for Niki's 10 000 AUD to double. (3 marks)

  c The Federal Bank of Australia offers a rate of interest which, compounded annually, will enable the amount to double in only 12 years. Calculate the rate of interest offered. (4 marks)

  d The Australian Credit Bank offers a nominal rate of interest of 3%, compounded quarterly. Sami deposits 5000 AUD. Calculate the amount of **interest** he will receive at the end of 6 years. (4 marks)

  e Niki and Sami travel from Australia to the Netherlands. They plan to take 5000 Euros with them. The Travellers Bank offers a rate of 1 Euro for 1.35 AUD and charges 1.5% commission. Calculate how many AUD they will pay for their Euros. (4 marks)

5 **a** The table below shows the depth of water (d) in a harbour at various times (t) in hours after midnight.

Time (t)	0	1	2	3	4	5	6
Depth (m)	12	17	20.6	22	20.6	17	12
Time (t)	7	8	9	10	11	12	
Depth (m)	7	3.4	2	3.4	7	12	

  i Using a horizontal scale of 1 cm to represent 1 hour and a vertical scale of 1 cm to represent 2 m, draw the graph of depth against time for $0 \leqslant t \leqslant 12$. (5 marks)

  ii High tide occurs at 3 am and low tide at 9 am.

    a Use your graph to determine the amplitude and period for this function.

    b The equation of the graph can be modelled by the function $d = a\sin(bt) + c$.
Write down the values of a, b and c (6 marks)

  b ABCD is a square piece of card from which four equal shaded squares are cut.

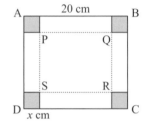

The remaining piece of card is folded along the dotted lines to form an open rectangular box with base PQRS. The length of AB is 20 cm. Each shaded square has sides of length x cm.

  i Write down the length of PQ in terms of x. (2 marks)

  ii Show that the volume, V, of the box is
$$4x^3 - 80x^2 + 400x.$$ (3 marks)

  iii Find $\dfrac{dV}{dx}$. (3 marks)

  iv Find the values of x for which $\dfrac{dV}{dx} = 0$. (3 marks)

  v State the value of x for which the volume is a maximum. (2 marks)

SPECIMEN EXAMINATION D

Paper 1

1 Calculate $\dfrac{\sqrt{2.068}}{1.203 \times 0.0237}$, giving the answer:

  a correct to 2 decimal places

  b correct to the nearest integer

  c correct to 6 significant figures

  d correct to the nearest ten thousandth

  e in the form $a \times 10^k$, where $1 \leqslant a < 10$ $(k \in \mathbb{Z})$.

2 Let p and q be the statements,

    p: Joshua studied hard at Mathematics

    q: Joshua passed Mathematics

  a Write the following logic statements in words

    i $\neg p \Rightarrow \neg q$ **ii** $\neg p \wedge q$

  b Write the following statement using symbols only.

    i If Joshua passed Mathematics then he had studied hard.

    ii Is the compound statement in **b i** the inverse, the converse or the contrapositive of $p \Rightarrow q$?

3 Before Maria left Italy for her holiday in Thailand, she converted her savings of 2400 Euro to Thai Baht to cover her travelling expenses. The exchange rate for Euro to Baht at the time was $1 : 46.184$. The bank charges a commission of 1.5% on each transaction.

  a Calculate the amount of Baht she received.

b Maria spent 90% of the Baht whilst on holiday. When she returned home, she converted the remaining Baht back to Euro, using the same bank. The exchange rate for Euro to Baht at that time was $1 : 45.865$.

Calculate the amount of Euro she received.

4 In a class of 28 Year 11, IB students; 12 study Economics, 17 study Math Studies and 6 students study neither of these.

a Use the information above to complete the Venn diagram alongside.

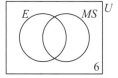

b Find the probability that a randomly chosen student from this class studies both Economics and Math Studies.

c A randomly chosen student from this class is known to study either Economics or Math Studies but not both.

Find the probability that this student studies Economics.

5 In triangle ABC, AB = 7.1 cm, BC = 4.7 cm and $\angle ABC = 92.7°$.

a Calculate the length of AC.

b Find the size of $\angle CAB$.

6 The population of a town t years after 1960 can be determined by the formula $P = 360 \times (1.045)^{\frac{t}{2}}$. Calculate:

a the population of the town in 1960

b the population of the town in 2005

c the year when the population reached 800.

7 The following passage contains 51 words that vary in length from 1 letter to 7 letters.

"Once a week we go to the shops. I ride in the cart while Bobby pushes. Up and down the aisles we go. We choose cereal and apples and cookies and raisins and a picture book. We pile them on the counter. Mommy pays and we all carry the bags home."

a Complete the table below for words containing 2 letters.

Number of letters	1	2	3	4	5	6	7
Number of words	3		12	11	5	5	4

b On a grid like the one provided, construct a *frequency polygon* to represent this data.

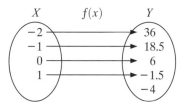

8 Yumiko places 2500 JPY in an investment account. Calculate the total amount of interest earned on this investment by the end of the fifth year if

a the account pays simple interest, of 3.2% per annum

b the rate is 3.2% per annum nominal interest, compounded quarterly.

9 The function $f : x \to f(x)$ maps the elements of X to elements of Y as shown below.

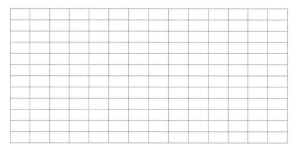

a **i** List the elements in the domain of f.
   ii List the elements in the range of f.

b The function f is of the form, $f(x) = ax^2 + bx + c$. Find the values of a, b and c.

10 The table below shows the length and weight of a sample of pumpkins.

	short	medium	long	Total
light	21	15	5	41
heavy	2	4	11	17
Total	23	19	16	58

a One pumpkin is chosen at random. Find the probability that it is

   i long and light

   ii not medium, given that it is light.

b A second pumpkin is chosen at random without the first one being replaced. Find the probability that the two pumpkins are both short and heavy.

11 A company's profits increase by 1.5% each year for a period of 10 years. In the first year the profit was 50 000 MAR.

a Calculate the profit in the 10th year.

b Find the total profit for the 10-year period, giving your answer correct to the nearest 5000 MAR.

12 A rectangle has its length 3 cm greater than its width. Let x be the width of the rectangle.

a Write down the length of the rectangle in terms of x.

b The rectangle has an area of 108 cm². Write down an equation in x that represents this information.

c Find the value of x by solving the equation.

d Find the values of the length and width of the rectangle.

13 David buys a new car for $45 000. At the end of the first year a new car decreases in value by 20%.

a Calculate the value of the car at the end of the first year.

b After the first year, the car decreases **further** in value by 12% per year. Calculate the value of the car at the end of the third year.

c David plans to sell the car when its value first falls below one third of its cost price. Calculate the number of years before he will sell the car.

14 Consider the function $y = (x - 2)^2 - 5$.

a Find $\dfrac{dy}{dx}$.

b Write down the gradient of the tangent to $y = (x-2)^2 - 5$ at the point $(3, -4)$.

c Determine the equation of the tangent to $y = (x - 2)^2 - 5$ at $(3, -4)$

15 A regular pentagon with sides of 15 cm is shown below. Diagonals BD and BE are drawn dividing the figure into three triangles. Triangle BED has area 173.12 cm².

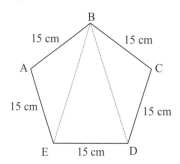

a The pentagon can be divided into 3 triangles as shown. Use this information to determine the size of each interior angle of the pentagon.

b Calculate the total area of the pentagon.

1 At the beginning of 1990 a toy company began with 25 employees. Since then, the number of employees has increased by an average rate of 4% per year.

    a Calculate the number of employees at the beginning of: **i** 1991 **ii** 2005   (3 marks)

    b Show that there were 32 employees at the company at the start of 1996.   (1 mark)

    c The table below shows the effect of average annual rates of inflation on the value of 1NZD for a number of time periods from 1990.

Years/Rate	4.5%	5.5%	$b\%$
5	1.246	1.307	1.370
10	1.553	1.708	1.877
15	a	2.232	2.572

    Find the values of a and b.   (3 marks)

    d The average salary paid to employees in the toy company was 18 000 NZD in 1991. Use the table of values to determine the average salary paid in 2005 if salaries had increased at a rate of 5.5% per year.   (2 marks)

    e Find the first year in which the average salary was more than 30 000 NZD if the average annual rate of inflation had been 4.5%.   (3 marks)

2 a At the end of a golf competition the individual scores of a number of competitors were recorded. The scores are given below.

    68, 73, 78, 84, 71, 67, 87, 66, 73, 73, 83, 79, 67, 70, 75

    i Represent the golf scores as an ordered stem and leaf diagram to show this.   (3 marks)

    ii Find the

        a median score

        b interquartile range of the scores.   (3 marks)

    iii Calculate the mean score.   (2 marks)

    iv The scores can be grouped in class intervals of 60 - 69, 70 - 79, and 80 - 89.
Copy and complete the frequency table.

Score	60 - 69	70 - 79	80 - 89
Frequency	4		

      (2 marks)

    v Calculate an estimate of the mean from the frequency table.   (2 marks)

    vi Calculate the percentage error of the estimate of the mean using your answers from **iii** and **v** above.   (2 marks)

    b The table below shows the number of vehicles using Holden Street between 7 am and 12 noon on a weekday.

Hour	frequency	Cumulative frequency
7:00 am -	14	14
8:00 am -	48	62
9:00 am -	35	
10:00 am -	24	
11:00 am -	22	

    i Copy and complete the table of **cumulative** frequencies.   (2 marks)

    ii Draw the cumulative frequency graph for this information. Use a scale of 2 units to represent 1 hour on the horizontal axis and 1 unit to represent 20 vehicles on the vertical axis.   (4 marks)

iii Use your graph to find:

    a the time when the 'median' vehicle drove down Holden Street

    b the approximate time of day when the 100th vehicle drove down the street

    c the number of cars which used the street between 9.30 am and 11.30 am

    d the time which would be considered to be the 25th percentile.   (4 marks)

3 Two vertical poles EG and FH stand on horizontal land, as shown in the diagram. The point D is 200 m to the left of the base of the pole FH. The angle from D to the top of the pole FH is $6.2°$. The distance from D to the top of the pole EG is DG = 57 m.

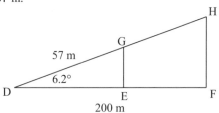

    a Find the distance between the base of the poles.   (3 marks)

    b Find the slant distance GH between the top of the poles.   (3 marks)

    c Find the size of the angle $F\widehat{E}H$, from E to the top of the pole FH.   (4 marks)

    d Determine the height of the shorter pole EG.   (2 marks)

    e Calculate the area of the triangle EGH.   (4 marks)

4 a Consider the propositions: p: The weather is fine.
                          q: The bus is late. r: I will walk to school.

p	q	r	$(p \wedge q)$	$\neg r$	$(p \wedge q) \Rightarrow r$	$(\neg p \vee \neg q)$	$(\neg p \vee \neg q) \Rightarrow \neg r$
T	T	T	T	F			
T	T	F	T	T			
T	F	T	F	F			
T	F	F	F	T			
F	T	T	F	F			
F	T	F	F	T			
F	F	T	F	F			
F	F	F	F	T			

    i Copy and complete the last three columns of the truth table.   (3 marks)

    ii State whether the compound statements, $p \wedge q \Rightarrow r$ and $\neg p \vee \neg q \Rightarrow \neg r$ are logically equivalent, tautologies, contradictions or none of these.   (1 mark)

    iii Write the statement $\neg p \vee \neg q \Rightarrow \neg r$ in words. Begin with "If the weather is not fine ......".   (2 marks)

    iv Write down the inverse of the statement, "If the bus is late then I will not walk to school."   (2 marks)

    b The probability that the weather is fine on any day is 0.7. The probability that the bus is late on any day is 0.4. Find the probability of:

    i the weather being fine on two consecutive days   (2 marks)

    ii the weather being fine and the bus not being late on two consecutive days.   (4 marks)

5 An object is travelling towards the ground. The vertical height H of the object, t seconds after it is first observed, is modelled by the function $H(t) = 1600 - 4t^2$ metres, $0 \leqslant t < 20$.

  a Sketch the graph of $y = H(t)$ for $0 \leqslant t < 20$, $0 \leqslant y \leqslant 1600$.   (3 marks)

  b **i** Show that the amount of time the object remains in the air, from the moment it is first observed, is 20 seconds.   (2 marks)

    ii Find the vertical height of the object at the moment it is first observed.   (2 marks)

    iii Find the average speed of the object's descent to the ground, given that average speed $= \dfrac{\text{distance}}{\text{time}}$.   (2 marks)

  c **i** Calculate $H(10)$.   (2 marks)

    ii Show that
$$H(10 + h) = 1200 - 80h - 4h^2.$$
  (3 marks)

    iii Simplify the expression
$$\frac{H(10 + h) - H(10)}{h} \text{ in terms of } h.$$
  (2 marks)

  d **i** Find $H'(t)$.   (2 marks)

    ii State if the function H is an increasing or decreasing function. Give a reason for your answer.   (2 marks)

    iii Find the values of $H'(5)$ and $H'(10)$.   (2 marks)

    iv Comment on the difference in the values found for $H'(5)$ and $H'(10)$.   (2 marks)

SPECIMEN EXAMINATION E

Paper 1

1 Given $x = 5$, $y = 12$, $z = 100$:

  a Find the value of x^2yz^3.

  b Write this number in the form $a \times 10^k$ where $1 \leqslant a < 10$ and $k \in \mathbb{Z}$.

  c Find the value of $\sqrt{x^2yz^3}$.

  d Give your answer to **c** correct to 2 significant figures.

2 In a recent test out of 40 marks, the students in a 2-Unit Maths class scored the following marks:

    35, 24, 28, 30, 18, 32, 38, 32, 19, 27

  a Rank these marks in **descending** order.

  b Calculate the median mark.

  c Find the probability that the result for a randomly chosen student was 5 marks or less from the median mark.

  d Find the probability that two students, chosen at random, both scored above 30 for the test.

3 Let $U = \{\text{all polygons}\}$
      $A = \{\text{all triangles}\}$ $B = \{\text{all quadrilaterals}\}$

  a Write down a subset of A.

  b Write down the name of a possible element of B'.

  c Represent the relationship between sets A and B on a Venn diagram.

  d Write down the number of elements in $A \cap B$.

4 Given two propositions, p and q.

  a Complete the truth table for the following statement:
$$(q \wedge \neg p) \Rightarrow (\neg q \vee p)$$

p	q	$\neg p$	$\neg q$	$(q \wedge \neg p)$	$(\neg q \vee p)$	$(q \wedge \neg p)$ $\Rightarrow (\neg q \vee p)$
T	T	F	F			
T	F	F	T			
F	T	T	F			
F	F	T	T			

  b State whether the final compound statement is a contradiction or not. Give a reason for your answer.

  c Write down, **in symbols**, the contrapositive of $(q \wedge \neg p) \Rightarrow (\neg q \vee p)$.

5 **a** Write down the factors of $m^2 - 6m - 27$.

  b Write down the zeros of $f(x) = 5x^2 + 53x - 84$.

  c Find the solutions of $3v^2 - 14v + 8 = 0$.

6 Let $A = \{-1, 0, 1, 2, 3\}$ and $B = \{1 \leqslant a < 9, a \in \mathbb{N}\}$. Draw the diagrams of the following mappings for A into B.

  a $m: \; a \rightarrow 3.5a + 1$ **b** $f: \; a \rightarrow a^2 - 1$

7 **a** On the axes below, sketch the graphs of

    i $y = \frac{3}{2}$ **ii** $2x - y - 3 = 0$.

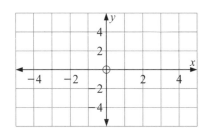

  b Find the **exact** value of the x-coordinate of the point of intersection of these two lines.

  c Write down the vertical distance from the line $y = \frac{3}{2}$ to the x-axis.

8 A sequence is given below.

    $\frac{1}{64}, \frac{1}{32}, \frac{1}{16}, \dots\dots, 16, 32, 64, 128, 256$

  a Write down the common ratio for the sequence.

  b Find the number of terms in this geometric sequence.

  c Calculate the sum of the sequence.

9 The heights (cm) of seedlings in a sample are shown below.

6	3 7	6 | 3 means 63
7	2 5 8	
8	3 6 6 8 8	
9	2 5 7 8	
10	3 6 6	
11	2 2	

  a Find the number of seedlings in the sample.

  b Write down the value of

    i the lower quartile   **ii** the median

    iii the upper quartile.

  c Draw a box and whisker plot for this data using a scale like the one below.

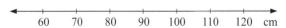

      60   70   80   90   100   110   120 cm

10 The cost ($\$C$), of producing a book, is given by $C(x) = 46\,000 + 11.50x$, where x represents the number of books produced. Each book sells for $\$30$.

  a Determine the profit if

    i 2000 books are produced and sold

    ii 5000 are produced and sold.

  b How many books must be sold for the publisher to break even, that is, for revenue to equal cost?

11 For the scalene triangle with dimensions shown:

  a Find the measure of angle BCA.

  b Determine the area of the triangle.

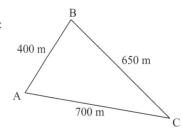

12 Philip invests 3500 AUD in an investment account which pays 5.2%, nominal interest, per annum.

   a Find how much the investment is worth at the end of the seventh year if:

     i the account pays 5.2% simple interest per annum

     ii the account pays nominal interest of 5.2% per annum, compounded monthly.

   b Determine the difference in the amount of interest paid.

13 Consider the graph of the quadratic function shown.

The axis intercepts are all integers.

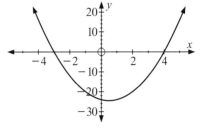

   a Write down the coordinates of the x-intercepts.

   b Determine the equation of the axis of symmetry.

   c Find the equation of the function.

   d Find the minimum value of the function.

14

P	25	45	70	55	45	90	35	45
Q	74	21	35	37	54	35	61	55

Using your graphic display calculator:

   a Write down the equation of linear regression and the coefficient of correlation.

   b Observe the scatter plot for this data. Remove the outlier and recalculate the equation of the regression line and the correlation coefficient.

   c Comment on the change in the gradient of the regression line and the strength of the relationship as a result of removing the outlier.

15 Consider the cubic function shown in the diagram.

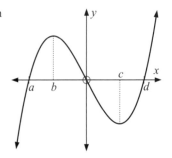

   a Using interval notation, and the letters a, b, c, and d, define where:

     i $f'(x) > 0$

     ii $f'(x) < 0$

   b For what values of x does $f'(x) = 0$?

Paper 2

1 a Alex, Carlos and Edwin decide to move to New York. They rent a flat for a monthly rate of 700 USD each.

     i Calculate the total rent paid by the three in the first year. (1 mark)

     ii The rental agreement says that the rent will be reviewed annually and increased by the annual rate of inflation. The annual inflation rate for the first two years is

Year 1	Year 2
2.8%	3.3%

     Calculate the total rent increase at the end of the first year. (2 marks)

     iii Find the amount of rent each person paid in the third year. (3 marks)

   b Alex, Carlos and Edwin work for the same company. Since the year 2000, the company has expanded its workforce by an extra 40 people each year. It is intended that the expansion will continue at the same rate indefinitely. There were 800 employees at the start of 2005.

     i Find how many employees the company will have at the start of 2009. (2 marks)

     ii Find how many employees the company had at the start of 2000. (2 marks)

     iii Calculate the year in which the company will first have more than 1000 employees. (3 marks)

2 a A rectangle has its length 5 cm greater than its width. Let x cm be the width of the rectangle.

     i Write down the length of the rectangle in terms of x. (1 mark)

     ii Write down an expression in x that represents the area of the rectangle. (2 marks)

     iii The rectangle has an area of 204 cm^2. Solve an equation to find the value of x. (2 marks)

     iv Find the value of the length and width of the rectangle. (2 marks)

   b A hemispherical enclosure has a volume of 7068 m^3. The enclosure is covered with waterproof material.

     i Find the radius of the enclosure. (3 marks)

     ii Calculate the amount of material covering the enclosure. (3 marks)

     iii The material costs $23.45 per 10 m^2 section. Find the total cost of the material covering the enclosure. (2 marks)

   c A box in the shape of a cuboid has dimensions 12.7 cm by 10.8 cm by 6.45 cm deep.

     i Find the length of the longest piece of string that can be stretched across the inside of the cuboid. (4 marks)

     ii Find the angle that the piece of string in **i** makes with the base of the box when stretched across the box. (2 marks)

3 a There are 60 packets of assorted sweets on a stand in a shop.

    42 packets contain peppermints

    36 contain chocolates

    21 contain liquorice

    11 of the packets contain at least some peppermints and some liquorice

    8 contain at least some liquorice and some chocolates

    6 contain peppermints only

    7 packets have all 3 types of sweets

    5 packets do not contain any of these 3 sweets

     i Copy and complete the diagram using the given information.

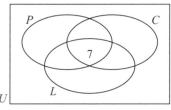

(3 marks)

     ii Find:

       a $n(P \cap C)$

       b $n(P \cup C')$

       c $n((L \cap P)' \cap (C \cup L))$ (4 marks)

   b **i** A box on a market stall contains pieces of assorted jewellery as shown in the table below.

	earrings	necklaces	bracelets
silver	15	8	12
bronze	7	11	10
gold	10	23	14

Write down the number of different pieces in the box. (1 mark)

ii Scarlett selects a piece of jewellery at random. Find the probability that the piece she chooses is:

   a gold earrings (2 marks)

   b not a silver bracelet. (2 marks)

iii Scarlett replaces the first piece and then randomly selects 2 pieces from the box. Find the probability that the pieces of jewellery she chooses are both silver given that they are both necklaces. (3 marks)

4 a The table below lists some values for the function $f(x) = 2x^2 - 6x - 20$.

x	-2	-1	0	1	2	3	4	5	6
y	0	a	-20	-24	b	-20	-12	0	16

   i Write down the values of a and b. (2 marks)

   ii Use the table of values above to draw the graph of $y = f(x)$ for $-3 \leqslant x \leqslant 7$.
Use 1 cm to represent 1 unit on the x-axis and 1 cm to represent 10 units on the y-axis. (4 marks)

   iii On the same axes, draw the graph of $y = 2x - 1$. (2 marks)

   iv Find the coordinates of the points where $f(x)$ meets the line $y = 2x - 1$. (2 marks)

b Consider the function $f(x) = \frac{5}{3}x^3 + 3x^2 - 8x + 2$ for $0 \leqslant x \leqslant 3$.

   i Find $f'(x)$. (3 marks)

   ii Find $f''(x)$. (2 marks)

   iii Determine the values of x for which $f'(x) = 0$. (3 marks)

   iv Find the largest and smallest values of $f(x)$, in the given domain. (5 marks)

5 a A company is testing a new fertiliser using two fields containing 100 plants. One field has been sprayed with an old fertiliser and the other field sprayed with new fertiliser. The results for the trials are displayed below.

Field A (old fertiliser)

Mean plant height	23 cm
Standard deviation (sd)	6 cm
Number of plants $\geqslant$ mean + 0.368 sd	22
Number of plants < 25 cm	52

Field B (new fertiliser)

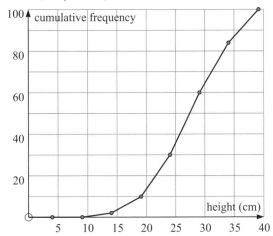

   i Using the information contained in the cumulative frequency graph for field B, construct a **frequency table** with intervals of: 0 - 4, 5 - 9, 10 - 14, etc. (2 marks)

   ii Use your frequency table data to determine the approximate mean and standard deviation for the plant heights in field B. (2 marks)

   iii Find the percentage difference of the means for the two fields expressed as a percentage of the mean for field B. (2 marks)

   iv **Use the cumulative frequency graph** to determine the number of plants in field B which are taller than 0.368 standard deviations above the mean. (2 marks)

b The company believes that the new fertiliser will increase plant growth significantly. They conduct two χ^2 tests to assist their analysis.

Test 1. "25 cm test"

The table lists the number of plants in field A, which are either equal to or greater than 25 cm, or are less than 25 cm.

	Plant Height	
	< 25 cm	$\geqslant$ 25 cm
field A	52	48
field B		

   i Enter the details for field B **using the information from your frequency table**. (1 mark)

   ii Write down the table of expected values for this test. (2 marks)

   iii Write down the calculated statistic. (2 marks)

Test 2. "standard deviation test"

   iv The table below displays the number of plants for field A whose height is greater than or equal to the mean height for field A plus 0.368 standard deviations. Enter the corresponding data for field B, calculated in part **a iv**. (1 mark)

	Plant Height	
	< mean + 0.368 s	$\geqslant$ mean + 0.368 s
field A	78	22
field B		

   v Perform the χ^2 test and write down the probability value. (2 marks)

   vi The hypothesis for both tests is, "there is no significant difference between the results for the two fields".
At the 5% significance level, what conclusion can you draw from your test results? Give a reason for your answer. (2 marks)

Short questions

1 a i $A = \{-1, 0\ 1, 2\}$ **ii** $B = \{2, 3, 5, 7, 11, 13\}$
    iii $C = \{-\sqrt{8}, +\sqrt{8}\}$

    b i false   **ii** true   **iii** true

2

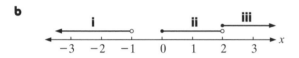

3 $A = \{0, 3, 6, 9\}$ $B = \{1, 2, 5, 10\}$

   a $A \cap B = \{\ \}$
   b $A \cup B = \{0, 1, 2, 3, 5, 6, 9, 10\}$
   c $(A \cup B)' = \{4, 7, 8, 11\}$

4 a

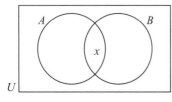

b

5 $P = \{1, 3, 5, 7, 9, 11\}$ $Q = \{1, 2, 3, 4, 6, 12\}$
   $R = \{5, 10\}$
   a $P \cap Q = \{1, 3\}$ **b** $(P \cap Q) \cup R = \{1, 3, 5, 10\}$
   c $Q \cap R = \{\ \}$ **d** $P' \cap (Q \cup R) = \{2, 4, 6, 10, 12\}$

6   **a** $n(P) = 22$ **b** $n(P \cup Q) = 47$
   c $n(Q \cap R) = 13$ **d** $n((P \cup Q \cup R)') = 3$
   e $n(Q') = 30$ **f** $n(P \cap R) = 0$

7 a If E is the set of students studying English and S those studying Spanish then
$$n(E \cup S) = n(E) + n(S) - n(E \cap S)$$
$$= 18 + 25 - 6$$
$$= 37$$
So, 37 IB students study English or Spanish.

   b Let F be the set of students studying in French and E be those studying in English. If all students must study either in French or English then 100% study in one of these languages.
$$n(F \cup E) = n(F) + n(E) - n(E \cap F)$$
Using percentages, $100\% = 60\% + 76\% - x\%$ where $x\%$ is the percentage of students studying in both languages.
$$x\% = (60 + 76 - 100)\% = 36\%$$
i.e., 36% of students study in both languages.

   c 20% of 25 = 5
Let A be the set of students studying art and D be those studying drama. This information is summarised in the Venn diagram (x is the number studying both art and drama).

$n(U) = 25$

$$n(A \cup D) = 25 - 5 = 20$$
Now $n(A \cup D) = n(A) + n(D) - n(A \cap D)$
$$\therefore \quad 20 = 13 + 9 - x$$
$$\therefore \quad x = 13 + 9 - 20 = 2$$
So, 2 students study both art and drama.

8 $\sqrt{\dfrac{32.76}{3.95 \times 2.63}} = 1.775\,806\,022\,....$

   a $= 1.776$ {correct to 3 d.p.}
   b $= 2$ {nearest integer}
   c $= 1.78$ {correct to 3 s.f.}
   d $= 1.78 \times 10^0$ {standard form}

9 Speed of light $= 186\,280 \times 1.609$ km/sec
$$= (186\,280 \times 1.609) \times 60 \text{ km/min}$$
$$= 17\,983\,471.2 \text{ km/min}$$

   a correct to 3 s.f. $= 18\,000\,000$ km/min
   (**Note:** The first zero is significant.)
   b In scientific notation, 1.80×10^7 km/min.
   c Time for light to reach Earth is
$$\frac{195\,000\,000}{18\,000\,000} = 10.8 \text{ minutes.}$$

10 a i Actual error is $5.65 - 5.645 = 0.005$ cm
     ii Relative error is $\dfrac{0.005}{5.645} = 0.000\,886$
     iii Relative percentage error is $0.000\,886 \times 100$
$$= 0.0886\%$$
   b i Actual error is $70 \times 3.2\% = 2.24$ kph.
     ii (70 ± 2.24)
     minimum 67.76 kph,   maximum 72.24 kph

11 a Error is $4 - 3.94 = 0.06$ m.
   b Length of joined pipes $= 5 \times 3.94 = 19.7$ m.
   c Error $= (5 \times 4) - (5 \times 3.94)$
$$= 0.3 \text{ m}$$
   d Percentage error is $\dfrac{0.3}{19.7} \times 100 = 1.52\%$

12 a $-9 - (-2) = -7$ So, this is an arithmetic sequence
     $-16 - (-9) = -7$ with common difference $= -7$.
     The sequence is $-2, -9, -16, -23, -30, ...$

   b

$m : n \to u_n$

1	-2
2	-9
3	-16
4	-23
5	-30

   c $u_n = u_1 + (n-1)d$
$$= -2 + (n-1)(-7)$$
$$= 5 - 7n$$

13 a $u_1 = 1(1+1) = 2$, $u_2 = 2(2+1) = 6$,
     $u_3 = 3(3+1) = 12$
   b $u_{15} = 15(15+1) = 240$
   c $n(n+1) = 600$ $n^2 + n - 600 = 0$
$$(n-24)(n+25) = 0$$
$$n = 24 \text{ or } -25$$
   But $n > 0$, so the 24th term is 600.

14 a Arithmetic, hence

$$(k - 166) - (-347) = -185 - (k - 166)$$
$$k - 166 + 347 = -185 - k + 166$$
$$2k = -200$$
$$k = -100$$

b Common difference is $(-100 - 166) + 347 = 81$

$$u_n = -347 + (n - 1)81$$
$$= -428 + 81n$$

c $-428 + 81n = 0$ if $n = \dfrac{428}{81} = 5.28$

The 6th term has the first positive value (58).

15 a $u_1 + 5d = 49 \quad \ldots\ldots (1)$
$u_1 + 14d = 130 \quad \ldots\ldots (2)$
$\therefore \quad 9d = 81 \quad$ {subtracting (1) from (2)}

Common difference $d = 9$.

b $u_1 + 5 \times 9 = 49$ First term is $u_1 = 4$.

c $4 + (n - 1)9 = 300$
$4 + 9n - 9 = 300$
$9n = 305$
$n = 33.9....$

The first 33 terms are less than 300.

16 a $\frac{7}{2}(2u_1 + (7 - 1)14) = 329$
$2u_1 + 84 = 94$
$2u_1 = 10 \qquad$ First term is 5.

b $\frac{n}{2}(2 \times 5 + (n - 1) \times 14) = 69\,800, \quad \therefore \quad n = 100$

17 a Common ratio $= \dfrac{6.75}{2.25} = 3$

b $u_n = 0.75 \times 3^{n-1}$

c $S_n = \dfrac{0.75 \times (3^{10} - 1)}{3 - 1} \approx 22\,143$

18 a Common ratio $= \dfrac{4.5}{5} = 0.9$

b Height of third bounce is $4.05 \times 0.9 = 3.645$

c Distance travelled is $5 + 2(4.5) + 2(4.05) + 2(3.645)$
$= 29.39$ m

19 a Half of $128 = 64$ clubs remain in the second round.
Half of $64 = 32$ clubs remain in the third round.

b $u_n = u_1 r^{n-1}$
i.e., $u_n = 128 \times (0.5)^{n-1}$ (or 2^{8-n})
remaining in the nth round.

c There are 7 rounds needed to find a winner.

20 a $u_1 r^{2-1} = 14.5, \quad u_1 r^{5-1} = 1.8125$

Substitute for $u_1 = \dfrac{14.5}{r}$

$\therefore \quad \dfrac{14.5 \times r^4}{r} = 1.8125$

$\therefore \quad r^3 = 0.125$

$\therefore \quad r = 0.5$

The common ratio is 0.5.

b Since $u_1(0.5) = 14.5$
then $u_1 = 29$ and the first term is 29.

c $S_5 = \dfrac{29(0.5^5 - 1)}{0.5 - 1} = 56.1875$

21 a Population in 2005 is $1200 \times 1.09^5 = 1846$.

b $1200 \times 1.09^n = 2500$

$\therefore \quad 1.09^n = \dfrac{2500}{1200} = \dfrac{25}{12}$

$\therefore \quad n \approx 8.52 \qquad$ {gdc}

Population reaches 2500 during the year 2009.

c If $1200 \times r^{10} = 3200$

then $r^{10} = \dfrac{3200}{1200} = \dfrac{32}{12}$

$\therefore \quad r = (\frac{32}{12})^{\frac{1}{10}} \approx 1.103$

Rate of increase is 10.3%.

22 a $178 - 4n = 7n + 57$
$\Leftrightarrow \quad 178 - 57 = 7n + 4n$
$\Leftrightarrow \quad 121 = 11n$

i.e., the sequences have a term in common if $n = 11$.
The term they have in common is
$178 - 4 \times 11 = 7 \times 11 + 57 = 134$.

b Break even when $R = C$
i.e., $25n = 21\,000 + 7.5n$
$\Leftrightarrow \quad 17.5n = 21\,000$
i.e., if $n = 1200$

Break even occurs when 1200 goods are produced and sold.

c $\dfrac{n(n + 1)}{2} > 435$

Solve $n(n + 1) = 870$
$n^2 + n - 870 = 0$
$(n + 30)(n - 29) = 0$
$n = -30$ or 29
but $n > 0$, so $n = 29$

The sum exceeds 435 for $n > 29$.

23 a i $s = 16, \quad r = 5$ **ii** $u_1 = 27, \quad d = 5$

b $a + 12p = 20$ and $a + 22p = 34$
Using a gdc, $a = 3.20$ and $p = 1.40$.

24 a Let l be the length, then $2x + 2l = 80$
i.e., $2l = 80 - 2x$
so the length is $40 - x$

b Area rectangle $=$ length $\times$ width
$= (40 - x)x$
i.e., $A = 40x - x^2$

c $40x - x^2 = 375$
i.e., $x^2 - 40x + 375 = 0$
$(x - 15)(x - 25) = 0$
$x = 15$ or 25

The length of the rectangle is 15 or 25 cm.

25 a $70t - 5t^2 = 0$
i.e., $5t(14 - t) = 0$
$t = 0$ or 14

The rocket is in the air for 14 seconds.

b $70t - 5t^2 = 30$
i.e., $-5t^2 + 70t - 30 = 0$
Using a gdc, $t = 0.443$ or 13.6

The rocket was above 30 m between 0.443 and 13.6 sec.

Long questions

1 a i is false since '2' is not included in $\{x \in \mathbb{R} \mid x < 2\}$

   ii is true

   iii is false since $2^2 + 2 = 4$ is false

 b i $A = \{14, 21, 28\}, \quad B = \{14, 28\},$

    $C = \{20, 22, 24, 26, 28\}$

   ii

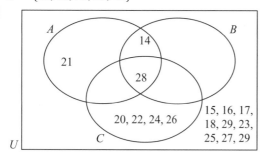

   iii a $A \cap B \cap C = \{28\}$

      b $(A \cap B) \cup C = \{14, 20, 22, 24, 26, 28\}$

      c $(A \cap B)' \cap C = \{20, 22, 24, 26\}$

      d $(A \cup C)' \cap B = \{\ \ \}$

 c ii is false. Consider $p = 1$, $q = 2$. $1 - 2 \neq 2 - 1$

2 a

 b

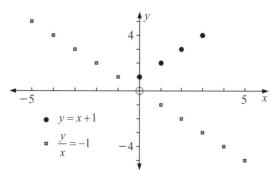

    ● $y = x + 1$

    ▫ $\dfrac{y}{x} = -1$

 c Let $x = -2$, $y = -3$, then $x^2 = 4$ and $y^2 = 9$

   and so $x > y$ but $x^2 < y^2$.

3 a $25.32 \times \dfrac{6.057}{2.4 \times \sqrt{5.14}} = 28.185\,67 \ldots$

   i $= 28.186 \quad \{\text{to 5 s.f.}\}$

   ii $= 28.2 \quad \{\text{to nearest tenth}\}$

   iii $= 30 \quad \{\text{to 1 s.f.}\}$

 b i Actual length covered is $3 \times 3.63 = 10.89$ m.

   ii Error between actual length and stated length is

     $10.89 - 10.80 = 0.09$ m

     Percentage error $= \dfrac{10.89 - 10.8}{10.89} \times 100$

                $= 0.826\%$

 c i Minimum volume needed is

     $10.89 \times 10.89 \times 0.095 = 11.27$ m^3 (11.1)

     Maximum volume needed is

     $10.89 \times 10.89 \times 0.105 = 12.45$ m^3 (12.5)

   ii Planned volume $= 10.8 \times 10.8 \times 0.1$

                  $= 11.66$ m^3 (11.7)

     Difference in cost is $(12.45 - 11.66) \times 47.50$

                      $= 37.53$ Euro

   iii Percentage difference in cost is

     $\dfrac{37.53}{11.66 \times 47.50} = 6.78\%$

4 a i 120, 123, 126   **ii** 4, 11, 18

 b i $120 + 3(n - 1) = 4 + 7(n - 1)$

   $\therefore \quad 120 + 3n - 3 = 4 + 7n - 7$

          $\therefore \quad 120 = 4n$ and so $n = 30$

   The 30th term is the same.

   ii $u_{30} = 120 + 3(30 - 1) = 4 + 7(30 - 1)$

                    $= 207$

 c $120 + (n - 1) \times 3 = 151, \quad \therefore \quad n = 11.3$

   or $\quad 4 + (n - 1) \times 7 = 151, \quad \therefore \quad n = 22$

   151 is a member of the second sequence.

 d $\dfrac{n}{2}(2 \times 120 + (n - 1) \times 3) = \dfrac{n}{2}(2 \times 4 + (n - 1) \times 7)$

     $\therefore \quad n(237 + 3n) = n(1 + 7n)$

     $\therefore \quad 237n + 3n^2 = n + 7n^2$

             $\therefore \quad 0 = 4n^2 - 236n$

             $\therefore \quad 0 = 4n(n - 59)$

   The sums of the first 59 terms are the same.

 e $\dfrac{n}{2}(2 \times 120 + (n - 1) \times 3)$

    $- \left(\dfrac{n}{2}(2 \times 4 + (n - 1) \times 7)\right) = 228$

   $\therefore \quad n(237 + 3n) - n(1 + 7n) = 2 \times 228$

   $\therefore \quad 237n + 3n^2 - (n + 7n^2) = 456$

      $\therefore \quad 0 = 4n^2 - 236n + 456$

      $\therefore \quad 0 = n^2 - 59n + 114$

      $\therefore \quad 0 = (n - 57)(n - 2)$

      $\therefore \quad n = 2$ or 57

   The sums of the sequences differ by 228 for both the 2nd and 57th terms.

5 a i $\dfrac{u_2}{u_1} = \dfrac{28}{56} = 0.5, \qquad \dfrac{u_3}{u_2} = \dfrac{14}{28} = 0.5$

   Since $\dfrac{u_2}{u_1} = \dfrac{u_3}{u_2}$, the sequence is geometric.

   ii $u_8 = u_1 r^{n-1} = 56 \times 0.5^7 = 0.4375$

   iii $S_8 = \dfrac{56 \times (1 - 0.5^8)}{1 - 0.5} = 111.5625$

 b i $u_1 r^2 = 24.5$ and $u_1 r^4 = 12.005$

         so $\quad r^2 = \dfrac{12.005}{24.5}$

           $\therefore \quad r = 0.7$

   Now $\quad u_1 \times (0.7)^2 = 24.5$

      $\therefore \quad u_1 = \dfrac{24.5}{(0.7)^2} = 50$

   ii General formula is $u_n = 50 \times 0.7^{n-1}$

 c $20 \times 0.8^{n-1} = 50 \times 0.7^{n-1}$

   $\therefore \quad \left(\dfrac{0.8}{0.7}\right)^{n-1} = \dfrac{50}{20} = 2.5$

     $\therefore \quad n - 1 = \dfrac{\log 2.5}{\log\left(\frac{0.8}{0.7}\right)}$

        $\therefore \quad n = 7.86$

   The first 7 terms of the sequence in **b** are larger than the first seven terms of $u_n = 20 \times 0.8^{(n-1)}$.

 d i $S_{30} = \dfrac{20 \times (1 - 0.8^{30})}{1 - 0.8} = 99.9$

   ii $S_{50} = 100$

   iii $S_{100} = 100$

   For large values of n the sum is about 100.

6 a i Interest of 12.5% is added for the year.

Amount owing is $20\,000 \times \dfrac{112.5}{100} = 20\,000 \times 1.125$

Payment of $\$k$ is made.

Amount owing is $(20\,000 \times 1.125) - k$

ii Amount owing at end of second year is
$$((20\,000 \times 1.125) - k) \times 1.125 - k$$

iii $(20\,000 \times 1.125) \times 1.125 - 1.125k - k = 17\,131.25$
$$\therefore \quad 25\,312.5 - 2.125k = 17\,131.25$$
$$\therefore \quad k = 3850$$

b i Percentage decrease $= \dfrac{24\,000 - 20\,400}{24\,000} \times 100\% = 15\%$

ii Value at the end of the 2nd year $= \$20\,400 \times 0.85$
$$= \$17\,340$$

iii Value after n years, $t_n = \$24\,000 \times (0.85)^n$

iv

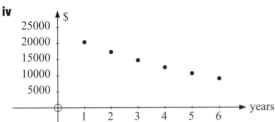

7 a i first month $250 + (5000 \times 1.2\%) = \$310$

ii second month $250 + (4800 \times 1.2\%) = \$307$

iii third month $250 + (4600 \times 1.2\%) = \$304$

b First term is 310. Common difference is -3.

Value of nth payment is $310 + (n-1) \times (-3)$
$$= \$(313 - 3n)$$

c When $n = 10$, $313 - 3(10) = \$283$

d $\dfrac{5000}{250} = 20$ monthly payments

e $S_{20} = \dfrac{20}{2}(2 \times 310 + (20-1) \times -3) = \$5630$

8 a i Weight at start of second year $= 200 \times 0.9 = 180$ g

Weight at start of third year $= 180 \times 0.9 = 162$ g

ii Common ration is 0.9

iii Weight at start of sixth year $= 200 \times 0.9^5 = 118.098$ g

iv

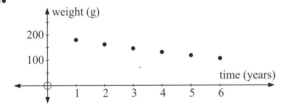

v As $200 \times 0.9^{n-1} = 20$ then $0.9^{n-1} = \dfrac{20}{200}$

$$\therefore \quad n \approx 22.9 \qquad \{\text{using a gdc}\}$$

The material will weigh less than 20 g at the start of the 23rd year.

b Amount of radioactive material at the beginning of the nth year is $120r^{n-1}$.

At the end of the 6th year, or the beginning of the 7th year, the amount is $120 \times r^{7-1} = 49.152$

$$\therefore \quad r^6 = \dfrac{49.152}{120}$$

$$\therefore \quad r = \left(\dfrac{49.152}{120}\right)^{\frac{1}{6}} = 0.862$$

Annual decrease is $1 - 0.862 = 0.138 = 13.8\%$.

Short questions

1 a $A = \{4, 8, 12, 16\}$, $B = \{2, 4, 6, 8\}$

$A \cup B = \{2, 4, 6, 8, 12, 16\}$

b $A \cap B = \{4, 8\}$

c $C = \{4, 8, 12\}$ or any subset of A that contains 3 elements.

2 a i -6 (or any integer)

ii $3\frac{7}{10}$ (or any number not an integer)

iii 29 (or any positive integer)

iv $\mathbb{Q}' \cap \mathbb{Z} = \varnothing$ and so there are no elements in $\mathbb{Q}' \cap \mathbb{Z}$.

b

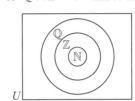

3 $A = \{9, 12, 15, 18\}$, $B = \{9, 12, 18\}$

a $A \cap B = \{9, 12, 18\}$

b $A' = \{8, 10, 11, 13, 14, 16, 17\}$

c

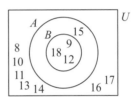

d i $B \subset A$ is true

ii $A' \cap B' = \{8, 10, 11, 13, 14, 16, 17\}$

so $n(A' \cap B') = 7$ is true.

iii Since $B \subset A$, $A \cup B = A$ is true.

4 $F = \{1, 2, 3, 4, 6, 8, 12\}$

$P = \{2, 3, 5, 7, 11, 13, 17, 19\}$

a $n(F) = 7$

b $P \cap F = \{2, 3\}$

c $P \cup F = \{1, 2, 3, 4, 5, 6, 7, 8, 11, 12, 13, 17, 19\}$

d $P' \cap F = \{1, 4, 6, 8, 12\}$

5 $A = \{2, 3, 4, 6, 8, 12, 16, 24, 48\}$

$B = \{6, 12, 18, 24, 30, 36, 42, 48\}$

$C = \{8, 16, 24, 32, 40, 48\}$

a $A \cap B \cap C = \{24, 48\}$

b $n(B) = 8$

c $A' \cap B = \{18, 30, 36, 42\}$

6 a Since b is a prime number less than 10, $b = 2$.

b $\mathbb{Q}$ is the set of even numbers less than 10.

c $a = 9$

7 a i $A \cap B = \varnothing$ is false as A and B have common elements.

ii $A \cap C = C$ is true as C lies entirely within A.

iii $B \subset A'$ is false as A and B have common elements.

iv $C \subset (A \cap B)$ is false as C has no elements in common with $A \cap B$.

b The shaded region is $A' \cap B$.

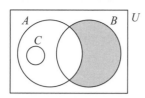

8 a $n(S \cap B \cap G) = 8$, and so 8 members play all three sports.

b $30 + 12$ play soccer but not basketball,
$20 + 9$ play basketball but not soccer and so
$(30 + 12) + (20 + 9) = 71$ play soccer or basketball but not both.

c 14 only play golf and no other sport.

d $30 + 12 + 14 = 56$ do not play basketball.

e $12 + 6 + 9 + 8 = 35$ play two or three sports.

f $30 + 6 = 36$ play soccer but do not play golf.

9 a $p \Rightarrow q$: If the sun is shining then I take the dog for a walk.

b $\neg p \vee q$: The sun is not shining or I take the dog for a walk.

c The converse of $p \Rightarrow q$ is $q \Rightarrow p$: If I take the dog for a walk then the sun is shining.

d $\neg q \Rightarrow \neg p$

e $\neg p \Rightarrow \neg q$ is the contrapositive of $p \Rightarrow q$.

10 a **i** $\neg q \Rightarrow \neg r$

  ii $\neg p \Rightarrow \neg r \wedge \neg q$ or $\neg p \Rightarrow \neg(r \vee q)$

b $\neg r \Rightarrow \neg(p \vee q)$: If Peter is not a student then he has neither black hair nor plays basketball.

11 a **i** $\neg p \wedge \neg q$: Wilson is not an active dog and Wilson does not dig holes.

  ii $p \veebar q$: Wilson is an active dog or Wilson digs holes but not both.

  iii $\neg p \Rightarrow q$: If Wilson is not an active dog then Wilson digs holes.

b

p	q	$\neg p$	$\neg p \Rightarrow q$
T	T	F	T
T	F	F	T
F	T	T	T
F	F	T	F

(Neither a contradiction nor a tautology.)

12 a **i** Inverse is $\neg p \Rightarrow \neg q$: If I do not like the beach then I do not live near the sea.

  ii Contrapositive is $\neg q \Rightarrow \neg p$: If I do not live near the sea then I do not like the beach.

b Converse is $q \Rightarrow p$.

13

p	q	$\neg q$	$p \Rightarrow \neg q$	$\neg p$	$\neg p \Rightarrow q$	$(p \Rightarrow \neg q) \vee (\neg p \Rightarrow q)$
T	T	F	F	F	T	T
T	F	T	T	F	T	T
F	T	F	T	T	T	T
F	F	T	T	T	F	T

This is a tautology.

14 a **i** $(\neg r \wedge \neg q) \vee p$: I do not buy an icecream and I have no money or the weather is hot.

  ii $(p \wedge q) \Rightarrow r$: If the weather is hot and I have money then I buy an icecream.

  iii $(\neg p \vee \neg q) \Rightarrow \neg r$: If the weather is not hot or I have no money then I do not buy an icecream.

b The contrapositive of $p \Rightarrow r$ is $\neg r \Rightarrow \neg p$:
If I do not buy an icecream then the weather is not hot.

15 a $\neg p \Rightarrow \neg q$: If Molly does not have a DVD player then Molly does not like watching Movies.

b

p	q	$p \Rightarrow q$
T	T	T
T	F	F
F	T	T
F	F	T

c

p	q	$\neg p$	$\neg q$	$\neg p \Rightarrow \neg q$
T	T	F	F	T
T	F	F	T	T
F	T	T	F	F
F	F	T	T	T

c As the final column is the same for both propositions then $q \Rightarrow p$ and $\neg p \Rightarrow \neg q$ are logically equivalent.

16 a

p	q	$p \wedge q$	$(p \wedge q) \Rightarrow p$
T	T	T	T
T	F	F	T
F	T	F	T
F	F	F	T

b As the final column only has T values, this is a tautology.

17 a $\neg q$: I do not visit the doctor.

b **i** $\neg p \Rightarrow q$: If I do not eat an apple every day then I visit the doctor.

  ii $(\neg p \vee q) \Rightarrow q$: If I do not eat an apple every day or I visit the doctor then I visit the doctor.

c

p	q	$\neg p$	$\neg p \vee q$	$(\neg p \vee q) \Rightarrow q$
T	T	F	T	T
T	F	F	F	T
F	T	T	T	T
F	F	T	T	F

As the last column contains some F values and some T values, this is neither a tautology nor a contradiction.

18 a

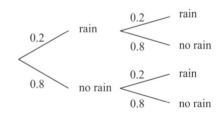

b **i** P(raining two days in a row) $= 0.2 \times 0.2$
            $= 0.04$

  ii P(raining on one day only)
   $= P((R \text{ and } NR) \text{ or } (NR \text{ and } R))$
   $= P(R \text{ and } NR) + P(NR \text{ and } R)$
   $= 0.2 \times 0.8 + 0.8 \times 0.2$
   $= 0.16 + 0.16$
   $= 0.32$

19 a **i** $A = \{2, 3, 5, 6\}$ and $n(A) = 4$

  ii $A \cap B = \{3, 6\}$ and $n(A \cap B) = 2$

b **i** $A \cup B \cup C = \{2, 3, 4, 5, 6, 7, 8\}$

  ii $(A' \cap B) \cup C = \{4, 5, 6, 7, 8\}$

20 a $n(P) = 4 + 1 + 2 + 4 = 11$

b $n(M \cup D) - n(M \cap D) = 8 + 1 + 2 + 6 = 17$

c $n(P \cap M') = 4 + 2 = 6$

d $n(D') = 8 + 1 + 4 + 3 = 16$

21

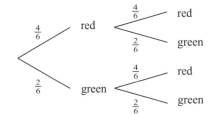

a P(two reds) $= \frac{2}{3} \times \frac{2}{3} = \frac{4}{9}$

b P(two greens) $= \frac{1}{3} \times \frac{1}{3} = \frac{1}{9}$

c P(one of each) $= \frac{2}{3} \times \frac{1}{3} + \frac{1}{3} \times \frac{2}{3} = \frac{4}{9}$

22 a
$$P(A \cup B) = P(A) + P(B) - P(A \cap B)$$
$$\therefore \quad 0.8 = 0.35 + 0.7 - P(A \cap B)$$
$$\therefore \quad P(A \cap B) = 1.05 - 0.8$$
$$\therefore \quad P(A \cap B) = 0.25$$

b

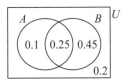

c $P(A' \cap B') = 0.2$

d If A and B are independent then
$$P(A \cap B) = P(A) \times P(B)$$
$$P(A) \times P(B) = 0.35 \times 0.7$$
$$= 0.245$$
but $\quad P(A \cap B) = 0.25$

$\therefore$ events A and B are not independent.

23 a $c = 1 - (0.3 + 0.4 + 0.2)$
$$= 0.1$$

b **i** $P(A \cup B) = 0.3 + 0.4 + 0.2 = 0.9$

ii $P(A \cap B) = 0.4$

iii $P(A' \cap B) = 0.2$

iv $P(A \mid B) = \dfrac{0.4}{0.6} = \frac{2}{3}$

v $P(B \mid A) = \dfrac{0.4}{0.7} = \frac{4}{7}$

24 a Number in class $= 7 + 9 + 3 + 4$
$$= 23$$

b $n(C \cap D) = 9$

c $n(D) - n(D \cap C) = 7$

d $n(C \cup D) = 7 + 9 + 3 = 19$

e $n((C \cup D)') = 4$

25 a **i** P(dark **or** hard) $= \frac{58}{90} \quad (\frac{29}{45}, 0.644)$

ii P(light $|$soft) $= \frac{18}{28} \quad (\frac{9}{14}, 0.643)$

b **i** P(mm) $= \frac{38}{90} \times \frac{37}{89} = \frac{1406}{8010} \quad (\frac{708}{4005}, 0.176)$

ii P(at least 1 soft $|$light)
$$= P(S \mid L) + P(L \mid S) + P(\text{both } S \mid L)$$
$$= \left(\frac{18}{90} \times \frac{72}{89}\right) + \left(\frac{72}{90} \times \frac{18}{89}\right) + \left(\frac{18}{90} \times \frac{17}{89}\right)$$
$$= \frac{2898}{8010} \quad \left(\frac{161}{445} \text{ or } 0.362\right)$$

Long questions

1 a **i** $P = \{2, 4, 6, 8, 10\}$ **ii** $Q = \{3, 6, 9\}$

iii $R = \{1, 2, 3, 4, 6\}$ **iv** $P \cap Q \cap R = \{6\}$

b **i** and **ii**

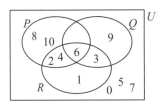

c **i** $P \cup Q$: The elements that are in set P or Q or both.

ii $P' \cap Q' \cap R'$: The elements that are not in P nor Q nor R.

d **i**

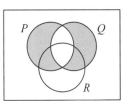

ii

p	q	r	$p \wedge r$	$p \veebar q$	$(p \wedge r) \Rightarrow (p \veebar q)$
T	T	T	T	F	F
T	T	F	F	F	T
T	F	T	T	T	T
T	F	F	F	T	T
F	T	T	F	T	T
F	T	F	F	T	T
F	F	T	F	F	T
F	F	F	F	F	T

iii An element of U for which $(p \wedge r) \Rightarrow (p \veebar q)$ is true is 2 which corresponds to the third entry in the table.

2 $\neg(p \vee q) \Rightarrow \neg p \wedge \neg q$

a **i**

p	q	$\neg p$	$\neg q$	$p \vee q$	$\neg(p \vee q)$	$\neg p \wedge \neg q$
T	T	F	F	T	F	F
T	F	F	T	T	F	F
F	T	T	F	T	F	F
F	F	T	T	F	T	T

$\neg(p \vee q) \Rightarrow \neg p \wedge \neg q$
T
T
T
T

ii This is a tautology.

b **i** $p \wedge q$: I work hard and I get a promotion.

ii Inverse $(\neg p \Rightarrow \neg q)$:

If I do not work hard then I do not get a promotion.

c **i**

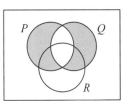

ii a P(both work hard) $= 0.8 \times 0.8$
$$= 0.64$$

b P(only one works hard) $= 0.8 \times 0.2 + 0.2 \times 0.8$
$$= 0.16 + 0.16$$
$$= 0.32$$

3 a i

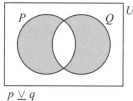

$p \veebar q$

ii

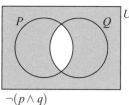

$\neg(p \wedge q)$

iii

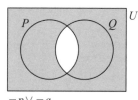

$\neg p \vee \neg q$

b Since **a ii** and **a iii** have the same areas shaded, $\neg(p \wedge q)$ and $\neg p \vee \neg q$ are logically equivalent.

c $\neg(p \wedge q) \Rightarrow \neg q$:

If the bush does not have thorns nor is it a rose bush then it is not a rose bush.

d

p	q	$p \wedge q$	$\neg(p \wedge q)$	$\neg q$	$\neg(p \wedge q) \Rightarrow \neg q$
T	T	T	F	F	T
T	F	F	T	T	T
F	T	F	T	F	F
F	F	F	T	T	T

The result is neither a tautology nor a contradiction.

4 a

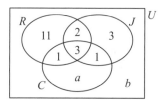

i Since 7 students like Classical music
$n(a) = 7 - (1 + 3 + 1) = 2$

ii The region containing 11 students are those who only like Rock music.

iii Since there are 30 senior students,
$n(b) = 30 - (11 + 2 + 3 + 1 + 3 + 1 + 2)$
$= 30 - 23$
$= 7$

iv Region b consists of the students who do not like any of the music.

b $R' \cap J$

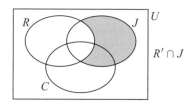

$R' \cap J$

c i P(likes all 3 types) $= \frac{3}{30} = \frac{1}{10}$

ii P(likes only Classical) $= \frac{2}{30} = \frac{1}{15}$

iii $P(R \mid J) = \frac{5}{9}$

d i P(both like Rock music only) $= \frac{11}{30} \times \frac{10}{29} = \frac{110}{870}$ (0.126)

ii P(one likes Rock only and the other likes all 3 types)
$= \left(\frac{11}{30} \times \frac{3}{29}\right) + \left(\frac{3}{30} \times \frac{11}{29}\right)$
$= \frac{66}{870}$ (or 0.0759)

5 a i and **ii**

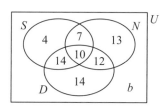

iii $4 + 7 + 10 + 14 + 13 + 12 + 14 = 74$
$\therefore 80 - 74 = 6$ students watched none.

b i P(watched only Drama) $= \frac{14}{80} = \frac{7}{40}$

ii $P(S \mid N) = \frac{17}{42}$

c i $p \Rightarrow q$: If you watch sport on television then you like sport.

ii $q \Rightarrow p$: If you like sport then you watch sport on television.

iii $\neg q \Rightarrow \neg p$

iv $\neg q \Rightarrow \neg p$ is the contrapositive of $p \Rightarrow q$.

6 a

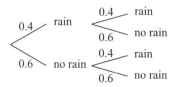

b i P(Rain on both days) $= 0.4 \times 0.4$
$= 0.16$

ii P(No rain on one day) $= 0.4 \times 0.6 + 0.6 \times 0.4$
$= 0.24 + 0.24$
$= 0.48$

c P(Fine on 5 consecutive days)
$= 0.6 \times 0.6 \times 0.6 \times 0.6 \times 0.6$
$= 0.0778$

d i $p \Rightarrow q$: If it is raining then I wear my raincoat.

ii $\neg q \Rightarrow \neg p$: If I do not wear my raincoat then it is not raining.

e i

p	q	$p \wedge q$	$\neg(p \wedge q)$	$\neg p$	$\neg(p \wedge q) \Rightarrow \neg p$
T	T	T	F	F	T
T	F	F	T	F	F
F	T	F	T	T	T
F	F	F	T	T	T

ii The argument is false when it is raining and I do not wear my raincoat.

7 a i

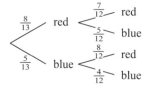

ii a P(two marbles same colour)
$= \left(\frac{8}{13} \times \frac{7}{12}\right) + \left(\frac{5}{13} \times \frac{4}{12}\right)$
$= \frac{76}{156}$
$= \frac{19}{39}$ (0.487)

b P(at least one blue marble) $= 1 - $ P(no blue)

$$= 1 - \text{P(two red)}$$
$$= 1 - \frac{8}{13} \times \frac{7}{12}$$
$$= \frac{100}{156}$$
$$= \frac{25}{39} \quad (0.641)$$

b

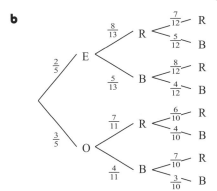

i P(even number on the spinner) $= \frac{2}{5}$

ii P(two blue marbles) $=$ P(EBB or OBB)

$$= \text{P(EBB)} + \text{P(OBB)}$$
$$= \frac{2}{5} \times \frac{5}{13} \times \frac{4}{12} + \frac{3}{5} \times \frac{4}{11} \times \frac{3}{10}$$
$$\approx 0.117$$

8 a i P(two chocolates) $= \frac{4}{11}$

ii Since $\dfrac{3}{10} + \dfrac{a}{b} = 1$,

then $a = 7, \; b = 10$ is one solution.

iii P(both hard) $= \dfrac{4}{11} \times \dfrac{3}{10}$

$$= \frac{6}{55}$$

iv P(one of each type) $= \dfrac{4}{11} \times \dfrac{7}{10}$

$$= \frac{14}{55}$$

b i

ii a P(both strawberry) $= \dfrac{5}{12} \times \dfrac{4}{11}$

$$= \frac{20}{132}$$
$$= \frac{5}{33} \quad (0.152)$$

b P(second is strawberry) $= \dfrac{5}{12} \times \dfrac{4}{11} + \dfrac{7}{12} \times \dfrac{5}{11}$

$$= \frac{55}{132} \quad (0.417)$$

iii P(selects 4 chocolates) $= \dfrac{7}{12} \times \dfrac{6}{11} \times \dfrac{5}{10} \times \dfrac{5}{9}$

$$= \frac{70}{396}$$
$$= \frac{35}{198} \quad (0.177)$$

SOLUTIONS TO TOPIC 4   **FUNCTIONS**

Short questions

1 a
$$m = \frac{y_2 - y_1}{x_2 - x_1} \qquad y\text{-intercept} = 1$$

$$\therefore \quad m = \frac{2 - 1}{2 - 0}$$

$$\therefore \quad m = \tfrac{1}{2}$$

and so $C(t) = \tfrac{1}{2}t + 1$

---

b For $t = 23$, $\quad C(23) = \tfrac{1}{2}(23) + 1$

$$C(23) = \$12.50$$

c $\tfrac{1}{2}t + 1 = 18.31, \quad t = 34.62$

$\therefore$ approximate time is 35 minutes.

2 a $h(t) = 1 - 2t^2$

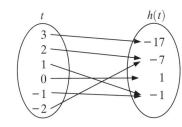

b $D = \{-2, -1, 0, 1, 2, 3\}$

c $R = \{-17, -7, -1, 1\}$

3 a 61%   **b** 5.6 years

c At $t = 19$, $\quad P = 100 \times 2^{-\frac{5 \times 19}{28}}$

$$\therefore \quad P = 9.52\% \quad (3 \text{ s.f.})$$

d Asymptote has equation $P = 0$

4 a $f(2) = 15 - 2(2) = 11$

b $g(-2) = 2^{-2} + 1 = 1\tfrac{1}{4}$

c $15 - 2x = 2^x + 1$ when $x = 3 \quad \{\text{gdc}\}$

5 a $N(0) = 120 \times (1.04)^0 = 120$

$\therefore$ settlement starts with 120.

b $N(4) = 120 \times (1.04)^4 \approx 140.4$

$\therefore$ 140 people after 4 years.

c
$$N(t) = 240 \quad (\text{double})$$
$$\therefore \quad 120 \times (1.04)^t = 240$$
$$\therefore \quad (1.04)^t = \frac{240}{120} = 2$$
$$\therefore \quad t = 17.7 \quad \{\text{using a gdc}\}$$

$\therefore$ 18 years for the population to double.

6 a $y = ax^2 + bx + c$

If y-int $= 9 \quad \Rightarrow \quad c = 9$

$\therefore \quad y = ax^2 + bx + 9$

b Axis of symmetry is $x = 1 \; \therefore \; \dfrac{-b}{2a} = 1$

$$\therefore \quad -b = 2a$$
$$\therefore \quad 2a + b = 0 \quad \text{...... (1)}$$

c $(1, 7)$ is a known point.

$$\therefore \quad a(1)^2 + b(1) + 9 = 7$$
$$a + b = -2 \quad \text{...... (2)}$$

d Solving equation (1) and (2) simultaneously (gdc)

$$a = 2, \quad b = -4$$

Hence, $a = 2, \quad b = -4$ and $c = 9$

7 Graphing $y = x^3 - 3x^2 - x + 3$ on $-2 \leqslant x \leqslant 3$:

a

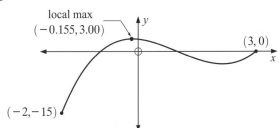

b Range: $-15 \leqslant y \leqslant 3.08$ (3 s.f.)

8 a $H(0) = 0$ m

Hence, the object begins at ground level.

b $H(t) = 19.6t - 4.9t^2$
$$= 4.9t(4 - t)$$
$$= 0 \quad \text{at} \quad t = 0 \quad \text{and} \quad t = 4$$

i.e., at ground level after 4 seconds.

c Object is in the air for $0 < t < 4$.

d Max. height occurs at $t = \dfrac{-b}{2a} = \dfrac{-19.6}{-9.8} = 2$ seconds.

Max. height is 19.6 m.

9 a $x^2 + 3x - 28 = (x + 7)(x - 4)$

b A$(-7, 0)$ and B$(4, 0)$

c $x = \dfrac{-b}{2a} = \dfrac{-3}{2(1)} = -\dfrac{3}{2}$

$\therefore \quad x = -1\frac{1}{2}$ is the axis of symmetry

d At $x = -\frac{3}{2}$, $y = -30.25$ $\therefore$ C$(-1\frac{1}{2}, -30\frac{1}{4})$

10 a i Amplitude $= 2$

ii Period $= \dfrac{360}{b} = \dfrac{360}{\frac{1}{2}} = 720°$

b

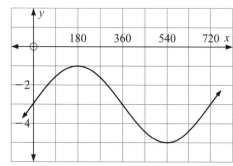

11 a $f(x) = 8x - 2x^2 = 2x(4 - x)$

b x-intercepts are $x = 0$ and $x = 4$

c Axis of symmetry is $x = \dfrac{-b}{2a} = \dfrac{-8}{-4} = 2$, i.e., $x = 2$

d $f(2) = 8(2) - 2(2)^2 = 8$ $\therefore$ vertex is at $(2, 8)$.

12 a i a Domain $= \{-2, -1, 0, 1, 2\}$

b Range $= \{-7, -2, 3, 8, 13\}$

ii Equation is linear

$\therefore \quad f(x) = ax + b$

$\therefore \quad a = \dfrac{y_2 - y_1}{x_2 - x_1} = \dfrac{13 - 8}{-2 + 1} = \dfrac{5}{-1} = -5$

$b = 3 \quad (x = 0)$

$\therefore \quad f(x) = -5x + 3$

b $g(x) = 4 \times 2^{3x} - 3$

Exponential graph has asymptote $y = -3$

$\therefore$ for $x \in \mathbb{R}$, $y > -3$

Range of g is $y > -3$.

13 a $N(0) = 30 - 3^3 = 30 - 27 = 3$

$\therefore$ 3000 ants initially.

b $N(2) = 30 - 3^{3-2} = 30 - 3 = 27$

$\therefore$ 27 000 ants present after 2 months.

c $N(t) = 20$

$\therefore \quad 30 - 3^{3-t} = 20$

$\therefore \quad 3^{3-t} = 10$

using a gdc $t \approx 0.904$ months i.e., in the 1st month

d Asymptote is $N = 30$

e Population approaches 30 000 ants, but theoretically never reaches it.

14 a amplitude $= 3$ period $= 360°$

Begins at Max. position

$\Rightarrow$ cosine function $\therefore$ $y = 3\cos x$

b amplitude $= 1$

period $= 60°$ $\therefore$ $b = \dfrac{360}{60} = 6$

Begins at mean position

$\Rightarrow$ sine function $\therefore$ $y = \sin 6x$

15 a y-int $= f(0) = \dfrac{2^0}{0 - 1} = -1$

b min $(2.44, 3.77)$ (gdc)

c Vertical asymptote is $x = 1$

d $f(5) = \dfrac{2^5}{5 - 1} = \dfrac{32}{4}$ $\therefore$ $f(5) = 8$

e Graph of $y = \dfrac{2^x}{x - 1}$

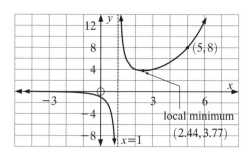

local minimum $(2.44, 3.77)$

16 a Graph of $y = 3 + \dfrac{1}{x - 2}$

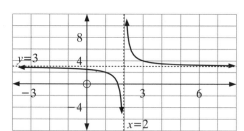

b Vertical asymptote is $x = 2$

Horizontal asymptote is $y = 3$

17 a $T(t) = A \times B^{-t} + 3$

and $T(0) = 27$

$\therefore$ $A \times B^0 + 3 = 27$ and so $A = 24$

b $T(3) = 6$

$\therefore$ $24 \times B^{-3} + 3 = 6$

$\therefore$ $B = 2$ {using a gdc}

c At $t = 5$, $T(5) = 24 \times 2^{-5} + 3$

$\therefore$ $T(5) = 3.75°$C

d $T(t) = 24 \times 2^{-t} + 3$ has an asymptote at $T = 3°$C.

Hence the refrigerator will approach $3°$C but will (theoretically) never reach it.

18 a $f(x) = ax^2 + bx + 7$

$f(2) = 7,$ then $4a + 2b + 7 = 7$

$\therefore \quad 4a + 2b = 0$

$2a + b = 0 \quad ......(1)$

$f(4) = 23,$ then $16a + 4b + 7 = 23$

$\therefore \quad 16a + 4b = 16$

$\therefore \quad 4a + b = 4 \quad ...... (2)$

b Solving equations (1) and (2) simultaneously

$2a + b = 0 \quad ...... (1)$

$4a + b = 4 \quad ...... (2)$

Equations $(2) - (1), \quad 2a = 4 \quad$ and so $\quad a = 2$

Substituting $\quad a = 2 \quad$ into (1) we have $\quad 2(2) + b = 0$

$\therefore \quad b = -4$

Therefore $\quad a = 2 \quad$ and $\quad b = -4$

c $f(-1) = 2(-1)^2 - 4(-1) + 7 = 2 + 4 + 7 = 13$

$\therefore \quad f(-1) = 13$

19 a Graph of $\quad P(x) = -50x^2 = 1000x - 2000$

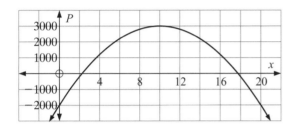

b 10 workers maximise the profit

c The maximum profit is €3000.

d $P(1) = -50 + 1000 - 2000 = -1050$

i.e., there is a loss of €1050.

20

Graph	Function
A	**e**
B	**c**
C	**b**
D	**d**

21

Graph	Function
$f(x)$	**E**
$g(x)$	**D**
$h(x)$	**B**

22 a **i** x-intercepts are $\quad x = 0, \quad x = 2, \quad x = 3$

ii local max. $(1.37, 2.64),$ local min. $(2.63, -4.24)$

b

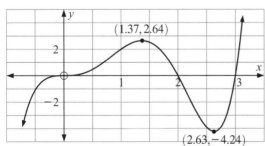

23 a

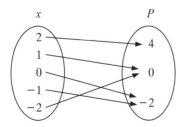

b Domain $\{-2, -1, 0, 1, 2\}$

c Range $\{4, 0, -2\}$

24 a x-intercepts are $\quad x = 1, \quad x = 5 \quad$ (touches)

$\therefore \quad y = a(x - 1)(x - 5)^2$

$\therefore \quad b = 1, \quad c = 5$

b $y\text{-int} = -50$

$\therefore \quad a(-1)(-5)^2 = -50$

$a = 2$

c Max. on $\quad 0 \leqslant x \leqslant 5 \quad$ is $\quad$ P(2.53, 19.0).

25 a Graph of $\quad y = x^4 - 2x^3 - 3x^2 + 8x - 4$

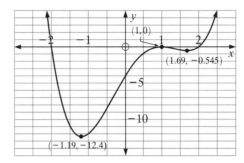

b Local minimums are $(1.69, -0.545)$ and $(-1.19, -12.4)$.
Local maximum is $(1, 0)$.

c x-intercepts are $(-2, 0), (1, 0)$ and $(2, 0)$.

$\therefore \quad x^4 - 2x^3 - 3x^2 + 8x - 4 = 0$

when $\quad x = 1 \quad$ or $\quad x = \pm 2$

Long questions

1 a **i** $C(20) = 20^2 + 400 = 800$

i.e., weekly cost is $800

ii $I(20) = 50 \times 20 = 1000$

i.e., weekly income is $1000

iii $P(20) = I(20) - C(20)$

$= 1000 - 800$

$= 200 \quad$ i.e., a profit of $200 is made.

b $P(x) = I(x) - C(x)$

$\therefore \quad P(x) = 50x - (x^2 + 400)$

c $P(x) = -x^2 + 50x - 400$

$\therefore \quad$ vertex occurs when $\quad x = -\dfrac{b}{2a} = \dfrac{-50}{2(-1)} = 25$

Hence, 25 CD-players must be made and sold to maximise profit.

d $P(25) = -(25)^2 + 50(25) - 400 = 225$

Profit **per** CD-player $= \dfrac{\$225}{25} = \$9$

e The function $P(x)$ has zeros at $\quad x = 10 \quad$ and $\quad x = 40$.

In order to make positive (non-zero) profit, 39 CD-players must be made.

2 a x-int occurs when $\quad y = 0 \quad \therefore \quad 2 + \dfrac{4}{x + 1} = 0$

$\therefore \quad \dfrac{4}{x + 1} = -2$

$\therefore \quad 4 = -2(x + 1)$

$\therefore \quad 4 = -2x - 2$

$\therefore \quad 2x = -6$

$\therefore \quad x = -3$

b y-int occurs when $\quad x = 0 \quad \therefore \quad y = 2 + \frac{4}{1} = 6$

c $f(-2) = 2 + \dfrac{4}{-2 + 1} \quad \therefore \quad f(-2) = -2$

d **i** $y = 2$ **ii** $x = -1$

e

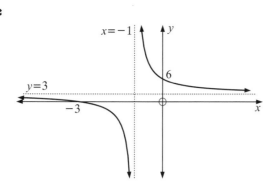

3 a i $x = \frac{3}{2}$ **ii** $y = 0$

b y-intercept at $x = 0$, $\therefore$ $y = a^0 = 1$

c Equation of the horizontal asymptote is $y = 0$.

d At $x = 2$, $a^2 = \dfrac{4}{2(2) - 3} = \dfrac{4}{1} = 4$

$$\therefore \quad a = \pm 2$$
$$\therefore \quad a = 2 \quad \{\text{as } a > 0\}$$

e Graph of $y = \dfrac{4}{2x - 3}$ and $y = 2^x$

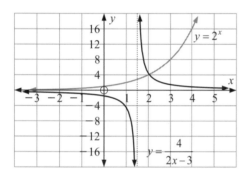

4 a

x	1	2	3	4	5	6
$W(x)$	7	4	3	2.5	2.2	2

b

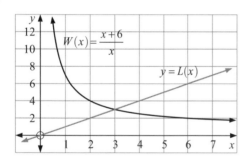

c Square base occurs when $L(x) = W(x)$.
From the graph, this occurs when $x = 3$ cm.

d Volume $= L \times W \times H = 36$ cm^3

$$\therefore \quad x \times \left(\frac{x + 6}{x}\right) \times H = 36$$
$$\therefore \quad H(x + 6) = 36$$
$$\therefore \quad H = \frac{36}{x + 6}$$

e $A(x) = 2(LW) + 2(LH) + 2(WH)$

$$= 2x\left(\frac{x + 6}{x}\right) + 2x\left(\frac{36}{x + 6}\right) + 2\left(\frac{x + 6}{x}\right)\left(\frac{36}{x + 6}\right)$$
$$= 2(x + 6) + \frac{72x}{x + 6} + \frac{72}{x}$$
$$= 2x + 12 + \frac{72x}{x + 6} + \frac{72}{x}$$

f Minimum area is 65.9 cm^2.

5 a

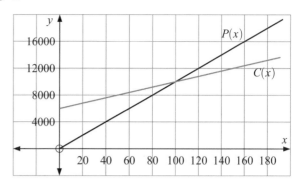

b The initial set-up cost $C(0) = \$6000$.

c Break-even occurs when $6000 + 40x = 100x$
$$\therefore \quad 6000 = 60x$$
$$\therefore \quad x = 100$$

d Total revenue of selling x bicycles $= \$100x$
Revenue per bicycle $= \$100$

e $P(x) = R(x) - C(x)$
$$= 100x - (6000 + 40x)$$
$$= 60x - 6000$$

f Profit from sale of 400 bicycles is
$$P(400) = 60 \times 400 - 6000 = \$18\,000$$

6 a

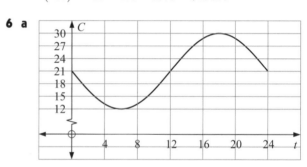

b At 1:30 pm, $t = 13.5$
$$C(13.5) = 21 - 9\sin(15 \times 13.5) = 24.4°\text{C} \quad (3 \text{ s.f.})$$

c Max. temp is $30.0°$C reached at $t = 18$, i.e., at 6:00 pm.

d At $t = 10$, $C(10) = 16.5°$C
At $t = 19.5$, $C(19.5) = 29.3°$C

However, max. temp of $30.0°$C occurs at $t = 18$
$\therefore$ range is between $30°$ and $16.5°$
$\therefore$ range $= 13.5°$C

e Temperature is rising on $6 \leqslant t \leqslant 18$
Temperature rising most rapidly at $t = 12$ as slope of $C(t)$ is greatest at this point.

7 a y-intercept $= 0$

b Max is $(4.33, 4.04)$

c $f(2) = 2$, $f(-1) = -2$

d and **e**

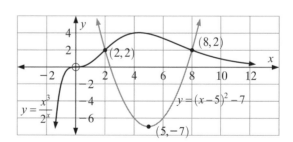

f $\dfrac{x^3}{2^x} + 7 = (x-5)^2$

$\therefore \dfrac{x^3}{2^x} = (x-5)^2 - 7$ and so $f(x) = g(x)$

Intersect at $(2, 2)$, $(8, 2)$, and so $x = 2$ or 8.

8 a 5 times per second $\equiv$ 1 time per $\frac{1}{5}$ second.

$\therefore$ one revolution takes 0.2 seconds.

b Mean position $= 12$ m   Period $= 0.2$

$\therefore$ $c = 12$ m

Amplitude $= 3$ m $\therefore$ $b = \dfrac{360}{0.2} = 1800$

$\therefore$ $P(t) = 3\cos(1800t) + 12$

c $R(t) = 11 - \cos(720t)$

$\therefore$ $b = 720 \Rightarrow$ period $= \dfrac{360}{b} = \dfrac{360}{720} = 0.5$ sec

d $P(t) = R(t)$ at $t = 0.0686$ secs

e Both $P(t)$ and $R(t)$ have a minimum at $t = 0.5$ secs.

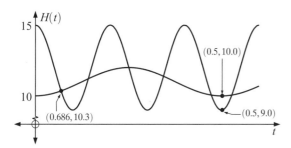

SOLUTIONS TO TOPIC 5   GEOMETRY AND TRIGONOMETRY

Short questions

1 a

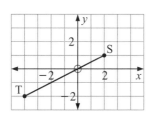

b Using the distance formula

$ST = \sqrt{(-4-2)^2 + (-2-1)^2}$

$= \sqrt{36 + 9}$

$= \sqrt{45}$ or 6.71 (3 s.f.)

c $SR = 5$ units

$\therefore$ $\sqrt{(b-2)^2 + (4-1)^2} = 5$ {distance formula}

$\therefore$ $(b-2)^2 + 9 = 25$

$\therefore$ $(b-2)^2 = 16$

$\therefore$ $b - 2 = \pm 4$ $\therefore$ $b = 6$ as $b > 0$

2

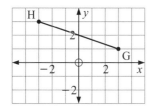

a Gradient GH $= \dfrac{1-3}{3--3} = \dfrac{-2}{6} = -\frac{1}{3}$ (or ≈ -0.333)

b Midpoint GH is $\left(\dfrac{3+-3}{2}, \dfrac{1+3}{2}\right)$, i.e., $(0, 2)$

c Perpendicular bisector has gradient 3 $\therefore$ $y = 3x + b$
passes through $(0, 2)$ $\therefore$ $2 = 3(0) + b$ and so $b = 2$

$\therefore$ equation is $y = 3x + 2$

3 L_1: $4x - 3y = 7$ L_2: $2x + ky = 5$

a $L_1:$ $4x - 3y = 7$

$\therefore$ $-3y = -4x + 7$

$\therefore$ $y = \dfrac{-4x}{-3} + \dfrac{7}{-3}$

$\therefore$ $y = \frac{4}{3}x - \frac{7}{3}$

$\therefore$ gradient of $L_1 = \frac{4}{3}$

b $L_2:$ $2x + ky = 5$

$\therefore$ $ky = -2x + 5$

$\therefore$ $y = -\dfrac{2}{k}x + \dfrac{5}{k}$

$\therefore$ gradient of $L_2 = -\dfrac{2}{k}$

i If L_1 and L_2 are parallel, $\dfrac{-2}{k} = \dfrac{4}{3}$

$\therefore$ $4k = -6$

$\therefore$ $k = \dfrac{-6}{4} = -\frac{3}{2}$

ii If L_1 and L_2 are perpendicular, $-\dfrac{2}{k} \times \dfrac{4}{3} = -1$

$\therefore$ $-8 = -3k$

$\therefore$ $\frac{8}{3} = k$

4 a

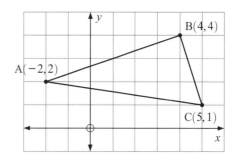

b Slope$_{AB} = \dfrac{4-2}{4--2} = \dfrac{2}{6} = \frac{1}{3}$

Slope$_{BC} = \dfrac{1-4}{5-4} = \dfrac{-3}{1} = -3$

Now   slope$_{AB} \times$ slope$_{BC} = \frac{1}{3} \times -3 = -1$

$\therefore$ lines are perpendicular and Δ is right angled at B.

c

$AC^2 = (5--2)^2 + (1-2)^2$ {Pythagoras}

$= 7^2 + 1^2$

$\therefore$ $AC = \sqrt{50}$ units   {length AC > 0}

5 a $L_1:$ $7x + 3y = 12$

$\therefore$ $3y = -7x + 12$

$\therefore$ $y = -\frac{7}{3}x + 4$

$\therefore$ gradient of $L_1 = -\frac{7}{3}$

$\therefore$ L_2 has gradient $-\frac{7}{3}$ {parallel lines}

b Perpendicular line has gradient $= \frac{3}{7}$ $\{\frac{3}{7} \times -\frac{7}{3} = -1\}$

$\therefore$ $y = \frac{3}{7}x + c$

$\therefore$ $1 = \frac{3}{7}(7) + c$ {subst $(7, 1)$}

$\therefore$ $1 = 3 + c$ and so $c = -2$

$\therefore$ equation is $y = \frac{3}{7}x - 2$

6 a $2x - 4y = 7$ meets the x-axis when $y = 0$

$\therefore$ $2x = 7$ and so $x = k = \frac{7}{2}$

b The line passing through $(3, 2)$ and $(-6, 0)$ has

gradient $= \dfrac{0-2}{-6-3} = \dfrac{-2}{-9} = \dfrac{2}{9}$

$$y = \tfrac{2}{9}x + c$$

$\therefore \quad 0 = \tfrac{2}{9}(-6) + c \quad$ {substituting $(-6, 0)$}

$\therefore \quad 0 = -\tfrac{12}{9} + c \quad$ and so $\quad c = \tfrac{12}{9}$

$\therefore \quad y = \tfrac{2}{9}x + \tfrac{12}{9}$

$\therefore \quad 9y = 2x + 12$

$\therefore \quad 0 = 2x - 9y + 12$

but the line has equation $\quad ax + by + d = 0$

$\therefore \quad a = 2, \quad b = -9, \quad d = 12 \quad$ {equating coefficients}

7

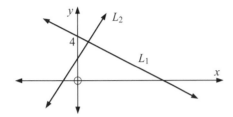

a $\qquad L_1$ has gradient $= -\tfrac{1}{2}$ and y-intercept $= 4$

$\therefore \quad$ equation of L_1 is $\quad y = -\tfrac{1}{2}x + 4$

$\therefore \quad 2y = -x + 8$

$\therefore \quad x + 2y - 8 = 0$

b Gradient of $L_2 = \dfrac{8 - -1}{4 - -2} = \dfrac{9}{6} = \dfrac{3}{2}$

$\therefore \quad y = \tfrac{3}{2}x + c$

$\therefore \quad -1 = \tfrac{3}{2}(-2) + c \quad$ {subst $(-2, -1)$}

$\therefore \quad -1 = -3 + c \quad$ and so $\quad c = 2$

$\therefore \quad y = \tfrac{3}{2}x + 2 \quad$ is the equation of L_2

L_1 and L_2 intersect when

$$-\tfrac{1}{2}x + 4 = \tfrac{3}{2}x + 2 \quad \text{(or use technology)}$$

$\therefore \quad 2 = \tfrac{4}{2}x \quad$ and so $\quad x = 1$

subst $x = 1$ in $y = \tfrac{3}{2}x + 2$

gives $\quad y = \tfrac{3}{2}(1) + 2 = 3\tfrac{1}{2}$

$\therefore \quad$ point of intersection is $(1, 3\tfrac{1}{2})$

8 a $kx + 3y = 7 \quad$ cuts x-axis at $(4, 0)$

$\therefore \quad 4k = 7 \quad$ and so $\quad k = \tfrac{7}{4}$

b

$$ax - y = 4h \quad \text{...... (1)}$$
$$ax + 2y = h \quad \text{...... (2)}$$

Solving simultaneously, $\quad -3y = 3h \quad \{(1) - (2)\}$

$\therefore \quad y = \dfrac{3h}{-3}$

i.e., lines intersect when $\quad y = -h$

but they intersect at $(1, -1)$, $\therefore \quad -1 = -h$ and so $h = 1$

Substituting $x = 1, \; y = -1, \; h = 1$ in (2) gives

$$a(1) + 2(-1) = 1$$

$\therefore \quad a - 2 = 1$

$\therefore \quad a = 3$

9 a $y = \dfrac{24}{x} \quad$ and $\quad y = 3x - 1$

intersect when $\quad \dfrac{24}{x} = 3x - 1$

$\therefore \quad 24 = 3x^2 - x$

$\therefore \quad 0 = 3x^2 - x - 24$

$\therefore \quad 0 = (3x + 8)(x - 3)$

$\therefore \quad 3x + 8 = 0 \quad$ or $\quad x - 3 = 0$

$\therefore \quad x = -\tfrac{8}{3} \quad$ or $\quad x = 3$

But $x > 0$, $\therefore \quad x = 3$

When $\quad x = 3, \quad y = 3(3) - 1 = 9 - 1 = 8$

$\therefore \quad$ intersect at $(3, 8)$. {In examinations solve using a gdc.}

b Gradient of $\quad y = 3x - 1 \quad$ is 3

$\therefore \quad$ gradient of perpendicular $= -\tfrac{1}{3}$

$\therefore \quad y = -\tfrac{1}{3}x + c$

$\therefore \quad 8 = -\tfrac{1}{3}(3) + c \quad$ {subst $(3, 8)$}

$\therefore \quad 8 = -1 + c$

$\therefore \quad 9 = c$

$\therefore \quad y = -\tfrac{1}{3}x + 9 \quad$ is the equation of the perpendicular line.

10

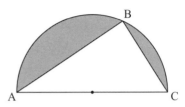

$AB = 8$ cm, $\quad BC = 6$ cm, $\quad AC = 10$ cm

a If right angled then $\quad 8^2 + 6^2 = 10^2 \quad$ {Pythagoras}

LHS $= 8^2 + 6^2 = 64 + 36 = 100$

RHS $= 10^2 = 100$

$\therefore \quad$ LHS $=$ RHS

$\therefore \quad \triangle ABC$ is right angled at B.

b Shaded area $=$ area semi circle $-$ area triangle

$= \tfrac{1}{2} \times \pi \times 5^2 \; - \; \tfrac{1}{2} \times 8 \times 6$

$= 15.3 \text{ cm}^2$

11

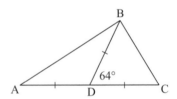

a $\angle DBC = \angle DCB = \dfrac{180° - 64°}{2} = 58° \quad$ {isosceles $\triangle$}

$\angle ADB = 180° - 64° = 116° \quad$ {straight angle}

$\angle DAB = \angle ABD = \dfrac{180° - 116°}{2} = 32° \quad$ {isosceles $\triangle$}

Now $\angle ABC = \angle ABD + \angle DBC$

$= 32° + 58°$

$= 90°$

b $AB^2 + 4.24^2 = 8^2 \quad$ {Pythagoras' Theorem}

$AB = \sqrt{(8^2 - 4.24^2)}$

≈ 6.78 cm

c Area $= \tfrac{1}{2}(\text{base} \times \text{height})$

$= \tfrac{1}{2} \times 4.24 \times 6.78$

$\approx 14.4 \text{ cm}^2$

12

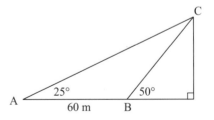

a $\angle ABC = 180° - 50° \quad$ {straight angle}

$= 130°$

$\therefore \quad \angle ACB = 180° - (25° + 130°)$

$= 25°$

b As $\triangle ACB$ is isosceles (base angles equal)

then $BC = AB = 60$ m

Let the tower have height x m.

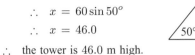

$\therefore \quad \sin 50^o = \dfrac{x}{60}$ 60 m

$\therefore \quad x = 60 \sin 50^o$

$\therefore \quad x = 46.0$

$\therefore$ the tower is 46.0 m high.

13

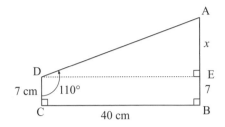

a $\angle ADE = 110^o - 90^o = 20^o$

Let AE be x cm.

$\therefore \quad \tan 20^o = \dfrac{x}{40}$

$\therefore \quad x = 40 \tan 20^o \approx 14.56$

$\therefore \quad AB = 14.56 + 7$

$\therefore \quad AB = 21.56$ cm   (2 dec. pl.)

b $\cos 20^o = \dfrac{40}{AD}$

$\therefore \quad AD = \dfrac{40}{\cos 20^o} = 42.6$ cm

c ABCD is a trapezium with DC $\parallel$ AB

area $= \dfrac{h}{2}(a+b)$

$\therefore$ area $= \dfrac{40}{2}(7 + 21.56) \approx 571$ cm^2

14 a

$\angle ABC = 60^o$ (equilateral $\triangle$)

b Each altitude bisects the angle and the base.
This gives triangle

$\tan 30^o = \dfrac{x}{25}$

$\therefore \quad x = 25 \tan 30^o$

$\therefore \quad x = 14.4$ cm

15 a

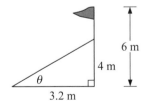

b The wire is secured to the pole at $\frac{2}{3}$ of its length.

Now $\frac{2}{3} \times 6 = 4$ m.

Let θ represent the angle the wire makes with the ground.

$\tan \theta = \dfrac{4}{3.2}$

$\therefore \quad \theta = \tan^{-1}\left(\dfrac{4}{3.2}\right)$

$\therefore \quad \theta = 51.3^o$

---

i.e.,   the wire makes an angle of 51.3^o with the ground.

c Let x be the length of each wire.

$4^2 + 3.2^2 = x^2$ {Pythagoras' theorem}

$\therefore \quad 16 + 10.24 = x^2$

$\therefore \quad x^2 = 26.24$

$\therefore \quad x = \sqrt{26.24}$ $(x > 0)$

$\therefore \quad x \approx 5.122$

$\therefore$ total length of the three wires $\approx 3 \times 5.122 \approx 15.4$ m

16

a Area $\triangle DEF = 120$ cm^2.   Let DF be x cm.

Using area of a triangle $= \frac{1}{2}bc \sin A$

we have $120 = \frac{1}{2} \times 12 \times x \sin 30^o$

$\therefore \quad 120 = 6 \times x \times \frac{1}{2}$

$\therefore \quad 120 = 3x$

$\therefore \quad 40 = x$

$\therefore \quad DF = 40$ cm

b In $\triangle EDG$, $\sin 30^o = \dfrac{EG}{12}$

$\therefore \quad EG = 12 \sin 30^o = 6$

i.e.,   the length of the perpendicular is 6 cm.

17 a

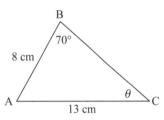

b Let $\angle BCA = \theta$.

$\therefore \quad \dfrac{\sin \theta}{8} = \dfrac{\sin 70^o}{13}$ {Sine Rule}

$\therefore \quad \sin \theta = \dfrac{8 \sin 70^o}{13}$

$\therefore \quad \theta = \sin^{-1}\left(\dfrac{8 \sin 70^o}{13}\right) \approx 35.3^o$

i.e., $\angle BCA = 35.3^o$

c To find the area of $\triangle ABC$ we need either length BC or $\angle BAC$.

$\angle BAC = 180^o - (70^o + 35.3^o) = 74.7^o$

$\therefore$ area $\triangle ABC = \frac{1}{2} \times 8 \times 13 \sin 74.7^o \approx 50.2$ cm^2

18 a

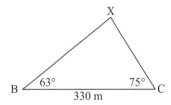

b To find BX we need $\angle BXC$.

$\angle BXC = 180^o - (63^o + 75^o) = 42^o$

Using the Sine Rule, $\dfrac{BX}{\sin 75^o} = \dfrac{330}{\sin 42^o}$

$BX = \dfrac{330 \sin 75^o}{\sin 42^o} \approx 476$

i.e.,   the distance of the landmark from B is 476 m.

Mathematical Studies SL – Exam Preparation & Practice Guide

19

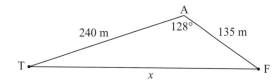

a Let the distance be x m.

Using the Cosine Rule,
$$x^2 = 240^2 + 135^2 - 2 \times 240 \times 135 \cos 128^o$$
$$\therefore \quad x \approx 340.18$$

i.e., the distance is 340 m.

b $\dfrac{\sin \angle ATF}{135^o} = \dfrac{\sin 128^o}{340.18}$

$\therefore \quad \angle ATF = \sin^{-1}\left(\dfrac{135 \sin 128^o}{340.18}\right) \approx 18.2^o$

20 a

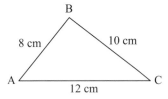

b Smallest angle is opposite the shortest side, i.e., $\angle BCA$.

Let $\angle BCA = \theta$.

Using the Cosine Rule, $\cos \theta = \dfrac{10^2 + 12^2 - 8^2}{2 \times 10 \times 12} = 0.75$

$$\therefore \quad \theta = \cos^{-1}(0.75) \approx 41.4^o$$

c Area $\triangle ABC = \frac{1}{2} \times 10 \times 12 \sin 41.4^o \approx 39.7$ cm^2

21

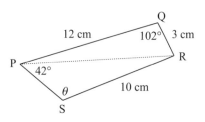

a Using the Cosine Rule
$$PR^2 = 12^2 + 3^2 - 2 \times 12 \times 3 \cos 102^o \approx 167.970$$
$$\therefore \quad PR \approx 12.960 \text{ cm, which is} \approx 13.0 \text{ cm}$$

b $\dfrac{\sin \theta}{PR} = \dfrac{\sin 42^o}{10}$ {Sine Rule}

$\therefore \quad \sin \theta = \dfrac{12.960 \times \sin 42^o}{10} \approx 0.867193$

$\therefore \quad \theta = \sin^{-1}(0.867193)$

$\therefore \quad \theta = 60.1^o$

22

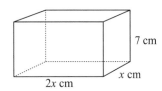

a Let the shorter side be x cm. $\therefore$ the longer side is $2x$ cm
$$V = 2x \times x \times 7 \text{ cm}^3$$

But $V = 350$ cm^3

$\therefore \quad 14x^2 = 350$

$\therefore \quad x^2 = \dfrac{350}{14} = 25$

$\therefore \quad x = \sqrt{25} = 5$ {as $x > 0$}

$\therefore$ dimensions are 5 cm $\times$ 10 cm $\times$ 7 cm.

b

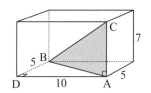

Longest pencil has the length of the diagonal of the box.

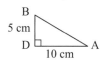

In $\triangle ABD$, $AB^2 = 10^2 + 5^2$ {Pythagoras}

$\therefore \quad AB^2 = 125$

In $\triangle ABC$, $BC^2 = AB^2 + 7^2$ {Pythagoras}

$\therefore \quad BC^2 = 125 + 49 = 174$

$\therefore \quad BC = \sqrt{174}$ {as BC > 0}

$\quad\quad\quad = 13.2$

$\therefore$ the longest pencil is 13.2 cm long.

23 a

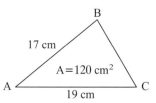

b Let $\angle BAC = \theta$.

Using area $= \frac{1}{2}bc \sin A$

$\frac{1}{2} \times 17 \times 19 \times \sin \theta = 120$

$\therefore \quad \sin \theta = \dfrac{120}{161.5}$

$\therefore \quad \theta = \sin^{-1}\left(\dfrac{120}{161.5}\right) \approx 48.0^o$

i.e., $\angle BAC = 48.0^o$

c Using the Cosine Rule,
$$BC^2 = 17^2 + 19^2 - 2 \times 17 \times 19 \cos 48.0^o$$
$$\therefore \quad BC = 14.8$$

i.e., the remaining side is 14.8 cm long.

d Volume = area cross-section $\times$ length
$$= 120 \times 13.5$$
$$= 1620 \text{ cm}^3$$

24 a

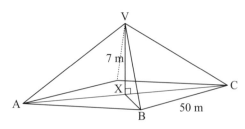

b Length of base diagonal

$= \sqrt{50^2 + 50^2} \approx 70.7$ m

Length of sloping edge

$= \sqrt{7^2 + \left(\dfrac{70.7}{2}\right)^2}$

≈ 36.036

≈ 36.0 m

c $\sin \theta = \dfrac{7}{36.036}$

$\therefore \quad \theta = \sin^{-1}\left(\dfrac{7}{36.036}\right) \approx 11.2^o$

i.e., angle between sloping edge and base diagonal is 11.2^o.

d

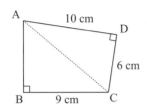

Height is $\sqrt{(36.036)^2 - 25^2} \approx 25.95$ m

Area of face is $\dfrac{50 \times 25.95}{2} \approx 649$ m^2

25

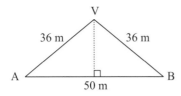

a In $\triangle ADC$, $AD^2 + DC^2 = AC^2$ {Pythagoras}

$\therefore \quad 10^2 + 6^2 = AC^2$

$\therefore \quad AC^2 = 136$

In $\triangle ABC$, $AB^2 + BC^2 = AC^2$ {Pythagoras}

$AB^2 + 9^2 = 136$

$AB^2 = 136 - 81 = 55$

$\therefore \quad AB = \sqrt{55}$ units

$\therefore \quad AB \approx 7.42$ units

b Area quadrilateral ABCD

$=$ area$_{\triangle ABC}$ + area$_{\triangle ADC}$

$= \dfrac{\sqrt{55} \times 9}{2} + \dfrac{10 \times 6}{2}$

≈ 63.37

≈ 63.4 cm^2

c Volume = area cross-section $\times$ length

$\therefore$ length of prism = $\dfrac{484}{63.37} \approx 7.64$ cm

Long questions

1 a

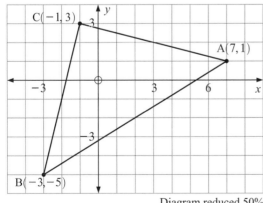

Diagram reduced 50%

b i length$_{AC} = \sqrt{(-1-7)^2 + (3-1)^2}$

$= \sqrt{(-8)^2 + 2^2}$

$= \sqrt{64 + 4}$

$= \sqrt{68}$

≈ 8.25 units

ii length$_{BC} = \sqrt{(-1--3)^2 + (3--5)^2}$

$= \sqrt{2^2 + 8^2}$

$= \sqrt{68}$

$=$ length AC

iii Gradient$_{AC} = \dfrac{3-1}{-1-7} = \dfrac{2}{-8} = -\dfrac{1}{4}$

iv gradient$_{BC} \times$ gradient$_{AC} = 4 \times -\dfrac{1}{4} = -1$

$\therefore \quad AC \perp BC$ and the angle at C is 90°

v Area $= \dfrac{1}{2}$ base $\times$ height

$= \dfrac{1}{2} \times \sqrt{68} \times \sqrt{68}$

$= 34$ units^2

c i Gradient$_{AB} = \dfrac{-5-1}{-3-7} = \dfrac{-6}{-10} = \dfrac{3}{5}$

$\therefore$ equation of AB is $y = \dfrac{3}{5}x + c$

$\therefore \quad 1 = \dfrac{3}{5}(7) + c$ {subst (7, 1)}

$\therefore \quad \dfrac{21}{5} + c = 1$

$\therefore \quad c = 1 - \dfrac{21}{5} = -\dfrac{16}{5}$

$\therefore \quad y = \dfrac{3}{5}x - \dfrac{16}{5}$

$\therefore \quad 5y = 3x - 16$

$\therefore \quad 3x - 5y = 16$

ii D is the midpoint of AB

$\therefore \quad$ D is $\left(\dfrac{7+-3}{2}, \dfrac{1+-5}{2}\right)$, i.e., $(2, -2)$

But DC is perpendicular to AB

$\therefore$ its gradient is $\dfrac{-5}{3}$.

$\therefore \quad y = -\dfrac{5}{3}x + c$

$\therefore \quad -2 = -\dfrac{5}{3}(2) + c$ {subst (2, -2)}

$\therefore \quad -2 = -\dfrac{10}{3} + c$

$\therefore \quad -2 + \dfrac{10}{3} = c$ and so $c = \dfrac{4}{3}$

$\therefore$ its equation is $y = -\dfrac{5}{3}x + \dfrac{4}{3}$

2 a

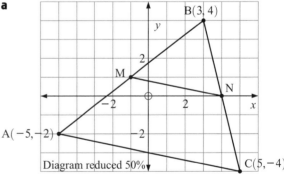

Diagram reduced 50%

b i Midpoint of AB is M $\left(\dfrac{-5+3}{2}, \dfrac{-2+4}{2}\right)$

i.e., M is $(-1, 1)$.

ii Midpoint BC is $\left(\dfrac{3+5}{2}, \dfrac{4+-4}{2}\right)$ i.e., $\left(\dfrac{8}{2}, \dfrac{0}{2}\right)$

i.e., N is $(4, 0)$

c i Gradient of MN $= \dfrac{0-1}{4--1} = -\dfrac{1}{5}$

ii Equation of the line through M and N is

$y = -\dfrac{1}{5}x + c$

$\therefore \quad 1 = -\dfrac{1}{5}(-1) + c$ {subst (-1, 1)}

$\therefore \quad 1 = \dfrac{1}{5} + c$ and so $c = \dfrac{4}{5}$

$\therefore \quad y = -\dfrac{1}{5}x + \dfrac{4}{5}$

$\therefore \quad 5y = -1x + 4$

$\therefore \quad x + 5y = 4$

d If AC is parallel to MN then they have the same gradient.

$$\text{Gradient}_{AC} = \frac{-4 - -2}{5 - -5} = -\frac{1}{5}$$

$\therefore$ AC is parallel to MN.

e Length AC $= \sqrt{(5 - -5)^2 + (-4 - -2)^2}$

$\qquad\qquad\quad = \sqrt{10^2 + (-2)^2}$

$\qquad\qquad\quad = \sqrt{104}$

$\qquad\qquad\quad = \sqrt{4 \times 26}$

$\qquad\qquad\quad = \sqrt{4} \times \sqrt{26}$

$\qquad\qquad\quad = 2\sqrt{26}$

$\therefore$ AC is twice as long as MN

$\quad or \quad$ AC $= \sqrt{104} \approx 10.20$ cm

and MN $= \sqrt{26} \approx 5.10$ cm

$\therefore$ AC is twice the length of MN.

f i

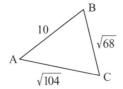

$$\cos \angle ABC = \frac{10^2 + \left(\sqrt{68}\right)^2 - \left(\sqrt{104}\right)^2}{2 \times 10 \times \sqrt{68}} \approx 0.3881$$

$\therefore$ $\angle ABC = \cos^{-1}(0.3881) \approx 67.2°$

ii Area $\triangle ABC = \frac{1}{2} \times 10 \times \sqrt{68} \sin 67.2° \approx 38.0$ units^2

iii

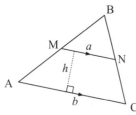

$\triangle ABC$ has area 38 units^2 and $\triangle BMN$ has area 9.5 units^2

$\therefore$ trapezium AMNC has area $38 - 9.5 = 28.5$ units^2

Now area of trapezium $= h\left(\dfrac{a+b}{2}\right)$

$\therefore$ $28.5 = h\left(\dfrac{\sqrt{26} + \sqrt{104}}{2}\right)$

$\therefore$ $57 = h\left(\sqrt{26} + \sqrt{104}\right)$

$\therefore$ $h = \dfrac{57}{\left(\sqrt{26} + \sqrt{104}\right)} \approx 3.73$ units

$\therefore$ the perpendicular distance is 3.73 units.

3 a i

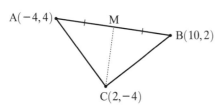

$\text{length}_{AC} = \sqrt{(2 - -4)^2 + (-4 - 4)^2}$

$\qquad\qquad = \sqrt{36 + 64}$

$\qquad\qquad = \sqrt{100}$

$\qquad\qquad = 10$

$\text{length}_{BC} = \sqrt{(2 - 10)^2 + (-4 - 2)^2}$

$\qquad\qquad = \sqrt{(-8)^2 + (-6)^2}$

$\qquad\qquad = \sqrt{100}$

$\qquad\qquad = 10$

---

ii $\triangle ABC$ is isosceles as   AC $=$ BC $= 10$ units

iii Midpoint$_{AB}$ is $\left(\dfrac{-4 + 10}{2}, \dfrac{4 + 2}{2}\right)$, i.e., (3, 3).

iv $\angle AMC = 90°$ {altitude bisects base of isosceles $\triangle$}

b i gradient$_{BC} = \dfrac{-4 - 2}{2 - 10} = \dfrac{-6}{-8} = \dfrac{3}{4}$

Now gradient$_{AC} \times$ gradient $_{BC} = -\dfrac{4}{3} \times \dfrac{3}{4} = -1$

$\therefore$ AC $\perp$ BC i.e., angle ACB $= 90°$.

ii

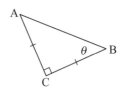

As $\triangle ABC$ is a right isosceles then $\angle CBA = 45°$

c i gradient$_{BC} = \dfrac{3}{4}$

$\therefore$ equation of the line through B and C is
$$y = \tfrac{3}{4}x + c$$

$\therefore$ $-4 = \tfrac{3}{4}(2) + c$ {subst (2, -4)}

$\therefore$ $-4 = \tfrac{3}{2} + c$ and so $c = -\tfrac{11}{2}$

$\therefore$ $y = \tfrac{3}{4}x - \tfrac{11}{2}$

$\therefore$ $4y = 3x - 22$

$\therefore$ $3x - 4y = 22$

ii a equation of a line $\parallel$ to BC is $3x - 4y = k$
$(k \in \mathbb{R})$ (i.e., k can be any real number)

b equation of a line $\perp$ to BC is
$$4x + 3y = k \quad (k \in \mathbb{R})$$

4

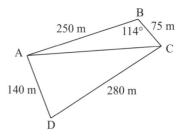

a i Using the cosine rule in $\triangle ABC$
$$AC^2 = 250^2 + 75^2 - 2 \times 250 \times 75 \cos 114°$$
$\therefore$ AC ≈ 289 m

ii Using the cosine rule in $\triangle ADC$
$$\cos \angle ADC = \frac{140^2 + 280^2 - 289^2}{2 \times 140 \times 280} \approx 0.1865$$
$\therefore$ $\angle ADC = \cos^{-1}(0.1865) \approx 79.3°$

iii Area $\triangle ADC = \frac{1}{2} \times 140 \times 280 \sin 79.3°$
$\qquad\qquad\quad = 19\,259.2$
$\qquad\qquad\quad \approx 19\,300$ m^2

iv Area $\triangle ABC = \frac{1}{2} \times 250 \times 75 \sin 114°$
$\qquad\qquad\quad = 8564.5$
$\qquad\qquad\quad = 8560$ m^2

$\therefore$ total area of park $\approx 19\,259.2 + 8564.5$
$\qquad\qquad\qquad\qquad \approx 27\,827.3$
$\qquad\qquad\qquad\qquad \approx 27\,800$ m^2

b

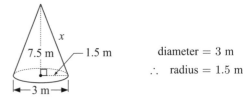

diameter $= 3$ m

$\therefore$ radius $= 1.5$ m

i Let the slant height be s m.

$\therefore \quad 7.3^2 + 1.5^2 = s^2 \quad$ {Pythagoras}

$\therefore \quad s^2 = 53.29 + 2.25$

$\therefore \quad s = \sqrt{55.54} \approx 7.45$

i.e., the slant height is 7.45 m.

ii Let the angle between base and slant height be θ.

$\therefore \quad \tan\theta = \dfrac{7.3}{1.5}$

$\therefore \quad \theta = \tan^{-1}\left(\dfrac{7.3}{1.5}\right) \approx 78.4^o$

iii Volume $= \frac{1}{3}\pi r^2 h$

$= \frac{1}{3}\pi(1.5)^2 \times 7.3$

$\approx 17.2 \text{ m}^3$

$\therefore \quad$ total volume $= 34.2 \text{ m}^3$

c Area of curved surface $= \pi r s$

$= \pi \times 1.5 \times 7.45$

$\approx 35.1 \text{ m}^2$

$\therefore \quad$ total area of curved surface is 70.2 m^2

$\therefore \quad$ require $70.2 \div 15 = 4.68$ litres of paint.

5 a i

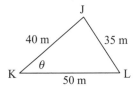

ii Let $\angle JKL = \theta$

Using the Cosine Rule,

$\cos\theta = \dfrac{40^2 + 50^2 - 35^2}{2 \times 40 \times 50} \approx 0.71875$

$\theta = \cos^{-1}(0.71875) \approx 44.0^o$

i.e., Kim must turn through 44.0^o.

b

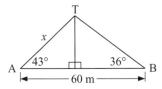

i $\angle ATB = 180^o - (43^o + 36^o) \quad$ {angle sum of $\triangle$}

$= 101^o$

ii $\dfrac{AT}{\sin 36^o} = \dfrac{60}{\sin 101^o} \quad$ {Sine Rule}

$\therefore \quad AT = \dfrac{60 \times \sin 36^o}{\sin 101^o} \approx 35.9$

i.e., the treasure is 35.9 m from point A.

iii

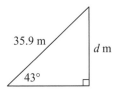

Let the vertical distance be d m.

Now $\sin 43^o = \dfrac{d}{35.9}$

$\therefore \quad 35.9 \times \sin 43^o = d$

$\therefore \quad 24.5 \approx d$

i.e., the vertical distance is 24.5 m.

c Area of $\triangle ATB \approx \frac{1}{2} \times 35.9 \times 60 \sin 43^o$

$\approx 735 \text{ m}^2$

6 a i

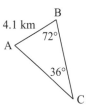

$\dfrac{AC}{\sin 72^o} = \dfrac{4.1}{\sin 36^o} \quad$ {Sine Rule}

$\therefore \quad AC = \dfrac{4.1 \sin 72^o}{\sin 36^o} \approx 6.63 \text{ km}$

And since EF is 20% longer than AC then
length EF $= 1.2 \times$ length AC

$= 7.96 \text{ km}$

ii

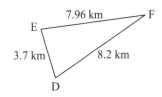

Using the Cosine Rule,

$\cos \angle DEF = \dfrac{7.96^2 + 3.7^2 - 8.2^2}{2 \times 3.7 \times 7.96} \approx 0.1666$

$\angle DEF \approx 80.4^o$

iii

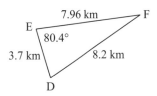

Area $\triangle DEF \approx \frac{1}{2} \times 3.7 \times 7.96 \sin 80.4^o$

$\approx 14.5 \text{ km}^2$

b i $\angle BAC = 180^o - (72^o + 36^o) = 72^o$

$\therefore \quad \triangle ABC$ is isosceles

$\therefore \quad BC = AC = 6.63 \text{ km}$

$\therefore \quad$ length of course 1 $\approx 4.1 + 6.63 + 6.63$

$\approx 17.4 \text{ km}$

ii Course 2 has length $= 3.7 + 8.2 + 7.96 \approx 19.9 \text{ km}$

Time to complete course 1 $= \dfrac{17.4}{14}$ h

$\approx 74.6 \text{ min}$

$\approx 1 \text{ hour } 15 \text{ minutes}$

Time to complete course 2 $= \dfrac{19.9}{10}$ h

$= 1.99 \text{ hours}$

$= 1 \text{ hour } 59 \text{ mins}$

$\therefore \quad$ it will take Wael 40 minutes extra to complete course 2 (nearest 10 mins).

7

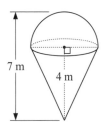

a i Height of the hemisphere is $7 - 4 = 3$ m

$\therefore \quad$ radius of cone $= 3$ m

ii Volume $= \frac{1}{3}\pi r^2 h + \frac{2}{3}\pi r^3$

$\qquad = \frac{1}{3}\pi \times 3^2 \times 4 + \frac{2}{3}\pi \times 3^3$

$\qquad \approx 37.7 + 56.5 \text{ m}^3$

$\qquad \approx 94.2 \text{ m}^3$

b i

$\tan\theta = \frac{4}{3}$

$\therefore \quad \theta = \tan^{-1}\left(\frac{4}{3}\right)$

$\therefore \quad \theta \approx 53.1^\circ$

ii slant height $s = \sqrt{3^2 + 4^2}$ {Pythagoras}

$\qquad\qquad = \sqrt{25}$

$\qquad\qquad = 5 \text{ m}$

iii Total surface area

$= $ surface area of hemisphere $+$ surface area of cone

$= \frac{1}{2} \times 4\pi r^2 + \pi r s$

$= \frac{1}{2} \times 4 \times \pi \times 3^2 + \pi \times 3 \times 5$

$\approx 104 \text{ m}^2$

c Weight of icecream $\approx 104 \times 1.23 \approx 128 \text{ kg}$

8 a

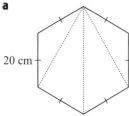

20 cm

The shape can be divided into 4 triangles with each triangle having an angle sum of 180°,

$\therefore$ angle sum hexagon

$= 4 \times 180^\circ = 720^\circ$

$\therefore$ each angle

$= \dfrac{720^\circ}{6} = 120^\circ$

b i As $OA = OB$, triangle AOB is isosceles.

As each vertex is bisected then $\angle OAB = \dfrac{120^\circ}{2} = 60^\circ$

$\therefore$ triangle AOB has all angles 60° (i.e., an equilateral triangle) $\therefore \angle AOB = 60^\circ$

ii $\triangle AOB$ is equilateral.

iii The sign is made up of 6 equilateral triangles.

The area of each triangle $= \frac{1}{2} \times 20 \times 20 \times \sin 60^\circ$.

$= 173.2 \text{ cm}^2$

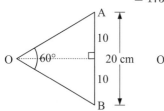 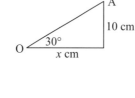

$\therefore$ total area of figure $= 6 \times 173.2$

$\qquad\qquad\qquad\qquad = 1039.2$

$\qquad\qquad\qquad\qquad \approx 1040 \text{ cm}^2$

c i Height (y) of sign $= $ length OA $\times 2 = 40 \text{ cm}$

ii Now $\tan 30^\circ = \dfrac{10}{x}$ and so $x = \dfrac{10}{\tan 30^\circ} \approx 17.32$

Width (x) of sign $\approx 2 \times 17.32 \approx 34.6 \text{ cm}$

iii Area $= $ height $\times$ width

$\qquad\quad = 40 \times 34.6$

$\qquad\quad = 1386 \text{ cm}^2$

$\qquad\quad = 1390 \text{ cm}^2$

d Wasted area $= $ area of rectangle $-$ area of hexagon

$\qquad\qquad\quad = 1386 - 1039$

$\qquad\qquad\quad = 347 \text{ cm}^2$

$\therefore$ cost of wasted material $= 0.35 \times 347 \text{ EUD}$

$\qquad\qquad\qquad\qquad\qquad = 121.45 \text{ EUD}$

Short questions

1 a Discrete data.   14, 16, 18, 23, 24, 25, 26, 26, 34

b Mean $= \dfrac{14 + 16 + \dots + 34}{9} = 22.9$, i.e., 23 customers/h

Median is $\dfrac{n+1}{2} = \dfrac{9+1}{2} = 5$ i.e., 5th value

$\therefore$ the median $= 24$ customers

Mode $= 26$

Range $= 34 - 14 = 20$

c Total income $= 206 \times \$14.20 = \$2925.20$

2 a Discrete data.

b and **c**

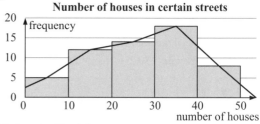

Number of houses in certain streets

c Modal class is 30 - 39

3 a $\dfrac{n+1}{2} = \dfrac{22+1}{2} = 11.5$ th value

But, 11th value $=$ 12th value $= 22$,

$\therefore$ median $= 22$ birds/day.

Q_1 lies between the 5th and 6th values

i.e., $Q_1 = \dfrac{14 + 17}{2} = 15.5$ birds/day

Q_3 lies between the 17th and 18th values

i.e., $Q_3 = \dfrac{35 + 36}{2} = 35.5$ birds/day

b IQR $= 35.5 - 15.5 = 20$ birds/day

$Q_1 - 1.5\times$ IQR $= 15.5 - 30 < 0$

$Q_3 + 1.5\times$ IQR $= 35.5 + 30 = 65.5$ birds/day

As the maximum number of birds present was 49, there are no outliers.

c On 5 days there are more than 35 birds in the park.

Let X be the number of birds in the park,

then $P(X > 35) = \frac{5}{22}$.

4 a Continuous data.

b Mid-interval values are: 4.5, 14.5, 24.5, 34.5, 44.5

c Lower boundary 9.5, upper boundary 19.5.

d Mean $= \dfrac{(4.5 \times 2) + (14.5 \times 15) + \dots + (44.5 \times 5)}{50}$

$\qquad\quad = 24.1$

5 a Cumulative frequencies: 2, 17, 38, 45, 50.

b

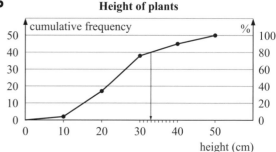

Height of plants

c 80th percentile is approximately 32 cm.

d 80th percentile is 40th plant. There are 10 plants taller than the 80th percentile.

6

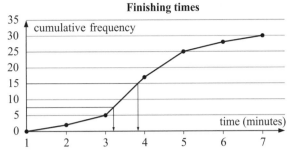

Finishing times

a median $\approx 15^{\text{th}}$ score ≈ 3.8 (or 3.9) min

b $Q_1 \approx 7\frac{1}{2}^{\text{th}}$ score ≈ 3.2 min

c 5 finish within 3 minutes and

25 finish within 5 min

∴ 20 finish between 3 and 5 minutes.

7 a 9, 10, a, 13, b, 16, 21

Sum $= 7 \times 14 = 98$

$(a + b) = 98 - (9 + 10 + 13 + 16 + 21) = 29$

In order, $a = 13$, $b = 16$.

b The median lies between 9 and 11 and so the median $= 10$.

Since median $=$ mean, mean $= 10$.

$$\text{mean} = \frac{1 + 5 + 9 + 11 + 16 + p}{6}$$

$$\therefore \quad 10 = \frac{42 + p}{6}$$

$$\therefore \quad 42 + p = 60 \quad \text{and so} \quad p = 18$$

8 a

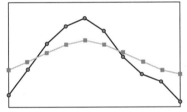

b Set 2 has the higher standard deviation, i.e., greater dispersion of data.

c Set 1 is likely to have the smaller IQR.

d Set 2 is likely to have more people on higher wages. Data is more spread and the median wage is slightly higher.

9 a $165 < \text{height} \leqslant 175$

b The frequency table is

Height (rounded, cm)	Frequency
140	2
150	6
160	14
170	17
180	9
190	2

Total number of students is 50.

Using calculator, mean height $= 166$ cm.

Standard deviation is 11.5 cm.

c $\overline{x} + 2s = 166 + 23 = 189$

There are at least 2 students taller than 2 standard deviations above the mean height.

10 a Midpoints are 89.5, 109.5, 129.5, 149.5, 169.5, 189.5

Using a calculator, mean rent $\approx \$138.49$

Standard deviation $\approx \$21.60$

b $30 + 14 + 1 = 45$ houses have rent greater than \$140.

There are 89 houses.

$\text{P(rent} > \$140) = \frac{45}{89}$

c $\overline{x} + 1s = \$138.49 + \$21.60 = \$160.09 \approx \$160$

Percentage of rent above \$160 is $\dfrac{14 + 1}{89} \times 100\%$

$= 16.9\%$

11 a Site 3 has the greatest range.

b Site 2 has the smallest spread.

c Site 1 has the highest median weight.

d The heaviest fungi were found at Site 3.

e Site 1 has the highest proportion of weights above 40 g.

f All sites have the same proportion (25%) above Q_3.

12 a $Q_1 \approx 175$, $Q_2 \approx 190$, $Q_3 \approx 200$.

b Range $\approx 220 - 130 = 90$

c IQR $\approx 200 - 175 = 25$

d $Q_1 - 1.5 \times \text{IQR} = 167 - 1.5(25) = 129.5$.

The minimum of 130 is only just not an outlier.

13 We start by displaying the data on a stem and leaf plot.

a min $= 25$, $Q_1 = 60$,

$Q_2 = 71$, $Q_3 = 78$,

max $= 87$

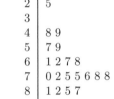

b

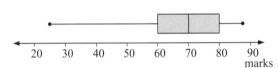

c IQR $= 78 - 60 = 18$

$Q_1 - 1.5 \times \text{IQR} = 60 - 1.5(18) = 33$

The minimum mark is an outlier. Student did not study; poor attendance or the student had a very bad day.

14 a

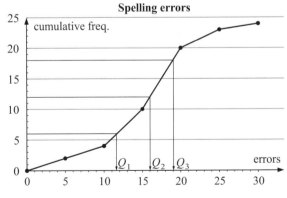

min $= 0$, $Q_1 = 12$, $Q_2 = 16$, $Q_3 = 19$, max $= 30$

b

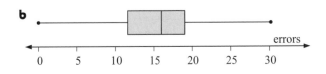

71

15 a Median is 5th value = $310 000

b Q_1 is between 2nd and 3rd value = $261 000,
Q_3 is between 7th and 8th value = $335 000
IQR = 335 000 − 261 000 = 74 000

c $Q_3 + 1.5(74 000) = 446 000$

The highest priced house is an outlier.

Median (with outlier omitted) = $295 000

d Percentage change is
$$\frac{310\,000 - 295\,000}{310\,000} \times 100\% = 4.84\%$$

16 a $r = \dfrac{s_{xy}}{s_x s_y} = \dfrac{405}{17.4 \times 25.6} = 0.909$

b strong, positive, relationship

c
$$(y - \overline{y}) = \frac{s_{xy}}{(s_x)^2}(x - \overline{x})$$
$$\therefore \quad (y - 110) = \frac{405}{17.4^2}(x - 63)$$
$$\therefore \quad y - 110 = 1.34(x - 63)$$
$$\therefore \quad y - 110 = 1.34x - 84.4$$
$$\therefore \quad y = 1.34x + 25.6$$

d $y = 1.34 \times 70 + 25.6 \approx 119$

17 a

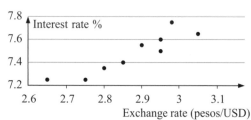

b $r = 0.915$

c There is a strong, positive, linear relationship between exchange rate and interest rate.

18 a $r = 0.795$ A moderate, positive relationship may exist between crop yield and rainfall.

b

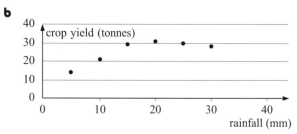

c The relationship between rainfall and crop yield does not appear to be linear and so r may not be appropriate for this data.

19 a The 2×2 contingency table is:

	Y_1	Y_2	sum
X_1	32	14	46
X_2	25	19	44
sum	57	33	90

The expected frequency table is:

	Y_1	Y_2
X_1	$\dfrac{46 \times 57}{90} = 29$	$\dfrac{46 \times 33}{90} = 17$
X_2	$\dfrac{44 \times 57}{90} = 28$	$\dfrac{44 \times 33}{90} = 16$

b The χ^2 calculation is:

f_o	f_e	$f_o - f_e$	$(f_o - f_e)^2$	$\dfrac{(f_o - f_e)^2}{f_e}$
32	29	3	9	0.310
14	17	−3	9	0.529
25	28	3	9	0.321
19	16	3	9	0.563
			Total	1.723

So $\chi^2_{\text{calc}} = 1.72$.

20 a H_0: Plant height is independent of light conditions.
H_A: Plant height is dependent on light conditions.

b The 3×2 contingency table is:

	$Ht < 60$ cm	$Ht \geqslant 60$ cm	sum
Sunlight	37	43	80
Shade	22	18	40
Dark	25	19	44
sum	84	80	164

The expected frequency table is:

	$Ht < 60$ cm	$Ht \geqslant 60$ cm
Sunlight	$\dfrac{80 \times 84}{164} = 41.0$	$\dfrac{80 \times 80}{164} = 39.0$
Shade	$\dfrac{40 \times 84}{164} = 20.5$	$\dfrac{40 \times 80}{164} = 19.5$
Dark	$\dfrac{44 \times 84}{164} = 22.5$	$\dfrac{44 \times 80}{164} = 21.5$

The χ^2 calculation is:

f_o	f_e	$f_o - f_e$	$(f_o - f_e)^2$	$\dfrac{(f_o - f_e)^2}{f_e}$
37	41.0	−4.0	16	0.390
43	39.0	4.0	16	0.410
22	20.5	1.5	2.25	0.110
18	19.5	−1.5	2.25	0.115
25	22.5	−2.5	6.25	0.278
19	21.5	2.5	6.25	0.291
			Total	1.594

$\chi^2_{\text{calc}} \approx 1.59$ (the calculated value may vary slightly depending on the rounding)

c $\chi^2_{2,\,05} = 5.991$

d $\chi^2_{\text{calc}} < \chi^2_{\text{crit}}$ do not reject H_0
The nursery's claim is justified according to this data. There is no significant difference in the height of the plants and the conditions they are growing under.

21 a Using a gdc, $\chi^2_{\text{calc}} = 6.88$
There are $(3-1)(3-1) = 4$ degrees of freedom
and $\chi^2_{4,\,0.05} = 9.488$
Since $\chi^2_{\text{calc}} < \chi^2_{4,\,0.05}$, we do not reject H_0, and accept that the factors are independent.
Note also that the p-value is $p = 0.142$
Since $p > 0.05$ we do not reject H_0.

b Expected value in Row 1/Column 1 is less than 5.

c Combined table

	Factor Y_a	Factor Y_b	Factor Y_c
Factor X_{a+b}	27	38	35
Factor X_c	16	11	22

$\chi^2_{\text{calc}} = 3.6246$ $\chi^2_{2,\,0.05} = 5.991$ **or** $p = 0.163\,27$

$\chi^2_{calc} < \chi^2_{2,\,0.05}$ or $p > 0.05$ do not reject H_0
                                        Factors are independent.

d Adding rows led to slightly greater p-value, but the difference was not significant.

22 a $y = -0.185x + 44.1$
   Number of potatoes $= -0.185$(median weight) $+ 44.1$

 b i Number of potatoes $= -0.185(100) + 44.1 = 26$

 ii Number of potatoes $= -0.185(200) + 44.1 = 7.1$

 c The first calculation is likely to be more reliable - it is an interpolated value. 200 grams is outside the range and the second calculation is an extrapolation.

23 a $y = -0.555x + 71.3$ $r = -0.647$

 b The outlier is $(50, 12)$.
   With the outlier removed, $y = -0.637x + 80.5$ and $r = -0.986$.

 c The slope of the line is steeper (gradient has become more negative). The relationship has changed from weak/moderate to very strong.

24 a $y = 2.43x + 32.0$

 b $70 = 2.43$ (hours) $+ 32.0$
   Tony studied for $\dfrac{70 - 32}{2.43} = 15.6$ hours.

 c The y-intercept (32%) is the estimate of the result for a student who did not do any study.
   The gradient of the line indicates that the result will increase by 2.43% for each additional hour studied.

25 a Using a gdc, $\chi^2_{calc} = 0.0171$
   With 2 degrees of freedom and assuming H_0
   $P(\chi^2_{calc} \geqslant 0.0171) = 0.991\,49$

   Probability value $p = 0.991\,49$
   lower tail $1 - p = 0.008\,51$

 b lower tail test
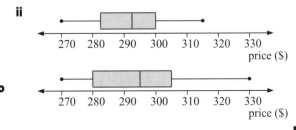

 c 1% level: reject H_0
   0.5% level: do not reject H_0
   At the 1% level, the deviation of the data from expected values may not necessarily be due to random chance. At the 0.5% level, the deviations from expected values are reasonable.

Long questions

1 a i $\dfrac{n+1}{2} = \dfrac{25+1}{2} = 13$
   so, the median is the 13th value. $\therefore$ median $= \$293$
   Range $= 316 - 271 = 45$
   Q_1 is $\left(\frac{n+1}{4}\right)$th value $= \left(\frac{25+1}{4}\right)$th value $= 6.5$th value,
   i.e., between 6th and 7th values, so $Q_1 = \$283$.
   Q_3 is 3×6.5th $= 19.5$th value,
   i.e., between 19th and 20th values, so $Q_3 = \$301$.

 ii
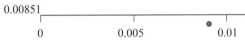

 b

c i New prices are more spread out.
 ii Mean price has increased slightly.   Some printers have increased in price; others have decreased.

 d Mean price has increased by $\$2$ from $\$293$ to $\$295$
   Percentage increase is $\frac{2}{293} \times 100\% = 0.683\%$.

2 a Mean $= \dfrac{3.6 + 5.4 + 4.5 + \ldots\ldots + 4.5 + 6.4}{40} = 5.265$

   Using a gdc, standard deviation is 0.856.

 b

Distance (m)	Cumulative frequency
3.5 - < 4.0	4
4.0 - < 4.5	7
4.5 - < 5.0	15
5.0 - < 5.5	22
5.5 - < 6.0	31
6.0 - < 6.5	39
6.5 - < 7.0	39
7.0 - < 7.5	40

 c
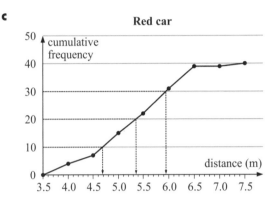

 d Median ≈ 4.8, $Q_1 \approx 5.4$, $Q_3 \approx 5.9$

 e
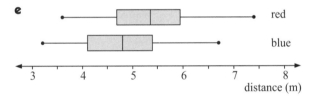

 f All values of the five-number summary, min, Q_1, median, Q_3 and max, for the red car are higher than those for the blue car. There is no evidence to support the view that the cars were made by the same machine.

3 a Mean $= \dfrac{312 + 312 + 308 + \ldots\ldots + 330 + 309 + 329}{24}$
   $= 319$ g
   Range $= 334 - 306 = 28$ g

 b

Weight (g)	Frequency	Weight (g)	Frequency
305 - 309	5	320 - 324	5
310 - 314	3	325 - 329	4
315 - 319	3	330 - 334	4

 c
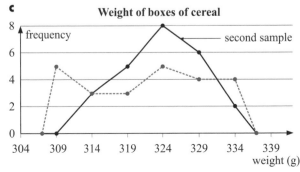

d The stated weight is higher than the average (mean) contents.

e Mean

$$= \frac{312 \times 3 + 317 \times 5 + 322 \times 8 + 327 \times 6 + 332 \times 2}{24}$$

$$= 322 \text{ g}$$

f on graph

g The mean weight is now higher. The spread of weights is less. The evidence suggests that an improvement in the production process has occurred.

4 a

b minimum is $120\,000$, maximum is $129\,999.99$

c Mean $= \dfrac{65 \times 3 + 75 \times 8 + 85 \times 11 + \dots\dots + 125 \times 8}{100}$

$\qquad = \$100\,500$

Using technology, standard deviation is $\$14\,800$.

d **i** $\overline{x} + 2s = 100\,500 + 2 \times 14\,800 = 130\,100$

ii No bonuses were paid.

e The top 8 sales staff sold more than $\$120\,000$.

This is $\$120\,000 - \$100\,500 = \$19\,500$ above the mean

and $\dfrac{19\,500}{14\,800} = 1.32$ standard deviations above the mean.

f $\overline{x} - 1.385s = 100\,500 - 1.385 \times 14\,800 = \$80\,002$

Approximately 11 staff may be retrenched.

5 a

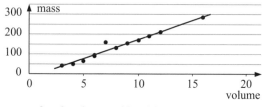

b **i** $\overline{x} = \dfrac{3 + 6 + 4 + \dots\dots 10 + 11}{12} = 8.08 \text{ cm}^3$

$\overline{y} = \dfrac{40 + 95 + 50 + \dots\dots + 170 + 190}{12} = 137 \text{ g}$

ii on graph

c An imperfect, positive relationship appears to exist between volume and mass of the samples of silver.

d $r = 0.980$

e **i** $M = 19.5V - 24.7$

ii $M = 19.5 \times 7 - 24.7 = 112 \text{ g}$

iii Percentage error between the given and expected mass

is $\dfrac{160 - 112}{112} \times 100\% = 42.9\%$.

6 a **i** $r = \dfrac{s_{xy}}{s_x s_y} = \dfrac{33.9}{7.25 \times 4.78} = 0.978$

ii A strong, positive relationship appears to exist between age and annual income.

b $(y - \overline{y}) = \dfrac{s_{xy}}{s_x^2}(x - \overline{x})$

$\therefore \quad y - 20 = \dfrac{33.9}{7.25^2}(x - 26.3)$

$\therefore \quad y - 20 = 0.645(x - 26.3)$

$\therefore \quad y = 0.645x - 17 + 20$

$\therefore \quad y = 0.645x + 3$

i.e., income $= 0.645\,(\text{age}) + 3$

c **i** At age 30, income $= 0.645(30) + 3 = 22\,350$

ii At age 60, income $= 0.645(60) + 3 = 41\,700$

d The age of 30 is within the given data range but 60 is outside the range. Predicting the income at 30 years is an interpolation and is more reliable than the extrapolation required for 60.

7 a

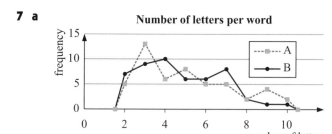

b

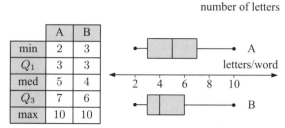

	A	B
min	2	3
Q_1	3	3
med	5	4
Q_3	7	6
max	10	10

c A: mean $= 5$, standard deviation $= 2.28$
B: mean $= 4.76$, standard deviation $= 2.02$

d

	< 5	$\geqslant 5$	sum
Story A	24	26	50
Story B	26	24	50
sum	50	50	100

e H_0: There is no difference in the stories.

Expected values:

	< 5	$\geqslant 5$
Story A	$\dfrac{50 \times 50}{100} = 25$	$\dfrac{50 \times 50}{100} = 25$
Story B	$\dfrac{50 \times 50}{100} = 25$	$\dfrac{50 \times 50}{100} = 25$

$\chi_{\text{calc}}^2 = 0.16 \quad \chi_{1,\,0.1}^2 = 2.706 \quad or \quad p = 0.689$

$\chi_{\text{calc}}^2 < \chi_{\text{crit}}^2 \quad or \quad p > 0.10$ hence, do not reject H_0

f There is no significant difference between the stories.

g The graphical evidence suggests that the stories may have been written by different authors.

The mean of B is lower and the standard deviation is smaller again, suggesting that the stories are by different authors.

However, the chi-square test suggests that the difference is not significant.

Overall, the statistical evidence is not strong enough to support the claim that the two stories were written by different authors.

8 a H_0: Choice of breakfast cereal is independent of gender.

b Contingency table:

	Muesli	Rolled Oats	Corn Flakes	Weetbix	sum
Female	2	7	24	12	45
Male	4	15	13	13	45
sum	6	22	37	25	90

Expected values:

	Muesli	Rolled Oats	Corn Flakes	Weetbix
Female	$\frac{45\times 6}{90}$ $= 3$	$\frac{45\times 22}{90}$ $= 11$	$\frac{45\times 37}{90}$ $= 18.5$	$\frac{45\times 25}{90}$ $= 12.5$
Male	$\frac{45\times 6}{90}$ $= 3$	$\frac{45\times 22}{90}$ $= 11$	$\frac{45\times 37}{90}$ $= 18.5$	$\frac{45\times 25}{90}$ $= 12.5$

c Combined contingency table:

	Muesli or Rolled Oats	Corn Flakes	Weetbix	*sum*
Female	9	24	12	45
Male	19	13	13	45
sum	28	37	25	90

Expected values:

	Muesli or Rolled Oats	Corn Flakes	Weetbix
Female	$\frac{28\times 45}{90} = 14$	18.5	12.5
Male	$\frac{28\times 45}{90} = 14$	18.5	12.5

d $\chi^2_{\text{calc}} = \frac{(9-14)^2}{14} + \frac{(24-18.5)^2}{18.5} + \frac{(12-12.5)^2}{12.5} + \ldots$
$+ \frac{(19-14)^2}{14} + \frac{(13-18.5)^2}{18.5} + \frac{(13-12.5)^2}{12.5} = 6.88$

e $df = (2-1)(3-1) = 2;$ $\chi^2_{2,\,0.05} = 5.991$
$\chi^2_{\text{calc}} > \chi^2_{\text{crit}}$ hence reject H_0

f The choice of breakfast cereal is dependent on gender.

g $\chi^2_{\text{calc}} = 6.89$ $\chi^2_{3,\,0.05} = 7.815$ *or* $p = 0.075\,62$
$\chi^2_{\text{calc}} < \chi^2_{\text{crit}}$ *or* $p = 0.075\,62 > 0.05$ hence do not reject H_0

He would have concluded that the choice of breakfast cereal and gender are not related.

SOLUTIONS TO TOPIC 7   CALCULUS

Short questions

1 a $y = x^3 - 4.5x^2 - 6x + 13$
$\therefore \frac{dy}{dx} = 3x^2 - 2 \times 4.5x - 6$
$\therefore \frac{dy}{dx} = 3x^2 - 9x - 6$

b When the gradient of the tangent is 6,
$$\frac{dy}{dx} = 6$$
$\therefore 3x^2 - 9x - 6 = 6$
$\therefore 3x^2 - 9x - 12 = 0$
$\therefore 3(x^2 - 3x - 4) = 0$
$\therefore 3(x-4)(x+1) = 0$
$\therefore x = 4$ or $x = -1$

So the x-coordinates of the points are 4 and -1.

2 a $y = ax^2 + bx + c$ $\therefore \frac{dy}{dx} = 2ax + b$

b When $x = k$, $\frac{dy}{dx} = 0$ $\therefore 2ax + b = 0$
$\therefore 2ax = -b$
$\therefore x = -\frac{b}{2a}$
i.e., $k = -\frac{b}{2a}$

c If $\frac{dy}{dx} < 0$, y is decreasing.

d When $x < k$, $\frac{dy}{dx} < 0$, and
when $x > k$, $\frac{dy}{dx} > 0$.
$\therefore \frac{dy}{dx}$ has sign diagram:
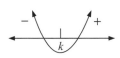
$\therefore x = k$ is a local minimum.

3 a $y = \frac{7}{x^3}$ $\therefore y = 7x^{-3}$

b $\frac{dy}{dx} = 7(-3)x^{-4} = -21x^{-4}$
$\therefore \frac{dy}{dx} = \frac{-21}{x^4}$

4 a $y = \frac{2x^4 - 4x^2 - 3}{x}$
$\therefore y = \frac{2x^4}{x} - \frac{4x^2}{x} - \frac{3}{x}$
$\therefore y = 2x^3 - 4x - 3x^{-1}$

b $\frac{dy}{dx} = 2(3)x^2 - 4 - 3(-1)x^{-2}$
$\therefore \frac{dy}{dx} = 6x^2 - 4 + \frac{3}{x^2}$

c At $x = -1$, $\frac{dy}{dx} = 6(-1)^2 - 4 + \frac{3}{(-1)^2}$
$= 6 - 4 + 3$
$= 5$
$\therefore$ at $x = -1$, the gradient is 5.

5 a $f(x) = 3x^2 - 4x^{-1} + 7$
$\therefore f'(x) = 3(2)x^1 - 4(-1)x^{-2}$
$= 6x + \frac{4}{x^2}$

b $f'(x) = 6x + 4x^{-2}$
$\therefore f''(x) = 6 + 4(-2)x^{-3}$
$= 6 - \frac{8}{x^3}$

6 a i $f(x)$ is increasing on $x > 0$.
ii $f(x)$ is decreasing on $x < 0$.

b $f'(x) = 0$ at $x = 0$ and $x = 2$.

c

7 a $f(x) = x^4 - 6x^2 - x + 3$
$\therefore f'(x) = 4x^3 - 12x - 1$

b $f''(x) = 12x^2 - 12$

c Max/min values of $f'(x)$ occur when
$$f''(x) = 0$$
$\therefore 12x^2 - 12 = 0$
$\therefore 12(x+1)(x-1) = 0$
$\therefore x = \pm 1$

8 a
$$g(x) = \left(3x - \frac{1}{x}\right)^2$$
$$= \left(3x - \frac{1}{x}\right)\left(3x - \frac{1}{x}\right)$$
$$= 9x^2 - 3x \times \frac{1}{x} - \frac{1}{x} \times 3x + \frac{1}{x} \times \frac{1}{x}$$
$$= 9x^2 - 3 - 3 + \frac{1}{x^2}$$
$$\therefore \quad g(x) = 9x^2 - 6 + \frac{1}{x^2}$$

b
$$g(x) = 9x^2 - 6 + x^{-2}$$
$$\therefore \quad g'(x) = 9(2)x + (-2)x^{-3}$$
$$\therefore \quad g'(x) = 18x - \frac{2}{x^3}$$

c The gradient of $g(x)$ at $x = -1$ is
$$g'(-1) = 18(-1) - \frac{2}{(-1)^3} = -18 + 2 = -16$$
$$\therefore \quad \text{gradient is } -16 \text{ at } x = -1$$

9 a
$$y = 2x^3 - 3x^2 - 264x + 13$$
$$\therefore \quad y' = 6x^2 - 6x - 264$$

b
$$y' = -12 \quad \text{when}$$
$$6x^2 - 6x - 264 = -12$$
$$\therefore \quad 6x^2 - 6x - 252 = 0$$
$$\therefore \quad 6(x^2 - x - 42) = 0$$
$$\therefore \quad 6(x - 7)(x + 6) = 0$$
$$\therefore \quad x = 7 \quad \text{or} \quad x = -6$$
$$\therefore \quad \text{the } x\text{-coordinates of the points are 7 and } -6.$$

10 a $f(x) = ax^2 + bx + c \quad \therefore \quad f'(x) = 2ax + b$

b
$$f'(x) = 2x - 6$$
$$\therefore \quad 2x - 6 = 2ax + b$$
Equating coefficients: $\quad 2a = 2 \quad$ and $\quad b = -6$
$$\therefore \quad a = 1 \quad \text{and} \quad b = -6$$

c i Min. value of f occurs when $f'(x) = 0$
$$\therefore \quad 2x - 6 = 0$$
$$\therefore \quad x = 3$$

ii When $x = 3$, y has min value 2.
$$\therefore \quad \text{substituting into } y = x^2 - 6x + c, \text{ we have}$$
$$(3)^2 - 6(3) + c = 2$$
$$\therefore \quad 9 - 18 + c = 2$$
$$\therefore \quad c = 11$$

11 a
$$v(t) = 7t - t^2$$
At $t = 1$, $v(1) = 7(1) - (1)^2 = 7 - 1 = 6$
$$\therefore \quad v(1) = 6 \text{ km/h}$$

b At $t = 1$, $v(1) = 6$ km/h
$$\therefore \quad 7t - t^2 = 6$$
$$\therefore \quad 0 = t^2 - 7t + 6$$
$$\therefore \quad 0 = (t - 6)(t - 1)$$
$$\therefore \quad \text{at } t = 6, \quad v(t) = 6 \text{ km/h}$$

c $v'(t) = 7 - 2t$

d Max. velocity occurs when
$$v'(t) = 0$$
$$\therefore \quad 7 - 2t = 0$$
$$\therefore \quad t = \tfrac{7}{2}$$
and $v\left(\tfrac{7}{2}\right) = 7\left(\tfrac{7}{2}\right) - \left(\tfrac{7}{2}\right)^2 = \tfrac{49}{2} - \tfrac{49}{4} = \tfrac{49}{4}$
$$v\left(\tfrac{7}{2}\right) = 12.25 \text{ km/h}$$
$$\therefore \quad \text{max. velocity is } 12.25 \text{ km/h.}$$

12 a The gradient of the tangent through A(6, 7) and B(0, −5) is
$$m = \frac{y_2 - y_1}{x_2 - x_1} = \frac{7 - -5}{6 - 0} = 2$$

b
$$y = x^2 - kx + 11$$
$$\therefore \quad \frac{dy}{dx} = 2x - k$$

c At $x = 4$, the gradient of the tangent is 2.
$$\therefore \quad \frac{dy}{dx} = 2$$
$$\therefore \quad 2(4) - k = 2 \quad \{\text{from } \textbf{b}\}$$
$$\therefore \quad k = 6$$

13 a $f(x) = x^2 \quad \therefore \quad f(2) = 2^2 = 4$

b
$$f(2 + h) = (2 + h)^2$$
$$\therefore \quad f(2 + h) = 4 + 4h + h^2$$

c
$$m = \frac{f(2 + h) - f(2)}{h}$$
$$\therefore \quad m = \frac{4 + 4h + h^2 - 4}{h}$$
$$\therefore \quad m = \frac{h(4 + h)}{h}$$
$$\therefore \quad m = 4 + h$$

14 a $y = 4x^{-1} + x \quad \therefore \quad \dfrac{dy}{dx} = 4(-1)x^{-2} + 1$
$$\therefore \quad \frac{dy}{dx} = \frac{-4}{x^2} + 1$$

b $\dfrac{dy}{dx} = 0$ when $1 - \dfrac{4}{x^2} = 0$
$$\therefore \quad \frac{4}{x^2} = 1$$
$$\therefore \quad x^2 = 4$$
$$\therefore \quad x = \pm 2$$

c At $x = 2$, $y = \dfrac{4}{2} + 2 = 4$
At $x = -2$, $y = \dfrac{4}{-2} + -2 = -4$
$$\therefore \quad \text{local minimum at } (2, 4)$$
and local maximum at $(-2, -4)$

15 a
$$H(t) = 80 - 5t^2$$
$$\therefore \quad H(0) = 80 - 5(0)^2$$
$$\therefore \quad H(0) = 80$$
i.e., the initial height is 80 m.

b The toy hits the ground when $H(t) = 0$.
Now $H(t) = 0$ when $80 - 5t^2 = 0$
$$\therefore \quad 80 = 5t^2$$
$$\therefore \quad t^2 = 16$$
$$\therefore \quad t = \pm 4$$
But $t > 0 \quad \therefore \quad t = 4$ seconds,
i.e., it hits the ground after 4 seconds.

c $H'(t) = -10t$

d $H'(2) = -10(2) = -20$ m/s
Hence, after 2 seconds of flight, the toy aeroplane is travelling at 20 m/s towards the ground.

16 a
$$\frac{4 - 3x + x^2}{x^2} = \frac{4}{x^2} - \frac{3x}{x^2} + \frac{x^2}{x^2}$$
$$= \frac{4}{x^2} - \frac{3}{x} + 1$$

b $\frac{d}{dx}\left(\frac{4}{x^2} - \frac{3}{x} + 1\right) = \frac{-8}{x^3} + \frac{3}{x^2}$

c $\frac{d}{dx}\left(\frac{4 - 3x + x^2}{x^2}\right) = 0$ when $\frac{-8}{x^3} + \frac{3}{x^2} = 0$
$$\therefore \quad \frac{3}{x^2} = \frac{8}{x^3}$$
$$\therefore \quad 3x^3 = 8x^2$$
$$\therefore \quad 3x^3 - 8x^2 = 0$$
$$\therefore \quad x^2(3x - 8) = 0$$
$$\therefore \quad x = 0 \quad \text{or} \quad x = \tfrac{8}{3}$$

17 a
$$y = ax^{-1} - x^2 + 1$$
$$\therefore \quad \frac{dy}{dx} = -ax^{-2} - 2x$$

But when $x = 2$, $\frac{dy}{dx} = -5$
$$\therefore \quad \frac{-a}{(2)^2} - 2(2) = -5$$
$$\therefore \quad -\frac{a}{4} - 4 = -5$$
$$\therefore \quad -\frac{a}{4} = -1 \quad \text{and so} \quad a = 4$$

b At $x = 2$, $y = \frac{4}{2} - 2^2 + 1 = -1$
$\therefore$ the point is $(2, -1)$.

c Tangent has gradient $m = -5$ at $x = 2$
$\therefore$ its equation is $y = -5x + c$
Substituting $(2, -1)$ gives
$$-1 = -10 + c$$
$$\therefore \quad c = 9$$
$\therefore$ tangent equation is $y = -5x + 9$

18 a
$$s = 2t^3 - 18t^2 + 54t$$
At $t = 0$, $s = 0$ km
At $t = 4$, $s = 2(4)^3 - 18(4)^2 + 54(4)$
$$= 56 \text{ km}$$
av. speed $= \frac{56}{4} = 14$ kmh^{-1}

b $\frac{ds}{dt} = 6t^2 - 36t + 54$

c Hikers have stopped when $\frac{ds}{dt} = 0$
$$\therefore \quad 6t^2 - 36t + 54 = 0$$
$$\therefore \quad 6(t^2 - 6t + 9) = 0$$
$$\therefore \quad 6(t - 3)^2 = 0$$
$$\therefore \quad t = 3$$

Hence, the hikers stop momentarily after 3 hours.
Now $s(3) = 2(3)^3 - 18(3)^2 + 54(3) = 54$
i.e., the hikers travel 54 km before stopping.

19 a $f(x) = x^3 - 3x^2 - 24x + 26$
$f'(x) = 3x^2 - 6x - 24$

b $f'(x) = 0$ when
$$3x^2 - 6x - 24 = 0$$
$$\therefore \quad 3(x^2 - 2x - 8) = 0$$
$$\therefore \quad 3(x - 4)(x + 2) = 0$$
$$\therefore \quad x = 4 \quad \text{or} \quad x = -2$$

c $f''(x) = 6x - 6$

d $f''(x) = 0$ when $6x - 6 = 0$
$$\therefore \quad x = 1$$

20 a $y = k^x$ is increasing for all $x \in \mathbb{R}$

b y-intercept occurs when $x = 0$
$$\therefore \quad y = k^0$$
$$\therefore \quad y = 1 \quad (k > 0)$$

c Tangent is located at $(0, 1)$ and has slope $m = 1$
$\therefore$ equation is $y = 1x + c$
Substituting $(0, 1)$ gives $1 = c$
$\therefore$ equation of tangent is $y = x + 1$

21 a
$$y = x^3 - x + 2$$
$$\frac{dy}{dx} = 3x^2 - 1$$
At $x = -1$, $\frac{dy}{dx} = 3(-1)^2 - 1$
$$= 3 - 1$$
$$\therefore \quad \frac{dy}{dx} = 2$$
$\therefore$ the gradient of the tangent at $x = -1$ is 2.

b If the tangents are parallel, then
$$\frac{dy}{dx} = 2 \quad \text{at} \quad x = k$$
$$\therefore \quad 3x^2 - 1 = 2$$
$$\therefore \quad x^2 = 1$$
$$\therefore \quad x = \pm 1$$
$$\therefore \quad k = 1$$

22 a
$$f(x) = \frac{6}{x} - \frac{2}{x^3}$$
$$\therefore \quad f(x) = 6x^{-1} - 2x^{-3}$$
Hence, $f'(x) = -6x^{-2} + 6x^{-4}$
$$= \frac{-6}{x^2} + \frac{6}{x^4}$$

b $f'(x) = 0$ when $\frac{-6}{x^2} + \frac{6}{x^4} = 0$
$$\therefore \quad \frac{6}{x^4} = \frac{6}{x^2}$$
$$\therefore \quad x^2 = x^4$$
$$\therefore \quad x^4 - x^2 = 0$$
$$\therefore \quad x^2(x^2 - 1) = 0$$
$$\therefore \quad x^2(x + 1)(x - 1) = 0$$
$$\therefore \quad x = 0 \text{ or } \pm 1$$
But if $x = 0$, $f(x)$ is undefined
$$\therefore \quad x = -1 \text{ or } 1$$

c At $x = 1$, $f(1) = 6 - 2 = 4$
$\therefore$ tangent has slope 0 at $(1, 4)$
$\therefore$ tangent equation is $y = 4$
At $x = -1$, $f(-1) = -6 + 2 = -4$
$\therefore$ tangent has slope 0 at $(-1, -4)$
$\therefore$ tangent equation is $y = -4$

23 a
$$s(t) = t^4 - 12t^3 + 48t^2 + 4t$$
$$\therefore \quad s'(t) = 4t^3 - 36t^2 + 96t + 4$$
At $t = 3$, $s'(3) = 4(3)^3 - 36(3)^2 + 96(3) + 4$
$$s'(3) = 76 \text{ km/h}$$

b $s(0) = 0$ km
$s(3) = (3)^4 - 12(3)^3 + 48(3)^2 + 4(3) = 201$ km

Hence $\dfrac{s(3) - s(0)}{3 - 0} = \dfrac{201 - 0}{3 - 0} = 67$ km/h

c The result from **b** is an average speed over the first 3 hours.

24 a $f(x) = \frac{1}{3}x^3 - x^2 - 15x + 15\frac{2}{3}$

$\therefore\ f'(x) = \frac{1}{3} \times 3x^2 - 2x - 15$

$\therefore\ f'(x) = x^2 - 2x - 15$

b $\qquad\qquad f'(x) = 0$ when

$x^2 - 2x - 15 = 0$

$\therefore\ (x - 5)(x + 3) = 0$

$\therefore\quad x = 5\ $ or $\ x = -3$

c

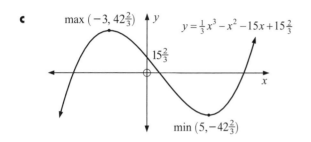

max $\left(-3, 42\frac{2}{3}\right)$

$y = \frac{1}{3}x^3 - x^2 - 15x + 15\frac{2}{3}$

$15\frac{2}{3}$

min $\left(5, -42\frac{2}{3}\right)$

25 a $y = x^3 - 3x + 2 \qquad \therefore\quad \dfrac{dy}{dx} = 3x^2 - 3$

b Min/max occur when $\dfrac{dy}{dx} = 0 \qquad \therefore\quad 3x^2 - 3 = 0$

$\therefore\quad 3(x^2 - 1) = 0$

$\therefore\quad 3(x + 1)(x - 1) = 0$

$\therefore\quad x = \pm 1$

At $x = 1$, $y = (1)^3 - 3(1) + 2 = 0$

At $x = -1$, $y = (-1)^3 - 3(-1) + 2 = -1 + 3 + 2 = 4$

$\therefore$ local max. at $(-1, 4)$ and local min at $(1, 0)$

c

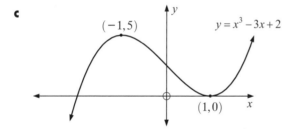

$(-1, 5)$

$y = x^3 - 3x + 2$

$(1, 0)$

Long questions

1 a $f(x) = 4x^2 - 3x - \dfrac{2}{x}$

$\therefore\ f(-1) = 4(-1)^2 - 3(-1) - \dfrac{2}{(-1)}$

$\therefore\ f(-1) = 4 + 3 + 2$

$\therefore\ f(-1) = 9$

b $f(x) = 4x^2 - 3x - 2x^{-1}$

$\therefore\ f'(x) = 4 \times 2x^1 - 3 - 2(-1)x^{-2}$

$\therefore\ f'(x) = 8x - 3 + \dfrac{2}{x^2}$

c $f'(-1) = 8(-1) - 3 + \dfrac{2}{(-1)^2}$

$\therefore\ f'(-1) = -8 - 3 + 2$

$\therefore\ f'(-1) = -9$

i.e., the gradient of the tangent at $x = -1$ is -9.

d Tangent passes through $(-1, 9)$ and has slope $m = -9$

$\therefore$ equation is $y = -9x + c$

Substituting $(-1, 9)$ gives $9 = -9(-1) + c$

$\therefore\quad 9 = 9 + c$

$\therefore\quad c = 0$

$\therefore$ equation of the tangent is $y = -9x$.

e Graphing $y = 4x^2 - 3x - \dfrac{2}{x}$ with $y = -9x$

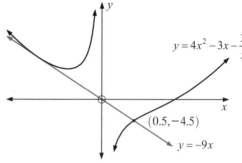

$y = 4x^2 - 3x - \dfrac{2}{x}$

$(0.5, -4.5)$

$y = -9x$

We find the tangent meets the curve again at $(0.5, -4.5)$.

2 a $C(x) = -0.2x^2 + 4x + 10$ for $0 \leqslant x \leqslant 10$

$C(5) = -0.2(5)^2 + 4(5) + 10 = \$25$

Hence, it costs \$25 to produce 5 bracelets.

b $C'(x) = -0.2 \times 2x + 4$

$C'(x) = -0.4x + 4$

c If C is measured in dollars and x is a number of bracelets, then $\dfrac{dC}{dx}$ has units "dollars per bracelet" (\$/bracelet).

d $C'(5) = -0.4(5) + 4$

$= 2$ \$/bracelet

e At $x = 5$, $\dfrac{dC}{dx} > 0$

$\therefore\ C(x)$ is increasing at $x = 5$

f $\qquad\qquad C'(x) = 0$

when $-0.4x + 4 = 0$

$\therefore\quad -0.4x = -4$

$\therefore\quad x = 10$

$\therefore$ maximum at $x = 10$

and $C(10) = -0.2(10)^2 + 4(10) + 10 = 30$

$\therefore$ max. value of $C(x)$ on $0 \leqslant x \leqslant 10$ is \$30.

3 a Substituting $(1, 8)$ into $y = x^3 + ax^2 + bx + 3$

gives $(1)^3 + a(1)^2 + b(1) + 3 = 8$

$\therefore\ a + b + 4 = 8$

$\therefore\ a + b = 4$ ...... (1)

b $\dfrac{dy}{dx} = 3x^2 + 2ax + b$

c i Tangent $y = 2x + 6$ has gradient $m = 2$

ii At $x = 1$, $\dfrac{dy}{dx} = 2$

$\therefore$ using the result from **b**

$3(1)^2 + 2a(1) + b = 2$

$\therefore\ 3 + 2a + b = 2$

$\therefore\ 2a + b = -1$ ...... (2)

iii Solving equations (1) and (2)

$2a + b = -1$

$-a - b = -4$

_____

$\therefore\ a = -5$ {adding}

Substituting $a = -5$ into (1)

gives $-5 + b = 4$

$\therefore \quad b = 9$

Hence, $a = -5$ and $b = 9$.

4 a $V(t) = 10t^2 - \frac{1}{3}t^3$ for $0 \leqslant t \leqslant 30$

$\therefore \quad V(5) = 10(5)^2 - \frac{1}{3}(5)^3$

$\therefore \quad V(5) = 208$ litres (3 s.f.)

After 5 minutes, the tank has 208 L of water in it.

b $V'(t) = 10(2)t - \frac{1}{3}(3)t^2$

$= 20t - t^2$

$= t(20 - t)$

c $V'(t)$ is measured in litres/minute.

d $V'(t) = t(20 - t)$

$\therefore \quad V'(t) = 0$ when

$t = 0$ mins or $t = 20$ mins

e $V'(5) = 5(15) = 75$ L/min

$V'(25) = 25(-5) = -125$ L/min

f $V'(t)$ is increasing for $V'(t) > 0$

$\therefore \quad$ increasing for $0 < t < 20$

g Max value on $0 \leqslant t \leqslant 30$ occurs when $t = 20$

$V(20) = 10(20)^2 - \frac{1}{3}(20)^3$

$\therefore \quad V(20) = 1333.33$ L

$\therefore \quad V(20) \approx 1330$ L (3 s.f.)

5 a $f(x) = Ax + \dfrac{B}{x}$

Tangent has equation $y = 3x + 2$ at $x = 1$.

At $x = 1$, $y = 3(1) + 2 = 5$

$\therefore \quad (1, 5)$ is the point of contact.

b $f(1) = 5$

$\therefore \quad A(1) + \dfrac{B}{(1)} = 5$ and so $A + B = 5$ ...... (1)

c $f'(x) = A - \dfrac{B}{x^2}$

d At $x = 1$, the gradient of the tangent $= 3$.

{tangent equation is $y = 3x + 2$}

e $f'(1) = 3$ $\therefore \quad A - B = 3$ ...... (2)

f $A + B = 5$ ...... (1)

$A - B = 3$ ...... (2)

Solving simultaneously, $A = 4$, $B = 1$

6 a Total perimeter $= 2x + y$

If 30 m of fence is available, then

$2x + y = 30$ and so $y = 30 - 2x$

b Area $= xy$

$\therefore \quad A(x) = x(30 - 2x)$

c If $A(x) = 100$, then $x(30 - 2x) = 100$

$\therefore \quad 30x - 2x^2 = 100$

$\therefore \quad -2x^2 + 30x - 100 = 0$

$\therefore \quad x^2 - 15x + 50 = 0$

$\therefore \quad (x - 10)(x - 5) = 0$

$\therefore \quad x = 10$ or $x = 5$

If $x = 10$, $y = 30 - 2(10) = 10$

If $x = 5$, $y = 30 - 2(5) = 20$

Hence, $A(x) = 100$ m^2 when the dimensions are 10 m $\times$ 10 m or 5 m $\times$ 20 m.

d $A(x) = 30x - 2x^2$ $\therefore \quad A'(x) = 30 - 4x$

Now $A'(x) = 0$

when $30 - 4x = 0$

$\therefore \quad 4x = 30$

$\therefore \quad x = 7.5$

For $x < 7.5$, $A'(x) > 0$

For $x > 7.5$, $A'(x) < 0$

Hence, $x = 7.5$ m is a maximum value.

$A(7.5) = (7.5)(30 - 2(7.5))$

$\therefore \quad A(7.5) = 112.5$ m^2

So, the largest area possible is 112.5 m^2.

7 a $f(x) = x^3$ $\therefore \quad f(1) = (1)^3 = 1$

$\therefore \quad$ A has coordinates $(1, 1)$

b B is located at $x = 1 + h$.

i When $h = 1$, $x = 2$ and $f(2) = (2)^3 = 8$

$\therefore \quad$ B$(2, 8)$

ii When $h = 0.1$, $x = 1.1$ and $f(1.1) = (1.1)^3$

$= 1.331$

$\therefore \quad$ B$(1.1, 1.331)$

iii When $h = 0.01$, $x = 1.01$ and $f(1.01) = (1.01)^3$

$= 1.0303$

$\therefore \quad$ B$(1.01, 1.0303)$

c i When $h = 1$, $m_{AB} = \dfrac{8 - 1}{2 - 1} = 7$

ii When $h = 0.1$, $m_{AB} = \dfrac{1.331 - 1}{1.1 - 1} = 3.31$

iii When $h = 0.01$, $m_{AB} = \dfrac{1.0303 - 1}{1.01 - 1} = 3.030$

d The smallest value, $h = 0.01$ would provide the best approximation to the tangent slope at $x = 1$.

e $f'(x) = 3x^2$

$\therefore \quad$ at $x = 1$, $f'(1) = 3(1)^2 = 3$

$\therefore \quad$ actual tangent slope is $m = 3$

8 a For an open top, total surface area $= x^2 + 4xy$.

b If TSA $= 1200$ cm^2

$\therefore \quad x^2 + 4xy = 1200$

$\therefore \quad 4xy = 1200 - x^2$ and so $y = \dfrac{1200 - x^2}{4x}$

c $V = x^2 y$

$V(x) = x^2 \left(\dfrac{1200 - x^2}{4x} \right) = \dfrac{x(1200 - x^2)}{4}$

$\therefore \quad V = 300x - \frac{1}{4}x^3$

d $V'(x) = 300 - \frac{1}{4}(3x^2)$ $\therefore \quad V'(x) = 300 - \frac{3}{4}x^2$

e $V'(x) = 0$

when $300 - \frac{3}{4}x^2 = 0$

$\therefore \quad \frac{3}{4}x^2 = 300$

$\therefore \quad x^2 = \dfrac{4 \times 300}{3} = 400$

$\therefore \quad x = \pm 20$

But $x > 0 \Rightarrow x = 20$

∴ maximum volume occurs when $x = 20$ cm.

When $x = 20$, $y = \dfrac{1200 - (20)^2}{4(20)} = 10$

i.e., dimensions for maximum volume are

20 cm $\times$ 20 cm $\times$ 10 cm.

f Maximum volume $= 20 \times 20 \times 10$ cm^3

∴ maximum volume is 4000 cm^3.

SOLUTIONS TO TOPIC 8   **FINANCE**

Short questions

1 a USD : GBP $= 1 : 0.5768$

So, GBP : USD $= 0.5768 : 1$

$= \dfrac{0.5768}{0.5768} : \dfrac{1}{0.5768}$

$= 1 : 1.7337$

b 365 USD $= 365 \times 0.5768$ GBP

$= 210.53$ GBP

c 500 GBP $= 500 \times 1.7337$ USD

$= 866.85$ USD

2 a EUR : JPY $= 1 : 141.9$

∴ 1000 EUR $= 1000 \times 141.9$ JPY

$= 141\,900$ JPY

After paying 1% commission,

$141\,900 \times \frac{99}{100} = 140\,481$ JPY would be received.

b 46 000 JPY $= 46\,000 \times \dfrac{1}{141.9} = 324.17$ EUR

After paying 1% commission,

$324.17 \times \frac{99}{100} = 320.93$ EUR would be received.

3 a 2000 CNY $= 2000 \times 6.684$ PHP $= 13\,368$ PHP

and 13 368 PHP $= 13\,368 \times 0.8559$ INR $= 11\,441.67$ INR

b 5000 INR $= 5000 \times \dfrac{1}{0.8559}$ PHP $= 5841.80$ PHP

and 5841.80 PHP $= 5841.80 \times \dfrac{1}{6.684}$ CNY $= 874.00$ CNY

4 a Selling GBP:

300 GBP $= 300 \times 1.9854$ CAD $= 595.62$ CAD

b Buying GBP:

300 CAD $= 300 \times \dfrac{1}{2.0113}$ GBP $= 149.16$ GBP

5 a Shelley is selling USD.

400 USD $= 400 \times 1.286$ CHF $= 514.40$ CHF

b Shelley is buying USD.

514.40 CHF $= 514.40 \times \dfrac{1}{1.311} = 392.37$ USD

c Cost of transactions in USD is $400 - 392.37 = 7.63$ USD

6 a 60 000 JPY $= 60\,000 \times 0.01106$ AUD $= 663.60$ AUD

A commission of 1.5% will cost

663.60 AUD $\times \frac{1.5}{100} = 9.95$ AUD

b Money received will be

$(663.60 - 9.95)$ AUD $= 653.65$ AUD

c If the money was converted back,

653.65 AUD $= 653.65 \times \dfrac{1}{0.011\,06}$ JPY $= 59\,100$ JPY

After paying a commission of 1.5% the amount received would be

$59\,100.36 \times \dfrac{98.5}{100}$ JPY $= 58\,214$ JPY

Note: This is not quite a loss of 3%.

7 Amount invested is $\dfrac{\$5000}{2} = \$2500$

$I = \dfrac{Crn}{100} = \dfrac{2500 \times 6.5 \times 3.5}{100} = 568.75$

and $2500 + 568.5 = 3068.75$

So, the amount in Annie and Dave's account is $3068.75

8 a Interest $= (15\,500 - 12\,500)$ PHP $= \$3000$ PHP

$$I = \dfrac{Crn}{100}$$

$$\therefore \quad 3000 = \dfrac{12\,500 \times R \times 4}{100}$$

$$\therefore \quad \dfrac{3000 \times 100}{12\,500 \times 4} = R$$

$$\therefore \quad R = 6$$

∴ annual interest rate $= 6\%$

b
$$\dfrac{12\,500 \times 7 \times T}{100} = 3000$$

$$\therefore \quad T = \dfrac{3000 \times 100}{12\,500 \times 7}$$

$$\therefore \quad T \approx 3.43$$

∴ time $= 3.43$ years

9 a
$$I = \dfrac{Crn}{100}$$

$$\therefore \quad 1800 = \dfrac{4000 \times 7.5 \times T}{100}$$

$$\therefore \quad \dfrac{1800 \times 100}{4000 \times 7.5} = T$$

$$\therefore \quad T = 6$$

∴ time $= 6$ years.

b Interest is $(6700 - 4000)$ CHF $= 2700$ CHF

$$\therefore \quad 2700 = \dfrac{4000 \times 7.5 \times T}{100}$$

$$\therefore \quad \dfrac{2700 \times 100}{4000 \times 7.5} = T$$

$$\therefore \quad T = 9 \text{ years}$$

So, it will take 3 more years.

10 Let the amount of interest be x.

∴ the original value is $6000 - x$

$I = \dfrac{Crn}{100}$ $\therefore \quad x = \dfrac{(6000 - x) \times 10 \times 5}{100}$

$$\therefore \quad x = \dfrac{6000 - x}{2}$$

$$\therefore \quad 2x = 6000 - x$$

$$\therefore \quad 3x = 6000$$

$$\therefore \quad x = 2000$$

The original value was $\$(6000 - 2000) = \$4000$

11 a Interest, $I = \dfrac{Crn}{100}$

$$= \dfrac{5600 \times 8.8 \times 3}{100}$$

$$= \$1478.40$$

b Jana has to repay $\$(5600 + 1478.40) = \$7078.40$

c The monthly repayment is $\dfrac{\$7078.40}{36} = \$196.62$

12 a Interest, $I = C\left(I + \frac{r}{100}\right)^n - C$

$$= 30\,000\left(1 + \frac{9}{100}\right)^6 - 30\,000$$

$$= 20\,313.00 \text{ rupees}$$

b
$$I = \frac{Crn}{100}$$

$$\therefore \quad 20\,313 = \frac{30\,000 \times R \times 6}{100}$$

$$\frac{20\,313 \times 100}{30\,000 \times 6} = R$$

$$R \approx 11.3$$

Equivalent simple interest rate is 11.3%

13 a $n = 4 \times 12 + 3 = 51$ months $\quad i = \dfrac{6.7}{12}$

$$F_v = C\left(1 + \frac{r}{100}\right)^n$$

$$= 4750 \times \left(1 + \frac{6.7}{1200}\right)^{51}$$

$$= \$6309.79$$

b Interest earned $= \$(6309.79 - 4750) = \$1559.79$

c If compounded annually, $\quad n = 4.25 \quad$ and $\quad i = 6.7$

$$I = C\left(1 + \frac{r}{100}\right)^n - C$$

$$= 4750\left(1 + \frac{6.7}{100}\right)^{4.25} - 4750$$

$$= 1507.38$$

Difference is $\quad \$(1559.79 - 1507.38) = \$52.41$

If compounded annually, \$52.41 less would be earned.

14 Multipliers are:

a 1.06 **b** $\left(1 + \frac{5.94}{400}\right)^4 = 1.0607$

c $\left(1 + \frac{5.9}{1200}\right)^{12} = 1.0606$

5.94%, compounding quarterly, gives highest return.

15 a $n = 25 \times 12 = 300 \quad i = 9.5 \div 12$

$$F_v = P_v\left(1 + \frac{r}{100}\right)^n$$

$$\therefore \quad 1\,000\,000 = P_v\left(1 + \frac{9.5}{1200}\right)^{300}$$

$$\therefore \quad \frac{1\,000\,000}{\left(1 + \frac{9.5}{1200}\right)^{300}} = P_v$$

$$\therefore \quad 93\,888.41 = P_v$$

Charles and Linda will need to invest \$93\,888.41

b Interest $I = \dfrac{Crn}{100}$

$$= \frac{\$93\,888.41 \times 9.5 \times 25}{100}$$

$$= \$222\,984.97$$

Difference is $\quad \$(1\,000\,000 - 93\,888.41) - \$222\,984$

$$= \$683\,126.62$$

16 a
$$I = C\left(1 + \frac{r}{100}\right)^n - C$$

$$\therefore \quad 2000 = 6500\left(1 + \frac{8}{400}\right)^n - 6500$$

$$\therefore \quad 8500 = 6500\left(1 + \frac{8}{400}\right)^n$$

$$\therefore \quad \frac{8500}{6500} = \left(1 + \frac{8}{400}\right)^n$$

$$n \approx 13.55 \text{ quarters} \quad \{\text{using a gdc}\}$$

It will take 14 quarters to earn a minimum \$2000 interest.

b In 14 quarters, the actual amount of interest would be

$$I = 6500 \times \left(1 + \frac{8}{400}\right)^{14} - 6500 = \$2076.61$$

Now $\qquad I = C\left(1 + \frac{r}{100}\right)^n - C$

$$\therefore \quad 2076.61 = 6500 \times \left(1 + \frac{r}{100}\right)^{3.5} - 6500$$

$$\therefore \quad 8576.61 = 6500 \times \left(1 + \frac{r}{100}\right)^{3.5}$$

$$\therefore \quad r \approx 8.24 \quad \{\text{using a gdc}\}$$

So, to earn the same amount of money over 14 months, the interest rate would have to be 8.24%.

17 a $F_v = C\left(1 + \frac{r}{100}\right)^n$

$$= 120\,000\left(1 + \frac{9.75}{1200}\right)^{3 \times 12}$$

$$= 160\,582.83$$

So, the total amount Sanya must repay is 160\,582.83 INR.

b $\dfrac{160\,582.83}{3 \times 4} = 13\,381.90$

So, Sanya will have to repay 13\,381.90 INR per quarter

c $120\,000 \times \left(1 + \frac{9.75}{200}\right)^{3 \times 2} = 159\,666.24$

and $\dfrac{159\,666.24}{12} = 13\,305.52$.

So, Sanya would have to pay

$(13\,381.90 - 13\,305.52)$ INR $= 76.38$ INR less per quarter.

18 a

Quarter	Capital	Interest	Repayment	Amount Outstanding
1	20\,000	600	900	19\,700
2	19\,700	591	900	19\,391
3	19\,391	581.73	900	19\,072.73
4	19\,072.73	572.18	900	18\,744.91

b Amount outstanding in quarters five and six are 18\,407.26 CNY and 18\,059.48 CNY.

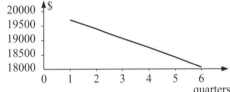

Amount outstanding

19 a The furniture has depreciated by 4800 EUR.

Average depreciation per year is $\dfrac{4800 \text{ EUR}}{5} = 960$ EUR

b Using $\quad F_v = C\left(1 - \frac{r}{100}\right)^n$

$$1200 = 6000 \times \left(1 - \frac{r}{100}\right)^5$$

$$\therefore \quad r = 27.5 \quad \{\text{using a gdc}\}$$

So, the rate is 27.5% per annum

c 4350, 3153.75, 2286.47, 1657.69, 1201.83 EUR

20 a

Year	Start Value	Depreciation (20% p.a.)	End Value
1	20\,000	4000	16\,000
2	16\,000	3200	12\,800
3	12\,800	2560	10\,240
4	10\,240	2048	8192

b Using $\quad F_v = C\left(1 - \frac{r}{100}\right)^n$

$$5000 = 20\,000 \times \left(1 - \frac{20}{100}\right)^n$$

$$5000 = 20\,000 \times (0.8)^n$$

$$\therefore \quad n = 6.21 \quad \{\text{using a gdc}\}$$

So, the van will fall below \$5000 in the 7th year.

21 a Book Value of computer $= 4500 \left(1 - \frac{22.5}{100}\right)^3$

$$= 2094.68 \text{ CAD}$$

b i If the original cost of the tractor was C, then

$$29\,000 = C \times \left(1 - \frac{17.5}{100}\right)^5$$

$$\therefore \quad \frac{29\,000}{\left(1 - \frac{17.5}{100}\right)^5} = C$$

$$\therefore \quad C = 75\,880$$

So, the original tractor cost GBP 75 880 GBP

ii Depreciation for 5 years is $\$(75\,880 - 29\,000) = \$46\,880$

So, the constant annual deduction would be

$$\frac{46\,880}{5} = 9376 \text{ GBP}.$$

22 a Value of home 10 years later $= 187\,000 \left(1 + \frac{6}{100}\right)^{10}$

$$= \$334\,888.52$$

b We have to solve $187\,000 \left(1 + \frac{r}{100}\right)^{10} = 360\,000$

$r \approx 6.77$ {using a gdc}

So, average rate of increase is 6.77%.

23 a

$$200 = 40 \times \left(1 + \frac{5}{100}\right)^n$$

$$\therefore \quad 5 = \left(1 + \frac{5}{100}\right)^n$$

$$\therefore \quad (1.05)^n = 5$$

$$\therefore \quad n \approx 32.99 \quad \{\text{using a gdc}\}$$

i.e. 33 years ago the cost of a pie was 40 cents.

b

$$250 = 200 \times \left(1 + \frac{5}{100}\right)^n$$

$$\therefore \quad \frac{250}{200} = (1.05)^n$$

$$\therefore \quad (1.05)^n = 1.25$$

$$\therefore \quad n \approx 4.574 \quad \{\text{using a gdc}\}$$

i.e., in 5 years time the cost of a pie will be $2.50.

24 a

year (n)	2.5%	3%	3.5%	4%	4.5%
1	1.025	1.03	1.035	1.04	1.045
2	1.0506	1.0609	1.0712	1.0816	1.0920
3	1.0769	1.0927	1.1087	1.1249	1.1412
4	1.1038	1.1255	1.1475	1.1699	1.1925
5	1.1314	1.1593	1.1877	1.2167	1.2462

b i $250 \times 1.1249 = \$281.23$

ii $\dfrac{1.68}{1.45} = 1.1586$ In the 3% column this is close to the multiplier of $n = 5$. The price was $1.45 about 5 years ago.

iii $\dfrac{611.52}{560} = 1.092$ In the 2 year row this corresponds to a rate of 4.5%.

25 a $S = 25\,000 \times 1.03^n$

b $E = 22\,500 \times 1.05^n$

c Marika's spending will be equal to her income if

$$25\,000 \times 1.03^n = 22\,500 \times 1.05^n$$

$$n \approx 5.48 \quad \{\text{using a gdc}\}$$

Marika's spending will start to exceed her income in the 6th year.

Long questions

1 a i Deposit is $27\,000 \times 15\% = \$4050$

ii Amount to borrow is $27\,000 - 4050 = \$22\,950$

iii Total to be repaid is $157.60 \times 48 \times 4 = \$30\,259.20$

Interest is $30\,259.20 - 22\,950 = \$7309.20$

iv Total amount to be paid for the boat is

$$27\,000 + 7309.20 = \$34\,309.20$$

b Amount to repay is $578.70 \times 5 \times 12 = \$34\,722$

c i $I = \dfrac{Crn}{100}$

$$= \frac{27\,000 \times 6 \times 4.5}{100}$$

$$= \$7290$$

Amount to repay $= 27\,000 + 7290 = \$34\,290$

ii Monthly repayment is $\dfrac{34\,290}{54} = \$635$

d Choosing the cheapest loan will save $34\,309.20 - 34\,290$

$$= \$19.20$$

2 a i Monthly repayment is $30 \times 20.3963 = \$611.90$

ii Total amount to repay is $611.90 \times 5 \times 12 = \$36\,714$

iii Interest paid is $36\,714 - 30\,000 = \$6714$

iv

$$I = \frac{Crn}{100}$$

$$\therefore \quad 6714 = \frac{30\,000 \times r \times 5}{100}$$

$$\therefore \quad \frac{6714 \times 100}{30\,000 \times 5} = r$$

$$\therefore \quad r \approx 4.48$$

Simple interest rate $= 4.48\%$

b i The required information is not in the table.

Using a gdc with

$n = 48$	$PMT = 0$
$I\% = 5$	$P/Y = 12$
$P_v = -30\,000$	$C/Y = 12$

gives $F_v = 36\,626.86$

total to be repaid $= \$36\,626.86$

$\therefore$ monthly repayment $= \$36\,626.86 \div 48 = \$763.06$

ii Total amount to be repaid is $690.88 \times 48 = \$33\,162.24$

c Marilia should be advised to take out the loan offered in **b** as she will save $\$(36\,714 - 33\,162.24) \doteqdot \$3550.00$

d One disadvantage is that Marilia has to make higher monthly payments.

3 a Amount at the end of 2001 is $1000 \times 1.072 = \$1072$

b End of 2002: $(1072 + 1000) \times 1.072 = \$2221.18$

2003: $(2221.18 + 1000) \times 1.072 = \$3453.10$

2004: $(3453.10 + 1000) \times 1.072 = \$4773.73$

c

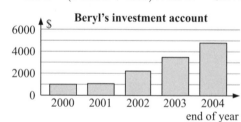

Beryl's investment account

d Using $F_v = C \left(1 + \frac{r}{100}\right)^n$

$$\therefore \quad 4773.73 = C \times 1.072^4$$

$$\therefore \quad \frac{4773.73}{(1.072)^4} = C$$

Lump sum required at the start of 2001 is $3614.75

e

$$I = \frac{Crn}{100}$$

$$\therefore \quad 773.73 = \frac{4000 \times r \times 4}{100}$$

$$\therefore \quad \frac{773.73 \times 100}{4000 \times 4} = r$$

$$\therefore \quad r = 4.84$$

A simple interest rate of 4.84% would have earned the same amount.

4 a $a = 1.01875$ $b = 1.00833$ $c = 1.125$

b i $4000 \times (1.006\,25)^{5 \times 12} = 5813.18$ CHF

ii $5000 = 4000 \times (1.025)^n$
$n \approx 9.04$ {using a gdc}   i.e.,   10 quarters

c $10\,000 = C \times (1.010\,417)^{7 \times 12}$

$\therefore \quad C = \dfrac{10\,000}{(1.010\,417)^{84}} \approx 4187.41$

Amount required now is 4187.41 CHF.

d i $6700 \times 1.2778 \times 0.985 = 8432.84$ CHF

ii $F_v = C\left(1 + \frac{r}{100}\right)^n$

$\qquad = 8432.84 \left(1 + \frac{6}{400}\right)^3$

$\qquad = 8818.04$ CHF

e $\dfrac{8814.04}{1.2778} \times 0.985 = 6797.44$ USD

f The exchange rate has remained constant.

5 a i Eddie's savings after 3 years will be

$F_v = C\left(1 + \frac{r}{100}\right)^n$

$\qquad = 1800 \left(1 + \frac{5.6}{400}\right)^{3 \times 4}$

$\qquad = \pounds 2126.81$

ii Additional amount to reach the target is
$\pounds(5500 - 2126.81) = \pounds 3373.19$

b Let C be the amount needed to accumulate to £5500.

Using $F_v = C\left(1 + \frac{r}{100}\right)^n$

$\therefore \quad 5500 = C \times \left(1 + \frac{5.6}{400}\right)^{3 \times 4}$

$\therefore \quad \dfrac{5500}{\left(1 + \frac{5.6}{400}\right)^{12}} = C$

$\qquad\qquad C = \pounds 4654.87$

Eddie's father needs to add $4654.87 - 1800 = \pounds 2654.87$

c i Using a gdc with

$n = 24 \qquad\qquad PMT = 0$
$I\% = 9 \qquad\qquad P/Y = 12$
$P_v = -5500 \qquad C/Y = 12$

gives $F_v = 6580.27$ $\therefore$ total to repay £6580.27

So, monthly repayment $= \pounds 6580.27 \div 24 = \pounds 274.18$

ii Total amount Thomas needs to repay is
$24 \times \pounds 251.27 = \pounds 6030.48$

d Thomas pays $\pounds(6580.27 - 4654.87) = \pounds 1925.40$ more.

6 a i $F_v = C\left(1 + \frac{r}{100}\right)^n = 5000\left(1 + \frac{6.8}{200}\right)^{4 \times 2} \approx 6533.33$

Value of investment is 6533.33 EUR

ii Interest earned is $6533.33 - 5000 = 1533.33$ EUR

b Amount of tax is $1533.33 \times 25\% = 383.33$ EUR

Ali and Sam have $1533.33 - 383.33 = 1150$ EUR

c Amount before tax is $5000\left(1 + \frac{6.5}{400}\right)^{4 \times 4} = 6471.11$ EUR

Tax is $(6471.11 - 5000) \times 25\% = 367.78$ EUR

Amount after tax is $(6471.11 - 5000 - 367.78)$ EUR
$\qquad\qquad\qquad\qquad = 1103.33$ EUR

Difference in after tax amount is $1150 - 1103.33$
$= 46.67$ EUR

d i If I is the before tax interest, then $I \times 0.75 = 430$

Interest $I = \dfrac{430}{0.75} = 573.33$ EUR

ii If r is the interest rate then

$5573.33 = 5000\left(1 + \frac{r}{100}\right)^{36}$

$\therefore \quad \left(1 + \frac{r}{100}\right)^{36} = \dfrac{5573.33}{5000}$

$\therefore \quad 1 + \frac{r}{100} = \left(\dfrac{5573.33}{5000}\right)^{\frac{1}{36}}$

$\therefore \quad r = 0.302\%$

Annual interest rate is $0.302 \times 12 = 3.62\%$

7 a i $F_v = C\left(1 + \frac{r}{100}\right)^n = 20\,000\left(1 + \frac{6.5}{400}\right)^4 \approx 21\,332.03$

Amount after one year is 21 332.03 SAR

ii $25\,884.45 = 20\,000\left(1 + \frac{6.5}{400}\right)^n$
$n = 16$ quarters $= 4$ years.   {using a gdc}

b i $I = \dfrac{Crn}{100} = \dfrac{21\,332.03 \times 9.5 \times 3}{100} = 6079.63$

Investment after 3 years is worth
$21\,332.03 + 6079.63 = 27\,411.66$ SAR,

ii Vitus can earn $27\,411.66 - 25\,884.45 = 1527.21$ SAR,
more with the company.

c Let x be amount Vitus keeps in the bank, then he invests
$21\,332.03 - x$ in the debenture.

After three years: the amount in the bank be $x\left(1 + \frac{6.5}{100}\right)^3$.

The interest in the debenture will be

$\dfrac{(21\,332.03 - x) \times 9.5 \times 3}{100}$

and so the total in the debenture will be

$\dfrac{(21\,332.03 - x) \times 9.5 \times 3}{100} + (21\,332.03 - x)$

After 3 years

$x\left(1 + \frac{6.5}{100}\right)^3 + \dfrac{(21\,332.03 - x) \times 28.5}{100} + (21\,332.03 - x)$

$= 26\,779.35$

Using gdc solver $x = 8206.43$

So Vitus left   8206.43 SAR   in the bank account.

8 a

Year	Book Value at start	Depreciation	Book Value at end
1	9500	1662.50	7837.50
2	7837.50	1371.56	6465.94
3	6465.94	1131.54	5334.00

b Year 4: $5334 \times 0.90 = \$4800.60$
Year 5: $4800.60 \times 0.90 = \$4320.54$

c i Total depreciation is $9500 - 4320.54 = \$5179.46$

ii Let r be the annual depreciation rate for the whole of
the five years.

then $4320.54 = 9500\left(1 - \frac{r}{100}\right)^5$

$\therefore \quad \left(1 - \frac{r}{100}\right)^5 = \dfrac{4320.54}{9500}$

$\therefore \quad 1 - \frac{r}{100} = \left(\dfrac{4320.54}{9500}\right)^{\frac{1}{5}}$ and so $r = 14.6\%$

d The value of Margarita's car 10 years after 1995 was
$F_v = C\left(1 + \frac{r}{100}\right)^n = 4320.54\left(1 + \frac{8}{100}\right)^{10}$
$\qquad\qquad\qquad\qquad = \$9327.72$

e Percentage change in the value of the MGB was

$\dfrac{(9500 - 9327.72)}{9500} \times 100 = 1.81\%$

i.e.,   there was a 1.81% decrease in value.

Paper 1

1 a $5, -5, \sqrt{16}$ {as $\sqrt{16} = 4$}

b $\frac{1}{3}, 5, -5, \sqrt{16}, 0.\dot{6}$ {as $0.\dot{6} = \frac{2}{3}$}

c $5, \sqrt{16}$

2 a $f: \quad x \mapsto 2x^2 + x - 3$

$\therefore \quad f(x) = 2x^2 + x - 3$

$f(-2) = 2(-2)^2 + (-2) - 3 = 8 - 2 - 3 = 3$

$f(-1) = 2(-1)^2 + (-1) - 3 = 2 - 1 - 3 = -2$

$f(0) = -3$

$f(1) = 2(1)^2 + 1 - 3 = 2 + 1 - 3 = 0$

$f(2) = 2(2)^2 + 2 - 3 = 8 + 2 - 3 = 7$

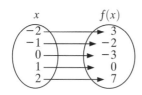

b i Domain $= \{x \in \mathbb{Z} \mid -2 \leqslant x \leqslant 2\}$

ii Range $= \{-3, -2, 0, 3, 7\}$

3 a Surface $= 9.85 \times 5.90$

$= 58.115 \text{ m}^2 \quad (= 58.1 \text{ m}^2)$

b Rounded measurements are 10 m by 6 m.

Surface area $= 10 \times 6$

$= 60 \text{ m}^2$

Percentage error $= \dfrac{60 - 58.115}{58.115} \times 100\%$

$= 3.24\%$

4 a

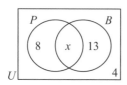

Total number of students $= 8 + 13 + 4 + x$

$\therefore \quad 30 = 25 + x$

$\therefore \quad x = 5$

$\therefore \quad$ 5 students like both plain and chocolate milk.

b

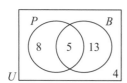

c P(likes only one type of milk) $= \dfrac{8 + 13}{30}$

$= \dfrac{21}{30}$

$= \dfrac{7}{10} \quad (= 0.7)$

5 a Total number of events $= 12 + 15 + 11 + 7 + 5$

$= 50$

P(ticket costs more than \$60) $= \dfrac{11 + 7 + 5}{50}$

$= \dfrac{23}{50} \quad (= 0.46)$

b

Cost (\$)	No. of events	Midpoint (x)
20 - 39	12	29.5
40 - 59	15	49.5
60 - 79	11	69.5
80 - 99	7	89.5
100 - 119	5	109.5
Total	50	

From a gdc, estimates are: mean $= \$60.70$

standard deviation $= \$25.35$

c 0.722 st dev above the mean is

$\$60.70 + 0.722 \times \$25.35 = \$79.00$

% of tickets less than \$79 $= \dfrac{12 + 15 + 11}{50}$

$= \dfrac{38}{50} \times 100$

$= 76\%$

6 a 2000 USD $= 2000 \times 0.75$ GBP

$= 1500$ GBP

b Amount remaining $= 1500 - 1200$

$= 300$ GBP

c 300 GBP $= 300 \times \dfrac{1}{0.80}$ USD

$= 375$ USD

7 a $u_1 r^6 = 320$ and $u_1 r^{10} = 5120$

Now $\dfrac{u_1 r^{10}}{u_1 r^6} = r^4$ and $\dfrac{5120}{320} = 16$

$\therefore \quad r^4 = 16$

$\therefore \quad r = 2$

b $u_1 2^6 = 320$

$\therefore \quad 64 u_1 = 320$

$\therefore \quad u_1 = 5$

c $u_{20} = u_1 r^{19}$

$= 5 \times 2^{19}$

$= 2\,621\,440$

8 a $F_v = C \left(1 + \frac{r}{100}\right)^n$

$= 20\,000 \times \left(1 + \frac{6.8}{1200}\right)^{48}$

$= \$26\,231.59$

i.e., value after 48 months is \$26 231.59

b Increasing original investment by 3.2% p.a. gives

$20\,000(1.032)^4 = \$22\,685.52$

c Real increase

$=$ actual increase $-$ original value indexed

$= 26\,231.59 - 22\,685.52$

$= \$3546.07$

9 a $Q_3 = 77, \quad Q_1 = 65$

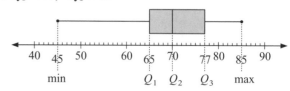

b IQR $= 77 - 65 = 12$

c minimum $= 45$

Testing for outliers $\quad Q_1 - 1.5 \times$ IQR

$= 65 - 1.5(12)$

$= 47$

but the minimum value is less than 47

$\therefore \quad$ the minimum value is an outlier.

10 a Profit = selling price − cost price

∴ for 100 boxes, profit = $12.50(100) − (9.5(100) + 45)$
$$= \$255$$

b Breakeven when $12.5x = 9.5x + 45$
$$\therefore \quad 3x = 45 \quad \text{and so,} \quad x = 15$$

i.e., 15 boxes must be produced and sold to breakeven.

c Profit > $1000 ∴ $12.50x − (9.5x + 45) > 1000$
$$\therefore \quad 3x − 45 > 1000$$
$$\therefore \quad x > 348.3$$

i.e., 349 boxes must be produced and sold.

11 a

$p \veebar q$	$\neg(p \wedge q) \vee q$	$(p \veebar q) \Rightarrow \neg(p \wedge q) \vee q$
F	T	T
T	T	T
T	T	T
F	T	T

b If Bozo does not have a red nose then Bozo is not a clown.

12 A is $(−2, −3)$, B is $(1, 3)$

a gradient of AB $= \dfrac{3 − (−3)}{1 − (−2)} = 2$

∴ equation of AB is $y = 2x + c$

substituting $(1, 3)$ gives $3 = 2(1) + c$ and so $c = 1$

i.e., equation of AB is $y = 2x + 1$
$$\text{or} \quad 2x − y + 1 = 0$$

b Midpoint of AB is $\left(\dfrac{−2+1}{2}, \dfrac{−3+3}{2}\right)$, i.e., $\left(−\tfrac{1}{2}, 0\right)$

gradient of perpendicular bisector is $−\tfrac{1}{2}$
$$\{\text{as} \quad 2 \times −\tfrac{1}{2} = −1\}$$

∴ equation is $y = −\tfrac{1}{2}x + c$

substituting $\left(−\tfrac{1}{2}, 0\right)$ gives $0 = −\tfrac{1}{2}\left(−\tfrac{1}{2}\right) + c$
$$\therefore \quad c = −\tfrac{1}{4}$$

∴ equation of perpendicular bisector is
$$y = −\tfrac{1}{2}x − \tfrac{1}{4}$$
$$\text{or} \quad 4y = −2x − 1$$
$$\text{or} \quad 2x + 4y + 1 = 0$$

13 a $f(x) = ax^2 + bx + d$ ∴ $f'(x) = 2ax + b$

b Now $f'(x) = 5x − 10$

Equating coefficients gives $2a = 5$ and $b = −10$
$$\therefore \quad a = 2.5 \quad \text{and} \quad b = −10$$

c $f'(x) = 0$ when $x = 2$

and $f(2) = 2.5 \times 2^2 − 10 \times 2 + d = d − 10$

So, $d − 10 = −4$ and ∴ $d = 6$

14 a

45 cm
60°
45 cm

The triangle which bisects the cone is equilateral with sides 45 cm.

∴ the diameter of the megaphone is 45 cm.

b

45 cm
x cm
60°
22.5 cm

Let the height be x cm.

Now $\tan 60° = \dfrac{x}{22.5}$
$$\therefore \quad x = 39.0$$
∴ height of cone is 39 cm.

Volume of cone $= \tfrac{1}{3}\pi r^2 h$
$$= \tfrac{1}{3}\pi \times 22.5^2 \times 39$$
$$= 20\,700 \text{ cm}^2 \quad (3 \text{ s.f.})$$

15 a i Amplitude $= \tfrac{1}{2}(\text{maximum} − \text{minimum})$
$$= \tfrac{1}{2}(5 − 1)$$
$$= 2$$

ii Period = length of 1 cycle = $120°$

b If $y = a\cos(bx) + c$,

where $a = $ amplitude $\qquad b = \dfrac{360}{\text{period}}$

$c = $ vertical translation

then for the graph given,
$$a = 2, \quad b = \dfrac{360}{120} = 3, \quad \text{and} \quad c = 3.$$

SOLUTIONS TO SPECIMEN EXAMINATION A

Paper 2

1 a

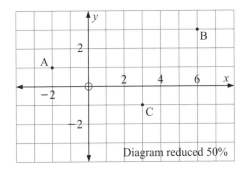

Diagram reduced 50%

b i gradient of BC $= \dfrac{−1 − 3}{3 − 6} = \dfrac{−4}{−3} = \dfrac{4}{3}$

ii Opposite sides of a parallelogram are parallel, and parallel lines have the same gradients.

∴ gradient of AD = gradient of BC

iii gradient of AD $= \dfrac{d − 1}{−5 − −2} = \dfrac{4}{3}$
$$\therefore \quad \dfrac{d − 1}{−3} = \dfrac{4}{3}$$
$$\therefore \quad d − 1 = \dfrac{4}{3} \times −3$$
$$\therefore \quad d − 1 = −4$$
$$\therefore \quad d = −3$$

c i length AB $= \sqrt{(6 − −2)^2 + (3 − 1)^2}$
$$= \sqrt{68}$$

ii $\cos \angle ABC = \dfrac{\sqrt{68}^2 + 5^2 − \sqrt{27}^2}{2 \times \sqrt{68} \times 5}$
$$\therefore \quad \angle ABC \approx 36.8°$$

d Area ABCD $\approx 2 \times$ area triangle ABC
$$\approx 2 \times \tfrac{1}{2} \times 5 \times \sqrt{68}\sin 36.8°$$
$$\approx 24.7 \text{ units}^2$$

2 a

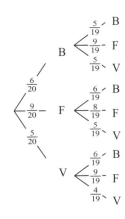

Mathematical Studies SL – Exam Preparation & Practice Guide

b i P(two basketballs)
= P(B and B)
= $\frac{6}{20} \times \frac{5}{19}$
= $\frac{30}{380}$

ii P(a basketball and a football)
= P(B and F) + P(F and B)
= $\frac{6}{20} \times \frac{9}{19} + \frac{9}{20} \times \frac{6}{19}$
= $\frac{108}{380}$

iii P(both balls are the same)
= P(B and B) + P(F and F) + P(V and V)
= $\frac{6}{20} \times \frac{5}{19} + \frac{9}{20} \times \frac{8}{19} + \frac{5}{20} \times \frac{4}{19}$
= $\frac{122}{380}$

c i With replacement

P(two volleyballs)
= P(V and V)
= $\frac{5}{20} \times \frac{5}{20}$
= $\frac{1}{4} \times \frac{1}{4}$
= $\frac{1}{16}$

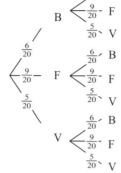

ii P(both B | the two balls are the same)

$$= \frac{\text{P(B and B)}}{\text{P(B and B)} + \text{P(F and F)} + \text{P(V and V)}}$$

$$= \frac{\frac{6}{20} \times \frac{6}{20}}{\frac{6}{20} \times \frac{6}{20} + \frac{9}{20} \times \frac{9}{20} + \frac{5}{20} \times \frac{5}{20}}$$

$$= \frac{18}{71} \quad (= 0.254)$$

3 a i
$T_P(0) = 61 \times (0.95)^0 + 18$
$= 61 + 18$
$= 79°C \qquad \therefore \quad a = 79°C$

$T_P(30) = 61 \times (0.95)^{30} + 18$
$\approx 31.1°C \qquad \therefore \quad b = 31.1°C$

ii We need to solve $61 \times (0.95)^t + 18 = 25$
So, $t \approx 42.2$ min {using gdc}

b
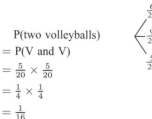

c i $T_F(0) = 53 \times (0.98)^0 + 18$
$= 53 + 18$
$= 71°C$

ii As $0.95 < 0.98$, the T_P function decreases at a faster rate than the T_F function.
∴ heat is lost faster in the plastic cup.

iii We need to solve
$53 \times (0.98)^t + 18 = 61 \times (0.95)^t + 18$
i.e., $53 \times (0.98)^t = 61 \times (0.95)^t$
From a gdc, $t \approx 4.52$

So it takes about $4\frac{1}{2}$ minutes for the temperatures in each cup to be equal.

d In the long term, $(0.95)^t$ and $(0.98)^t$ are virtually 0 (t is very large).
So, $T_P(t) = T_F(t) = 18°C$.

4 a ii a $s_{xy} = 93.7$ so
$$r = \frac{s_{xy}}{s_x s_y} = \frac{93.7}{4.78 \times 21.4} \approx 0.916$$

b A strong positive relationship exists between max. temperature and pool attendance.

ii The regression line is
$$y - \overline{y} = \frac{s_{xy}}{s_x^2}(x - \overline{x})$$
i.e., $y - 87.3 = \dfrac{93.7}{4.78^2}(x - 29.9)$
i.e., $y - 87.3 \approx 4.101(x - 29.9)$
$y \approx 4.101x - 122.62 + 87.3$
$y \approx 4.10x - 35.32$
i.e., attendance $\approx 4.10 \times$ max. temp $- 35.3$

iii a i When $x = 20$
$y \approx 4.10 \times 20 - 35.32$
$\therefore \quad y \approx 47$ people

ii When $x = 40$
$y \approx 4.10 \times 40 - 35.32$
$\therefore \quad y \approx 129$ people

b The estimate at $20°C$ is more reliable as it is an interpolated value.

iv Since the value of r is high, the manager's plan seems sensible.

b i H_0: Attendance by gender is independent of the max. temperature.

ii $\chi^2_{\text{calc}} \approx 2.79$ and p-value ≈ 0.0950

iii As p-value > 0.05 we *do not* reject H_0.

5 a $f(x) = 3x^3 - 4x + 5$
i $f(1) = 3 - 4 + 5 = 4$
ii $f'(x) = 9x^2 - 4$
iii $f'(1) = 9 - 4 = 5 \quad \therefore$ gradient is 5 at $x = 1$
iv At (1, 4) the tangent has gradient 5.
$\therefore$ equation is $y - 4 = 5(x - 1)$
i.e., $y - 4 = 5x - 5$
i.e., $y = 5x - 1$
v The tangent $y = 5x - 1$ meets $y = f(x)$
where $3x^3 - 4x + 5 = 5x - 1$
i.e., $3x^3 - 9x + 6 = 0$
or $x^3 - 3x + 2 = 0$
From a gdc, this has solutions $x = 1, 1$ and -2
$\therefore$ they meet when $x = -2$, $y = -11$
i.e., at $(-2, -11)$

b i Volume = length × width × height
$\therefore V = x \times x \times y$
i.e., $V = x^2y$

ii $V = x^2\left(\dfrac{30\,000 - x^2}{2x}\right)$
$\therefore V = \frac{1}{2}x(30\,000 - x^2)$
$\therefore V = 15\,000x - \frac{1}{2}x^3$

iii $\dfrac{dV}{dx} = 15\,000 - \frac{3}{2}x^2$

iv $\dfrac{dV}{dx} = 0$ when $\frac{3}{2}x^2 = 15\,000$
$\therefore 3x^2 = 30\,000$
$\therefore x^2 = 10\,000$
$\therefore x = 100 \quad \{x > 0\}$

Note: graph of V against x is

$\therefore$ max V when $x = 100$.

Paper 1

1 a **C** and **D**

  b $0.0518 = 5.18 \times 10^{-2}$

  c Percentage error in rounding is
$$\frac{0.0518 - 0.051\,76}{0.051\,76} \times 100\% = 0.0773\%$$

2 a $2 + 5 + 8 + 12 + 5 + 6 + 2 = 40$ sheep were weighed

  b Mean weight
$$= \frac{2 \times 10 + 5 \times 20 + 8 \times 30 + \ldots + 2 \times 70}{40}$$
$$= \frac{1590}{40}$$
$$= 39.75 \text{ kg}$$

  c 150% of the mean weight is $39.75 \times 1.50 \approx 59.625$ kg

  Percentage of sheep with weight more than 60 kg going to market is $\dfrac{6+2}{40} \times 100$
$$\frac{8}{40} \times 100$$
$$= 20\%.$$

3 a $\cos 38^o = \dfrac{DC}{10}$

  $10 \times \cos 38^o = DC$

  $\therefore\ DC \approx 7.88$ cm

  [Triangle diagram: A, 10 cm, D right angle, 38° at C]

  b $\sin 38^o = \dfrac{AD}{10}$

  $10 \times \sin 38^o = AD$

  $\therefore\ AD \approx 6.16$ cm

  Now $AB^2 = AD^2 + BD^2$

  $\therefore\ BD^2 = AB^2 - AD^2$

  $\therefore\ BD^2 = 8.5^2 - 6.16^2$

  $\therefore\ BD = \sqrt{8.5^2 - 6.16^2}$

  $\therefore\ BD \approx 5.86$ cm

  [Triangle diagram: A, 8.5 cm, 6.16 cm, B, D]

4 a Revenue is $22 \times 42.50 = 935$ EUR

  b Cost $C(22) = 15.6 \times 22 + 245$
$$= 588.20 \text{ EUR}$$

  c Profit is $935 - 588.20 = 346.80$ EUR

  d Profit per pair of jeans is $\dfrac{346.80}{22} = 15.76$ EUR

5 a $P = \{2, 3, 5, 7, 11, 13\}$

  b $Q = \{1, 2, 3, 4, 6, 8, 12\}$

  c $P \cup Q = \{1, 2, 3, 4, 5, 6, 7, 8, 11, 12, 13\}$
  $\therefore\ (P \cup Q)' = \{9, 10\}$

6 In the tree diagram,

  T = triangle, R = rectangle, H = rhombus.

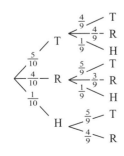

a P(both triangles) $= \dfrac{5}{10} \times \dfrac{4}{9} = \dfrac{2}{9}$

b P(one is a rhombus)
$$= \frac{5}{10} \times \frac{1}{9} + \frac{4}{10} \times \frac{1}{9} + \frac{1}{10} \times \frac{5}{9} + \frac{1}{10} \times \frac{4}{9}$$
$$= \frac{1}{5}$$

c From the tree diagram, the probability that the second is a rectangle is $\dfrac{5}{10} \times \dfrac{4}{9} + \dfrac{4}{10} \times \dfrac{3}{9} + \dfrac{1}{10} \times \dfrac{4}{9} = \dfrac{36}{90}$

  Probability of selecting 2 rectangles is $\dfrac{4}{10} \times \dfrac{3}{9} = \dfrac{12}{90}$

  Probability of the first being a rectangle is $\dfrac{12}{90} \div \dfrac{36}{90}$
$$= \frac{12}{36}$$
$$= \frac{1}{3}$$

7 a Domain $= \{x \in \mathbb{Z} \mid -5 \leqslant x \leqslant 0\}$

  b Range $= \{-8, -5, -2, 1, 4, 7\}$

  c If $x = 0$, $y = 7$

  Since $y = mx + c$
  $\therefore\ 7 = 0 + c$
  $\therefore\ c = 7$

  Also, if $x = -1$, $y = 4$
  $\therefore\ 4 = m(-1) + 7 \Rightarrow m = 3$
  $\therefore\ 4 = -m + 7$
  $\therefore\ m = 3$

  So, the equation is $y = 3x + 7$.

8 a If \$2500 is invested,

  the interest $I = \dfrac{CRN}{100}$
$$= \frac{2500 \times 7.5 \times 3.5}{100}$$
$$= \$656.25$$

  The amount in account $= \$2500 + \$656.25$
$$= \$3156.25$$

  b To return an amount of \$3400, the interest must be \$900.

  If the rate is R, then, $900 = \dfrac{2500 \times R \times 3.5}{100}$
$$\frac{900 \times 100}{2500 \times 3.5} = R$$
$$\therefore\ R \approx 10.3\%$$

  i.e., rate is 10.3%

9 a $y = 2x^3 - 3x^2 - 264x + 13$
$$\therefore\ \frac{dy}{dx} = 2(3x^2) - 3(2x) - 264$$
$$= 6x^2 - 6x - 264$$

  b The gradient is -12 if $6x^2 - 6x - 264 = -12$
  $\therefore\ 6x^2 - 6x - 252 = 0$
  $\therefore\ 6(x^2 - x - 42) = 0$
  $\therefore\ 6(x - 7)(x + 6) = 0$

  i.e., if $x = 7$ or $x = -6$, the gradient is -12

10 a $4r + 3p = 19$ ...... (1)

  b $3r - 2p = 10$ ...... (2)

  c $\quad 8r + 6p = 38$ ...... $2 \times$ (1)
  $\quad \underline{9r - 6p = 30}$ ...... $3 \times$ (2)
  $\quad 17r \qquad = 68$ {adding the equations}
  $\quad \therefore\ r = 4$

  If $r = 4$ then $16 + 3p = 19$ i.e., $p = 1$

  Cost of buying 5 reams of paper and 5 pens is
  $\quad 5 \times 4 + 5 \times 1 = £25$

11

	Climbing	Swimming	Mountain Bike	Sum
Female	9	18	8	35
Male	15	16	24	55
Sum	24	34	32	90

a Expected values

	Climbing	Swimming	Mountain Bike
Female	$\frac{24 \times 35}{90} = 9.33$	$\frac{34 \times 35}{90} = 13.2$	$\frac{32 \times 35}{90} = 12.4$
Male	$\frac{24 \times 55}{90} = 14.7$	$\frac{34 \times 55}{90} = 20.8$	$\frac{32 \times 55}{90} = 19.6$

b $\chi^2_{calc} \approx 5.44$

c With 2 degrees of freedom the p-value is 0.0658

d Since $0.05 < 0.0658$ we do not have enough evidence to reject the hypothesis that activities chosen are independent of sex.

12 a We are given, $n = 20$, $S_{20} = 560$ and $u_n = 66$

$$S_n = \frac{n}{2}(u_1 + u_n)$$

$$\text{So,} \quad 560 = \frac{20}{2}(u_1 + 66)$$

$$\therefore \quad 560 = 10(u_1 + 66)$$

$$56 = u_1 + 66$$

The first term, $u_1 = 56 - 66 = -10$

b
$$\text{As} \quad u_1 + (n-1)d = u_n,$$
$$-10 + 19d = 66$$
$$\therefore \quad 19d = 76$$

The common difference is $d = 4$.

13 a Graph of $y = \sin(2x) - 1$ for $0° \leqslant x \leqslant 360°$.

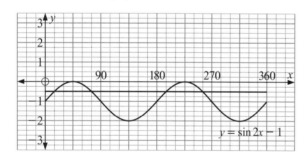

b $\sin(2x) - 1 = -\frac{1}{2}$ if $x = 15°$ or $x = 75°$

14 a At $x = 3$, $y = \dfrac{2^3}{3-2} = 8$

b When $x = 0$, $y = \dfrac{2^0}{0-2} = \dfrac{1}{-2} = -\dfrac{1}{2}$

$\therefore$ y-intercept is $-\frac{1}{2}$.

c $y \approx 7.54$ is the minimum value for $x \geqslant 2$

d Vertical asymptote is $x = 2$

15 a

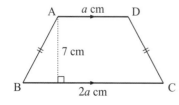

Area = 42 cm^2

b Area of trapezium $= \frac{1}{2}(a + b)h$

i.e., $42 = \frac{1}{2}(a + 2a) \times 7$

$\therefore \quad 84 = 7 \times 3a$

$\therefore \quad 12 = 3a$

$\therefore \quad a = 4$

The parallel sides of the trapezium have lengths 4 cm and 8 cm.

SOLUTIONS TO SPECIMEN EXAMINATION B

Paper 2

1 a To increase an amount by 2.5%, we multiply it by 1.025

$\therefore$ Amount in bank $= 500(1.025) + 500$
$= 1012.50$ USD

b The amount she will have one year later will be
$(500(1.025) + 500) \times 1.025 + 500$
$= 500(1.025)^2 + 500(1.025) + 500$
$= 1537.81$ USD

c i Amount after n years the day before she makes her next deposit will be

$500(1.025) + 500(1.025)^2 + \ldots\ldots + 500(1.025)^n$

which is a geometric progression with first term $500(1.025)$ and common ratio 1.025

$$\therefore \quad \text{amount} = \frac{512.50 \times (1.025^n - 1)}{1.025 - 1}$$

ii At midnight December 31st 2015 the amount will have been there for 11 years but a day before Jaime puts another 500 USD in the bank.

Amount will be

$500(1.025) + 500(1.025)^2 + \ldots\ldots + 500(1.025)^{11}$

$= 500(1.025) \times \left[\dfrac{(1.025)^{11} - 1}{1.025 - 1} \right]$

$= 6397.78$ USD

d i Over 11 years Jaime invested $11 \times 500 = 5500$ USD

ii Amount of interest earned is
$6397.78 - 5500 = 897.78$ USD

2 a

3	2 8
4	0 5 5 5 5 5 8
5	4 5 5 8
6	0 0 5 5 8 8
7	0 5 5 5 5 8 8
8	0 5 5 8

Key 3 | 2 means 32

b From a gdc, mean mark ≈ 61.8

c From a gdc,

i Median = 62.5   **ii** Lower quartile = 45

iii Upper quartile = 75

d

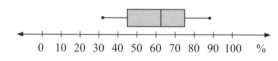

e

Class intervals	Frequency	Midpoint
30 - 39	2	34.5
40 - 49	7	44.5
50 - 59	4	54.5
60 - 69	6	64.5
70 - 79	7	74.5
80 - 89	4	84.5

f Modal groups 40 - 49 and 70 - 79

g From a gdc, estimate of mean ≈ 61.5

h Error in estimating mean is $61.8 - 61.5 = 0.3$

3 a

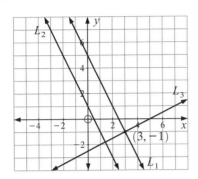

b i $y = 5 - 2x = -2x + 5$ has a gradient of -2.

$y = kx + c$ has the same gradient $\therefore$ $k = -2$.

Now $(2, -3)$ lies on $y = -2x + c$

$\therefore$ $-3 = -2(2) + c$

$\therefore$ $c = 1$ and so $y = -2x + 1$

ii See the graph above.

c i Substitution of $x = 3$ in L_1 gives

$y = 5 - 2(3) = -1$ ✓

So, $(3, -1)$ lies on the line.

ii See the graph above.

d i L_2 it has gradient -2 which is $\frac{-2}{1}$

$\therefore$ L_3 has gradient $\frac{1}{2}$

Since $(3, -1)$ lies on L_3, the equation of L_3 is

$y - -1 = \frac{1}{2}(x - 3)$

$\therefore$ $2y + 2 = x - 3$

$\therefore$ $2y = x - 5$

$\therefore$ $x - 2y - 5 = 0$

ii L_2 is $y = -2x + 1$ and L_3 is $y = \frac{x - 5}{2}$

Using a gdc to solve these simultaneously, we get $x = 1.4$ and $y = -1.8$ and so the lines intersect at $(1.4, -1.8)$.

4 a

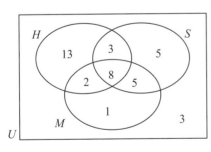

b i P(History only) = $P(H) = \frac{13}{40}$

ii P(does not like Music) = $P(M')$

$= \frac{13 + 3 + 5 + 3}{40}$

$= \frac{24}{40}$

$= \frac{3}{5}$

iii P(M or S but not H) $= \frac{5 + 5 + 1}{40}$

$= \frac{11}{40}$

iv P(at least one) $= \frac{37}{40}$

---

c i $P(S \cap M) = \frac{8 + 5}{40}$

$= \frac{13}{40}$

ii $P((H \cap S \cap M)') = \frac{40 - 8}{40}$

$= \frac{32}{40}$

$= \frac{4}{5}$

iii $P(H' \cap S') = \frac{3 + 1}{40}$

$= \frac{4}{40}$

$= \frac{1}{10}$

d $P(H \mid M) = \frac{2 + 8}{1 + 2 + 8 + 5}$

$= \frac{10}{16}$

$= \frac{5}{8}$

e P(first likes H and S) $= \frac{11}{40}$

P(second likes H and S) $= \frac{10}{39}$

P(both like H and S) $= \frac{11}{40} \times \frac{10}{39}$

$= \frac{11}{156}$

5 a i B lies on the exponential function (not the parabola).

So, when $x = 0$ $y = 2^0 = 1$

So the y-intercept is 1.

ii A and C are at the intersection of the curves.

So we need to solve $8 - x^2 = 2^{-x}$

Using a gdc, the solutions are $x = -2$ and $x \approx 2.80$.

So, A is at $(-2, 4)$ and B is at $(2.80, 0.143)$.

iii When $2^{-x} > 8 - x^2$ the graph of $y = 2^{-x}$ is **above** the graph of $y = 8 - x^2$

So, $x < -2$ or $x > 2.80$

b i a $y = \sin\left(\frac{x}{2}\right)$ is increasing for

$0^\circ < x < 180^\circ$ or $540^\circ < x < 720^\circ$

b $y = \sin\left(\frac{x}{2}\right)$ is decreasing for

$180^\circ < x < 540^\circ$

ii a $\frac{dy}{dx} = 0$ when $x = 180^\circ$ or 540°.

b The gradient is at its steepest at $x = 0^\circ, 360^\circ, 720^\circ$.

SOLUTIONS TO SPECIMEN EXAMINATION C

Paper 1

1 a $\frac{M}{EI} = \frac{6 \times 10^4}{(1.5 \times 10^8) \times (8 \times 10^2)}$

$= 5 \times 10^{-7}$ {using a gdc}

b $\sqrt[3]{\frac{34.5^2 - 103}{50.5 + 19}} = 2.5010067.......$

i $= 2.501$ {to 4 s.f.}

ii $= 3$ {to nearest integer}

2 a Mean temperature $= 20.2^\circ$C {gdc}

b Median temperature $= 19.5^\circ$C {gdc}

c Percentage error is $\frac{20.2 - 20}{20.2} \times 100\%$

$= 0.990\%$

3 a If x is a prime number then x is not a factor of 12.

b If $x = 2$ or 3, p is true, but $\neg q$ is false.

so $p \Rightarrow \neg q$ is false.

c The inverse of $p \Rightarrow \neg q$ is $\neg p \Rightarrow \neg(\neg q)$

i.e., $\neg p \Rightarrow q$

In words,

if x is not a prime number then x is a factor of 12.

d The inverse is not true for all values of x since 10 is not a prime number and it is not a factor of 12.

4 a gradient $= \dfrac{5-2}{1-(-2)} = \dfrac{3}{3} = 1$

$\therefore$ the line has equation $y - 5 = 1(x-1)$

i.e., $y = -1 + 5$

i.e., $y = x + 4$

b We need to solve simultaneously

$y = 3 - x$ and $y = x + 4$.

The solution is: $x = -0.5$ and $y = 3.5$

So, the point of intersection is $(-0.5, 3.5)$.

5 a By Pythagoras' Theorem

$AC^2 = AB^2 + BC^2$

$\therefore AC^2 = 20^2 + 20^2 = 800$

$\therefore AC = \sqrt{800}$

$\therefore AC \approx 28.3$ cm

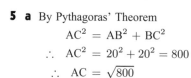

b $CM^2 = AC^2 + AM^2$

$\therefore CM^2 = 800 + 10^2$

$\therefore CM^2 = 900$

$\therefore CM = 30$ cm

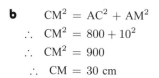

c Let N be the midpoint of CR

$\sin \alpha = \dfrac{CN}{CM} = \dfrac{10}{30}$

$\alpha \approx 19.47^o$ and so $2\alpha \approx 38.9^o$

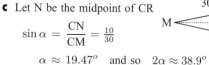

6 $u_2 - u_1 = u_3 - u_2 = -7$ and so the series is arithmetic with common difference -7.

a Let n be the number in the series then $u_n = -48$

But $u_n = u_1 + (n-1)d$

$\therefore -48 = 85 - 7(n-1)$

$\therefore 7(n-1) = 133$

$\therefore n - 1 = 19$

$\therefore n = 20$

So, the number of terms in the series is 20.

b Using $S_n = \dfrac{n}{2}(u_1 + u_n)$

$S_{20} = \dfrac{20}{2} \times (85 + -48)$

$= 10 \times 37$

$= 370$

7 a The number of green beads is $\frac{1}{5}$ of $40 = 8$.

There are 8 green beads in the bag and 32 yellow beads.

b P(Y and Y) $= \frac{32}{40} \times \frac{31}{39}$

$= \frac{124}{195}$

c We need to find x such that $\dfrac{8+x}{40+x} = \dfrac{1}{2}$

$\therefore 16 + 2x = 40 + x$

$\therefore x = 24$

So, we need to add 24 green beads.

8 a The factors of f are $(x+1)$ and $(x-3)$

Now $(x+1)(x-3) = x^2 - 2x - 3$

and so $a = -2$, $b = -3$

b $f(x) = x^2 - 2x - 3$, $\therefore f'(x) = 2x - 2$

c Minimum occurs when $f'(x) = 0$,

i.e., when $2x - 2 = 0$ and so $x = 1$.

When $x = 1$, $y = 1 - 2 - 3 = -4$

The point is $(1, -4)$.

9 a $x > 9$

b In order they are:

$\underbrace{0\ 0\ 1\ 2\ 2\ 2}_{6}\ \overset{\uparrow}{3}\ \underbrace{4\ 4\ 4\ 4\ 4\ 4}_{6}$ $\therefore y = 6$

median

c Mean mark is 1 $\therefore \dfrac{\sum fx}{\sum f} = 1$

$\therefore \dfrac{0 + 4 + 6 + 6 + 4}{z + 4 + 3 + 2 + 1} = 1$

i.e., $\dfrac{20}{z + 10} = 1$

i.e., $z = 10$

10 a $\angle XZY = (180 - 80 - 65)^o = 35^o$

By the Sine Rule $\dfrac{XZ}{\sin 65^o} = \dfrac{5}{\sin 35^o}$

$\therefore XZ = \dfrac{5 \times \sin 65^o}{\sin 35^o}$

$\therefore XZ \approx 7.90$ km

b By cosine rule

$XW^2 = 5^2 + 6^2 - 2 \times 5 \times 6 \times \cos 50^o$

$\therefore XW = \sqrt{5^2 + 6^2 - 60 \times \cos 50^o}$

$\therefore XW = 4.74$ km

11 a Using difference between squares

$x^2 - 49 = (x-7)(x+7)$

b $2 + 7x - 2x^2 = 4(1 + x^2)$

$2 + 7x - 2x^2 = 4 + 4x^2$

$0 = 2 - 7x + 6x^2$

i.e., $6x^2 - 7x + 2 = 0$

$(3x - 2)(2x - 1) = 0$

i.e., $x = \frac{2}{3}$ or $x = \frac{1}{2}$

12 a $r = \dfrac{s_{xy}}{s_x\, s_y} = \dfrac{10.6}{2.58 \times 4.35} \approx 0.944$

b $r = 0.944$ indicates a strong, positive relationship between x and y.

c The regression line is $y - \bar{y} = \dfrac{s_{xy}}{s_x^2}(x - \bar{x})$

$y - 24 = \dfrac{10.6}{2.58^2}(x - 15.5)$

$y \approx 1.592(x - 15.5) + 24$

$y \approx 1.59x - 0.683$

13 a

p	q	$\neg q$	$p \vee \neg q$
T	T	F	T
T	F	T	T
F	T	F	F
F	F	T	T

b

p	q	$\neg q$	$p \wedge q$	$(p \wedge q) \vee \neg q$
T	T	F	T	T
T	F	T	F	T
F	T	F	F	F
F	F	T	F	T

c $p \vee \neg q$ and $(p \wedge q) \vee \neg q$ are logically equivalent since the two final columns are the same.

14 a $y = \dfrac{10}{x} - x^2 = 10x^{-1} - x^2$

$$\frac{dy}{dx} = 10(-1)x^{-2} - 2x$$
$$= -10x^{-2} - 2x$$
$$= \frac{-10}{x^2} - 2x$$

b At $x = -2$, $\dfrac{dy}{dx} = \dfrac{-10}{(-2)^2} - 2(-2) = -2.5 + 4 = 1.5$

and so, the gradient is 1.5

15 a 1 hour $= 60 \times 60 = 3600$ sec.

So in 1 hour, 50×3600 cm of water pass by

$\therefore$ volume in one hour $= \pi r^2 h$
$$= \pi \times 4^2 \times 50 \times 3600 \text{ cm}^3$$
$$= 9\,047\,787 \text{ cm}^3$$
$$= (9\,047\,787 \div 1000) \text{ L}$$
$$\approx 9050 \text{ L}$$

b Volume of swimming pool $= 10 \times 4.50 \times 1.50 \text{ m}^3$
$$= 67.5 \text{ m}^3$$
$$= 67.5 \times 1000 \text{ L}$$
$$= 67\,500 \text{ litres}$$

$\therefore$ time to fill the pool is $\dfrac{67\,500}{9047.78} \approx 7.46$ hours

SOLUTIONS TO SPECIMEN EXAMINATION C

Paper 2

1 a i

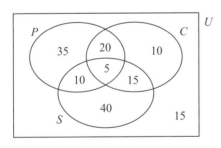

ii $150 - 135 = 15$ are not members of any of the clubs.

iii $P(P) = \dfrac{35 + 20 + 10 + 5}{150}$
$$= \frac{70}{150}$$
$$= \frac{7}{15}$$

iv $P(P \text{ or } C, \text{ but not both}) = \dfrac{35 + 10 + 10 + 15}{150}$
$$= \frac{70}{150}$$
$$= \frac{7}{15}$$

v $P(S \mid C) = \ = \dfrac{5 + 15}{20 + 5 + 15 + 10}$
$$= \frac{20}{50}$$
$$= \frac{2}{5}$$

b i H_0: Belonging to a club is independent of gender.

ii Expected value for females belonging to the sports club is $\dfrac{100 \times 110}{250} = 44$

iii $\chi^2_{\text{calc}} \approx 25.4$ with p-value $= 3.04 \times 10^{-6}$

iv As the p-value < 0.05, we reject the H_0, that belonging to a club is independent of gender. There is strong evidence that this is so.

$$\chi^2 \text{ critical value} < \chi^2 \text{ test statistic}$$

2 a Number affected after 1 day is $10 \times 1.2 = 12$.

b Number affected after 1 week is $10 \times (1.2)^7 \approx 36$

c i $N = 10$ **ii** $a = 1.2$

d

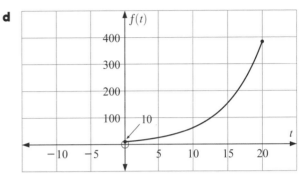

e $f(-10) = 10 \times (1.2)^{-10} = 2$ (nearest integer)
$f(20) = 10 \times (1.2)^{20} = 383$ (nearest integer)
Range is the interval $2 \leqslant y \leqslant 383$.

f The horizontal asymptote is $y = 0$.

3 a The median temperature for Nice $= 24°C$.

b The lower quartile for Nice $= 23.5°C$

c Range for Nice $= 26 - 21 = 5°C$
Interquartile range $= 25 - 23.5 = 1.5°C$

d On the whole Nice is hotter as the median is higher than for that of Geneva.

e The middle half of the days have temperatures more spread out in Geneva.

f i There are 30 days in September.
There are 25% of $30 = 7$ days above the upper quartile.
Nice maximum = Geneva upper quartile value.
Smallest number of days $= 1$

ii Maximum number of days $= 7$

4 a Amount after 5 years $= 10\,000(1.035)^5$
$$= 11\,876.863......$$
$$\approx 11\,900 \text{ AUD}$$

b To double when $10\,000(1.035)^n = 20\,000$
Using a gdc, $\therefore n = 20.148......$
So, 21 years are needed.

c If the bank pays $r\%$ per annum, we need to solve:
$$\left(1 + \frac{r}{100}\right)^{12} = 2$$
Using a gdc, $r = 5.9463.....$
$$\therefore r \approx 5.95\%$$

d After 6 years Sami will have $5000\left(1 + \frac{3}{100 \times 4}\right)^{6 \times 4}$
$$= 5982.07 \text{ AUD}$$

Interest $= 5982.07 - 5000$
$$= 982 \text{ AUD}$$

e Cost of 5000 EUR is $= 5000 \times 1.35$
$$= 6750 \text{ AUD}$$

Commission of 1.5% added means they need

$6750 \times (1.015) = 6851.25$ AUD

5 a i

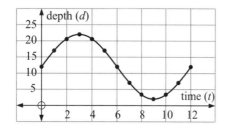

ii (1) Max. $d = 22$ and Min. $d = 2$

Amplitude $= \dfrac{\text{Max.} - \text{Min.}}{2} = \dfrac{22 - 2}{2} = 10$ m

Period $= 12$ hours

(2) If $d = a\sin(bt) + c$ then

$a = 10, \quad \dfrac{360}{b} = 12$ and so $b = 30$

and $c = \dfrac{22 + 2}{2} = 12$

i.e., $d = 10\sin(30t) + 12$.

b i $PQ = (20 - 2x)$ cm **Note:** $0 < x < 10$

ii Area of square base is

$(20 - 2x)^2 = 400 - 80x + 4x^2$ cm^2

Volume of box with height x cm is

$\begin{aligned} V &= x(400 - 80x + 4x^2) \\ &= (4x^3 - 80x^2 + 400x) \text{ cm}^3 \end{aligned}$

iii $\dfrac{dV}{dx} = 12x^2 - 160x + 400$

iv $\dfrac{dV}{dx} = 0$ if $x = \dfrac{10}{3}$ or 10 {from a gdc}

v $x = 10$ is not possible.

Maximum occurs if $x = 3\frac{1}{3}$

as from a gdc the graph is:

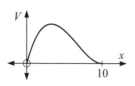

SOLUTIONS TO SPECIMEN EXAMINATION D

Paper 1

1 $\dfrac{\sqrt{2.068}}{1.203 \times 0.0237} = 50.438\,399\,11......$

a $= 50.44$ {to 2 d.p.}

b $= 50$ {to the nearest integer}

c $= 50.4384$ {to 6 s.f.}

d $= 50.4384$ {to nearest 10 thousandth}

e $= 5.043\,839...... \times 10^1$

2 a i If Joshua does not study hard at Mathematics then Joshua does not pass Mathematics.

ii Joshua did not study hard at Mathematics and Joshua passed Mathematics.

b i $q \Rightarrow p$ **ii** the converse

3 a Euro : Baht $= 1 : 46.184$

Now $2400 \times 46.184 = 110\,841.6$ Baht

and she gets 98.5% of these

$= 0.985 \times 110\,841.6$

$= 109\,178.98$

b She has 10% of the Baht left, i.e., $10\,917.90$ Baht.

Since the exchange rate is now $1 : 45.865$ she gets

$10\,917.90 \times \dfrac{1}{45.865} \times 0.985 = 234.47$ Euro

---

4 a

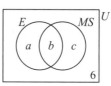

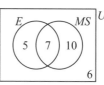

$a + b + c + 6 = 28$

$\therefore \quad a + b + c = 22$

$a + b = 12$

$b + c = 17$

Thus, $c = 10, \ b = 7, \ a = 5$

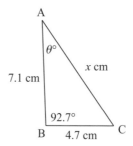

b $P(E \text{ and } MS) = \dfrac{7}{28}$ or $\dfrac{1}{4}$

c $P(E \mid E \text{ or } MS \text{ but not both}) = \dfrac{5}{5 + 10} = \dfrac{1}{3}$

5

a By the Cosine Rule,

$x^2 = 7.1^2 + 4.7^2 - 2 \times 7.1 \times 4.7 \times \cos 92.7^\circ$

$\therefore \quad x^2 \approx 75.64......$

$\therefore \quad x \approx 8.6973......$

So, $AC \approx 8.70$ cm long.

b By the Sine Rule,

$\dfrac{\sin \theta}{4.7} = \dfrac{\sin 92.7^\circ}{8.6}$

$\therefore \quad \sin \theta = \dfrac{4.7 \times \sin 92.7^\circ}{8.6973....} \approx 0.539\,797$

$\therefore \quad \theta \approx 32.7^\circ$

So, $\angle CAB$ is about 32.7°.

6 $P = 360 \times (1.045)^{\frac{t}{2}}$

a When $t = 0$, $P = 360 \times (1.045)^0$

$= 360$ people

b In 2005, $t = 45$

$\therefore \quad P = 360 \times (1.045)^{22.5}$

≈ 969 people

c When $P = 800$, $800 = 360 \times (1.045)^{\frac{t}{2}}$

which has solution $t \approx 36.3$ {gdc}

So will reach 800 in $1960 + 37$ i.e., 1997.

7 a

Number of letters	1	2	3	4	5	6	7
Number of words	3	11	12	11	5	5	4

Others add to 40, so this one is 11.

b

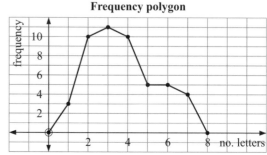

8 a $I = Crn = 2500 \times \frac{3.2}{100} \times 5$
$$= 400 \text{ JPY}$$

b $I = C \times \left(1 + \frac{r}{100}\right)^n - C$
$$= 2500 \times \left(1 + \frac{3.2}{400}\right)^{5 \times 4} - 2500$$
$$= 432 \text{ JPY}$$

9 a **i** domain $= \{-2, -1, 0, 1\}$
ii range $= \{-1.5, 6, 18.5, 36\}$

b $f(x) = ax^2 + bx + c$
$f(0) = 6 \quad \therefore \quad 0 + 0 + c = 6$
$\qquad\qquad$ So, $c = 6$
$f(1) = -1.5 \quad \therefore \quad a + b + c = -1.5$
$\qquad\qquad \therefore \quad a + b + 6 = -1.5$
$\qquad\qquad\qquad \therefore \quad a + b = -7.5 \quad \ldots\ldots \text{ (1)}$
$f(-2) = 36$
$\qquad \therefore \quad a(4) + b(-2) + 6 = 36$
$\qquad\qquad \therefore \quad 4a - 2b = 30$
$\qquad\qquad\qquad \therefore \quad 2a - b = 15 \quad \ldots\ldots \text{ (2)}$

$\qquad\qquad\qquad a + b = -7.5$
$\qquad\qquad\qquad \underline{2a - b = 15}$
$\qquad\qquad\qquad \therefore \quad 3a \qquad = 7.5 \quad$ and so $\quad a = 2.5$

In (1), when $a = 2.5$, $b = -10$.
So, $a = 2.5$, $b = -10$, $c = 6$.

10 a **i** 5 of the 58 are long and light.
$\qquad \therefore \quad$ P(long and light) $= \frac{5}{58}$

ii There are 41 lights of which $21 + 5$ are not medium.
$\qquad \therefore \quad$ P(not medium | light) $= \frac{26}{41}$

b P(both short and heavy) $= \frac{2}{58} \times \frac{1}{57} = \frac{1}{1653}$

11 a Profits are geometric with $u_1 = 50\,000$ and $r = 1.015$
and $u_{10} = u_1 \times r^9$
$\qquad\qquad = 50\,000 \times (1.015)^9$
$\qquad\qquad \approx 57\,169.50 \text{ MAR}$

b Total profit $= u_1 + u_2 + u_3 + \ldots\ldots + u_{10}$
$$= \frac{50\,000(1.015^{10} - 1)}{1.015 - 1}$$
$$\approx 535\,136.08, \quad \text{i.e.,} \quad 535\,000 \text{ MAR}$$

12

x cm

$(x + 3)$ cm

a Length $= (x + 3)$ cm

b Area $=$ length $\times$ breadth
$\qquad \therefore \quad x(x + 3) = 108$

c $\qquad x^2 + 3x - 108 = 0$
$\qquad \therefore \quad (x + 12)(x - 9) = 0 \quad$ and so $\quad x = -12 \text{ or } 9$

d $x > 0$ as lengths are positive $\therefore \quad x = 9$
So rectangle is 12 cm by 9 cm.

13 a Value $= 80\%$ of $\$45\,000$
$\qquad\qquad = 0.8 \times \$45\,000$
$\qquad\qquad = \$36\,000$

b Value at end of year 3 $= \$36\,000 \times (0.88)^2$
$\qquad\qquad\qquad\qquad = \$27\,878.40$

c $\$45\,000 \div 3 = \$15\,000$
We need to find $n + 1$ when
$36\,000 \times (0.88)^n = 15\,000$
Solving gives $n \approx 6.85 \quad \{\text{gdc}\}$
$\therefore \quad$ number of years is $\quad 7 + 1 = 8$

14 a $\qquad\qquad y = (x - 2)^2 - 5$
$\qquad \therefore \quad y = x^2 - 4x + 4 - 5$
$\qquad \therefore \quad y = x^2 - 4x - 1$
So, $\frac{dy}{dx} = 2x - 4$

b at $(3, -4)$, $x = 3 \quad \therefore \quad \frac{dy}{dx} = 2 \times 3 - 4 = 2$
So, gradient of tangent is 2.

c The equation of the tangent is $\qquad y - -4 = 2(x - 3)$
$\qquad\qquad\qquad\qquad \text{i.e.,} \quad y + 4 = 2x - 6$
$\qquad\qquad\qquad\qquad \text{i.e.,} \quad y = 2x - 10$

15 a The sum of the interior angles $= 3 \times 180^o = 540^o$
So, each interior angle is $\frac{540^o}{5} = 108^o$

b Area of $\triangle \text{EAB} = \frac{1}{2} \times 15 \times 15 \times \sin 108^o$
$\qquad\qquad\qquad \approx 106.99 \text{ cm}^2$
$\therefore \quad$ total area $= (2 \times 106.99 + 173.12) \text{ cm}^2$
$\qquad\qquad\qquad \approx 387.11 \text{ cm}^2$

SOLUTIONS TO SPECIMEN EXAMINATION D

Paper 2

1 a **i** Number of employees $= 25 \times 1.04 = 26$
ii Number of employees $= 25 \times (1.04)^{15} = 45$

b At the start of 1996, the power is 6
$\qquad \therefore \quad$ number $= 25 \times (1.04)^6$
$\qquad\qquad\qquad = 31.63 \ldots\ldots \text{ i.e.,} \quad 32$

c $a = (1.045)^{15} \approx 1.935$
For $b\%$, $\left(1 + \frac{b}{100}\right)^{10} = 1.877$
which has solution $b = 6.5 \quad \{\text{gdc}\}$

d Estimate of 2005 salary $= 18\,000 \times 2.232 = 40\,176 \text{ NZD}$

e We need to solve for n when
$18\,000 \times (1.045)^n = 30\,000$
$\qquad$ solution is $\quad n \approx 11.6$
So, this occurs in the 12th year.

2 a **i**
$\qquad 6 \mid 6\,7\,7\,8 \qquad\qquad\qquad n = 15$
$\qquad 7 \mid 0\,1\,3\,3\,3\,5\,8\,9$
$\qquad 8 \mid 3\,4\,7 \qquad\qquad 6 \mid 7 \quad$ means $\quad 67$

ii a median $=$ 8th score $= 73$

$\quad$ **b** $Q_1 = $ 4th score $= 68$
$\qquad Q_3 = $ 12th score $= 79$
$\qquad \therefore \quad \text{IQR} = Q_3 - Q_1 = 11$

iii mean $= \dfrac{\text{sum of scores}}{15} = \dfrac{1114}{15} \approx 74.27$

iv

Score	60 - 69	70 - 79	80 - 89
Freq.	4	8	3

v Midpoints are $64.5, 74.5, 84.5$
$\therefore \quad$ estimate of mean
$$= \frac{4 \times 64.5 + 8 \times 74.5 + 3 \times 84.5}{15}$$
$$= \frac{1107.5}{15}$$
$$= 73.83$$

vi % error $= \dfrac{74.27 - 73.83}{74.27} \times 100\% \approx 0.592\%$

b i

Hour	Freq.	Cum. freq.
7.00 am -	14	14
8.00 am -	48	62
9.00 am -	35	97
10.00 am -	24	121
11.00 am -	22	143

ii

Traffic in Holden Street

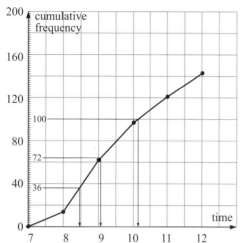

iii a median $= \left(\dfrac{143+1}{2}\right)$th score

$= $ 72nd score

$\approx$ 9.15 am

b 100th vehicle at about 10:10 am

c CF for 9:30 is 80

CF for 11:30 is 132

$\therefore$ number of cars $\approx 132 - 80$

≈ 52

d 25th percentile $= \dfrac{143+1}{4} = $ 36th score

which is $\approx$ 8:30 am

3 a In $\triangle$DGE,

$\cos 6.2^o = \dfrac{x}{57}$

$\therefore 57 \times \cos 6.2^o = x$

$\therefore x \approx 56.67$

So, EF $= 200 - x$

$= 200 - 56.67$ $(= 143.33)$

≈ 143 m

i.e., the poles are 143 m apart.

b In $\triangle$DHF,

$\cos 6.2^o = \dfrac{200}{y}$

$\therefore y = \dfrac{200}{\cos 6.2^o} \approx 201.18$

$\therefore$ GH $\approx 201.18 - 57$

≈ 144.18

≈ 144 m

c First we need to find FH.

$\tan 6.2^o = \dfrac{h}{200}$

$\therefore h = 200 \times \tan 6.2^o$

$\therefore h \approx 21.73$

$\tan \theta = \dfrac{21.73}{143.33}$

$\therefore \theta \approx 8.62^o$

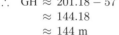

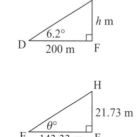

d $\sin 6.2^o = \dfrac{h}{57}$

$\therefore h = 57 \times \sin 6.2^o \approx 6.16$ m

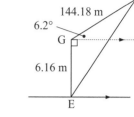

e

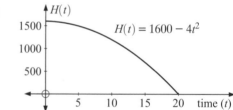

$\angle$EGH $= 90^o + 6.2^o$

$= 96.2^o$

Area $= \frac{1}{2} \times 6.16 \times 144.18 \times \sin 96.2^o$

≈ 441 m^2

4 a i

$(p \wedge q) \Rightarrow r$	$(\neg p \vee \neg q)$	$(\neg p \vee \neg q) \Rightarrow \neg r$
T	F	T
F	F	T
T	T	F
T	T	T
T	T	F
T	T	T
T	T	F
T	T	T

ii none of these

iii If the weather is not fine or the bus is not late then I will not walk to school.

iv If the bus is not late then I will walk to school.

b i P(fine then fine)

$= 0.7 \times 0.7$

$= 0.49$

ii P(fine and not late)   So, P(fine and not late **twice**)

$= 0.7 \times 0.6$ $= 0.42 \times 0.42$

$= 0.42$ ≈ 0.176

5 a

b i When $H(t) = 0$, $1600 - 4t^2 = 0$

$\therefore 4t^2 = 1600$

$\therefore t^2 = 400$

$\therefore t = 20$ $\{t \geqslant 0\}$

$\therefore$ is in the air for 20 seconds.

ii When $t = 0$, $H(0) = 1600$ m

$\therefore$ vertical height $= 1600$ m

iii Average speed $= \dfrac{\text{total distance fallen}}{\text{total time taken}}$

$= \dfrac{1600 \text{ m}}{20 \text{ sec}}$

$= 80$ ms^{-1}

c i $H(10) = 1600 - 4 \times 10^2$

$= 1200$ m

ii $H(10 + h) = 1600 - 4(10 + h)^2$

$= 1600 - 4(100 + 20h + h^2)$

$= 1600 - 400 - 80h - 4h^2$

$= 1200 - 80h - 4h^2$

iii $\dfrac{H(10 + h) - H(10)}{h}$

$= \dfrac{1200 - 80h - 4h^2 - 1200}{h}$

$$= \frac{-80h - 4h^2}{h}$$

$$= \frac{-80h}{h} - \frac{4h^2}{h}$$

$$= -80 - 4h$$

d i $H'(t) = 0 - 8t = -8t$

  ii As t is > 0, $-8t$ is negative.

∴ $H'(t)$ is negative for all $t > 0$

∴ H is a decreasing function.

  iii $H'(5) = -8 \times 5 = -40$

$H'(10) = -8 \times 10 = -80$

  iv The gradient at $t = 10$ is -80 compared with -40 at $t = 5$

∴ is steeper as t increases.

(This shows that the speed increases as t increases.)

SOLUTIONS TO SPECIMEN EXAMINATION E

Paper 1

1 a $x^2yz^3 = 5^2 \times 12 \times 100^3$

$= 300\,000\,000$

  b $300\,000\,000 = 3 \times 10^8$

  c $\sqrt{x^2yz^3} = \sqrt{300\,000\,000}$

$\approx 17\,320.50..... \approx 17\,300$ {to 3 s.f.}

  d $17\,000$ {to 2 s.f.}

2 a $38, 35, 32, 32, 30, 28, 27, 24, 19, 18$

$n = 10$

  b median $= \dfrac{\text{5th} + \text{6th}}{2} = \dfrac{30 + 28}{2} = 29$

  c P(within 5 of median)

$= $ P(X is from 24 to 34 inclusive)

$= \frac{6}{10}$

$= \frac{3}{5}$ or 0.6

  d P(first student is above 30) $= \frac{4}{10}$

P(2nd student is above 30) $= \frac{3}{9}$

∴ P(both above 30) $= \frac{4}{10} \times \frac{3}{9} = \frac{2}{15}$

3 a {equilateral triangles} is a subset

So is {equilateral Δs, isosceles Δs}, etc.

  b A possible element of B' is 'all pentagons'.

  c

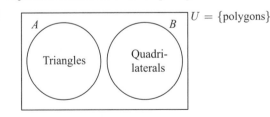

$U = $ {polygons}

  d $n(A \cap B) = 0$

4 a

$(q \wedge \neg p)$	$(\neg q \vee p)$	$(q \wedge \neg p) \Rightarrow (\neg q \vee p)$
F	T	T
F	T	T
T	F	F
F	T	T

  b As all entries are not F, the final statement is not a contradiction.

  c The contrapositive of the statement is

$\neg(\neg q \vee p) \Rightarrow \neg(q \wedge \neg p)$

5 a $m^2 - 6m - 27 = (m+3)(m-9)$

  b $f(x) = 5x^2 + 53x - 84 = (5x - 7)(x + 12)$

So, $f(x) = 0$ when $x = \frac{7}{5}$ or -12

∴ zeros are $\frac{7}{5}$ and -12.

  c $3v^2 - 14v + 8 = 0$

∴ $(3v - 2)(v - 4) = 0$ and so $v = \frac{2}{3}$ or 4

6 a $f(a) = 3.5a + 1$ $B = \{1, 2, 3, 4, 5, 6, 7, 8\}$

$f(-1) = -2.5$

$f(0) = 1$

$f(1) = 4.5$

$f(2) = 8$

$f(3) = 11.5$

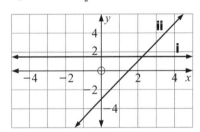

  b $f(a) = a^2 - 1$

$f(-1) = 0$

$f(0) = -1$

$f(1) = 0$

$f(2) = 3$

$f(3) = 8$

7 a i $y = \frac{3}{2}$ is a horizontal line through $(0, \frac{3}{2})$.

  ii $2x - y = 3$

when $x = 0$, $y = -3$

when $y = 0$, $x = \frac{3}{2}$

  b When $y = \frac{3}{2}$, $2x - \frac{3}{2} - 3 = 0$

∴ $2x = \frac{9}{2}$

∴ $x = \frac{9}{4}$

∴ $x = 2\frac{1}{4}$

  c The distance is $1\frac{1}{2}$ units.

8 a $\frac{32}{16} = 2$, $\frac{64}{32} = 2$, etc. So, $r = 2$

  b $u_1 = \frac{1}{64}$ and $u_n = 256$

But $u_n = u_1 \times r^{n-1}$

∴ $256 = \frac{1}{64} \times 2^{n-1}$

∴ $16\,384 = 2^{n-1}$

and so $n = 15$ {using a gdc}

i.e., there are 15 terms in the sequence.

  c $S_n = \dfrac{u_1(r^n - 1)}{r - 1}$

$= \dfrac{\frac{1}{64}(2^{15} - 1)}{2 - 1}$

$= \frac{1}{64}(2^{15} - 1)$

$= \dfrac{32\,767}{64}$ {exact answer}

≈ 512 {3 s.f.}

9 a $2 + 3 + 5 + 4 + 3 + 2 = 19$

    i.e., 19 seedlings

b As $n = 19$, $\frac{n+1}{4} = 5$, $\frac{n+1}{2} = 10$

   i $Q_1 = $ 5th score $= 78$ cm

   ii median $= $ 10th score $= 88$ cm

   iii $Q_3 = $ 15th score $= 103$ cm

c

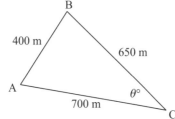

10 $C(x) = 46\,000 + 11.50x$ dollars, $R(x) = 30x$ dollars

  a **i** When $x = 2000$,

$$C(2000) = 46\,000 + 11.5 \times 2000$$
$$= \$69\,000$$
$$\text{Profit} = R - C$$
$$= 30 \times 2000 - 69\,000$$
$$= -\$9000$$

    i.e., a loss of $9000

   ii When $x = 5000$,

$$C(5000) = 46\,000 + 11.5 \times 5000$$
$$= \$103\,500$$
$$\text{Profit} = R - C$$
$$= 30 \times 5000 - 103\,500$$
$$= \$46\,500$$

  b Break even occurs when $C(x) = R(x)$

$$\text{i.e.,} \quad 30x = 46\,000 + 11.5x$$

    which has solution $x \approx 2486.486\,.....$

    i.e., 'break even' occurs when 2490 are sold.

11

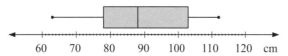

  a By the Cosine Rule,

$$\cos\theta = \frac{700^2 + 650^2 - 400^2}{2 \times 700 \times 650}$$

$$\therefore \quad \cos\theta \approx 0.826\,923\,......$$
$$\therefore \quad \theta \approx 34.216\,......$$

    i.e., $\angle BCA \approx 34.2^\circ$

  b Area $= \frac{1}{2} \times 700 \times 650 \times \sin\theta$

$$\approx 127\,927$$
$$\approx 128\,000 \text{ m}^2$$

12 a **i** $I = 3500 \times \frac{5.2}{100} \times 7$

$$= 1274 \text{ AUD}$$
$$\therefore \quad \text{investment} = 3500 + 1740$$
$$= 4774 \text{ AUD}$$

   ii $A = 3500 \times \left(1 + \frac{5.2}{1200}\right)^{7 \times 12}$

$$\approx 5032.80 \text{ AUD}$$

  b Difference in interest paid $= (5032.80 - 4774)$ AUD

$$= 258.80 \text{ AUD}$$

---

13 a x-intercepts are -3 and 4

  b $\frac{-3+4}{2} = \frac{1}{2}$ $\therefore$ axis is $x = \frac{1}{2}$

  c The function has equation $y = a(x+3)(x-4)$, $a \neq 0$

    But when $x = 0$, $y = -24$

$$\therefore \quad -24 = a(3)(-4) \quad \text{and so} \quad a = 2$$
$$\therefore \quad \text{function is} \quad y = 2(x+3)(x-4)$$

  d When $x = \frac{1}{2}$, $y = 2\left(\frac{7}{2}\right)\left(-\frac{7}{2}\right) = -\frac{49}{2}$

$$\therefore \quad \text{min. value is} \quad -24.5, \quad \text{when} \quad x = \frac{1}{2}$$

14 a $Q = -0.543P + 74.3$ with $r = -0.642$

  b The scatterplot is:

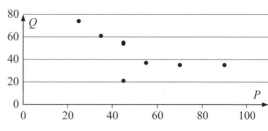

$$Q = -0.614P + 82.2 \quad \text{with} \quad r = -0.897$$

  c The gradient is steeper (negative).

    As r is closer to -1, the relationship is much stronger.

15 a **i** $f'(x) > 0$ when the function is increasing.

    This is when $x < b$ and when $x > c$.

   ii $f'(x) < 0$ when the function is decreasing.

    This is when $b < x < c$.

  b $f'(x) = 0$ where tangents are horizontal. This is at local max. and min. points, i.e., when $x = b$ or c.

SOLUTIONS TO SPECIMEN EXAMINATION E

Paper 2

1 a **i** Total rent $= 700 \times 12 \times 3$

$$= 25\,200 \text{ USD}$$

   ii Rent increase at end of year 1 $= 25\,200 \times 0.028$

$$= 705.60 \text{ USD}$$

   iii Each person pays (in year 3)

$$700 \times 12 \times 1.028 \times 1.033 = 8920.16 \text{ USD}$$

  b **i** $u_1 = 800$, $d = 40$

$$u_1 + 4d = 800 + 160 = 960, \quad \text{i.e., 960 employees}$$

   ii $u_1 - 5d = 800 - 200 = 600$, i.e., 600 employees

   iii When the number of employees is 1000, it is one year after 2009, i.e., 2010.

    So, for > 1000 it would be year 2011.

2 a **i** Length $= (x + 5)$ cm

   ii Area $=$ length $\times$ width

$$\therefore \quad A = (x+5)x$$
$$\text{i.e.,} \quad A = x^2 + 5x \text{ cm}^2$$

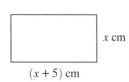

   iii If area is 204 cm^2

$$\text{then} \quad x^2 + 5x = 204$$
$$\therefore \quad x^2 + 5x - 204 = 0$$

    This has solutions $x = 12$ or -17.

   iv However, lengths are non-negative $\therefore$ $x = 12$.

    So, the length is 17 cm, width is 12 cm.

b i The volume of a sphere $= \frac{4}{3}\pi r^3$

$$\therefore \quad \frac{1}{2}\left(\frac{4}{3}\pi r^3\right) = 7068 \text{ m}^3$$
$$\therefore \quad \frac{2}{3}\pi r^3 = 7068$$
$$\therefore \quad r^3 = \frac{7068 \times 3}{2 \times \pi}$$
$$\therefore \quad r = 15.0 \text{ m} \quad \{\text{using a gdc}\}$$

ii Surface area of a sphere $= 4\pi r^2$

$$\therefore \quad \text{surface area of hemisphere} = 2\pi r^2$$
$$= 2 \times \pi \times (15.0)^2$$
$$= 1413.72$$
$$\approx 1410 \text{ m}^2$$

iii There are 142 lots of 10 m² required.

$$\therefore \quad \text{total cost} = 142 \times \$23.45 = \$3329.90$$

c i
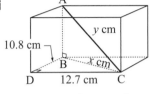

In ΔBCD, $\quad x^2 = 10.8^2 + 12.7^2$

In ΔABC, $\quad y^2 = x^2 + 6.45^2$

So, $\quad y^2 = 10.8^2 + 12.7^2 + 6.45^2$

$$\therefore \quad y = \sqrt{10.8^2 + 12.7^2 + 6.45^2}$$
$$\approx 17.8754......$$

$\therefore$ longest piece of string is 17.9 cm

ii $\tan\theta = \dfrac{6.45}{BC}$

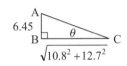

$$\therefore \quad \theta = \tan^{-1}\left(\frac{6.45}{\sqrt{10.8^2 + 12.7^2}}\right)$$
$$\therefore \quad \theta = 21.1°$$

3 a i
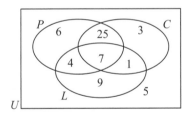

$n(U) = 60$

$a = 6 \quad \{6 \text{ contain peppermints only}\}$

$7 + e = 8 \quad \{8 \text{ contain some of each of } L \text{ and } C\}$

$\therefore \quad e = 1$

Likewise $d = 4$

$\{11 \text{ contain some of each of } P \text{ and } L\}$

So, $b + 6 + 4 + 7 = 42 \quad \therefore \quad b = 25$

$c + 25 + 7 + 1 = 36 \quad \therefore \quad c = 3$

$f + 4 + 7 + 1 = 21 \quad \therefore \quad f = 9$

ii a $n(P \cap C) = 25 + 7 = 32$

b $n(P \cup C') = 60 - 1 - 3 = 56$

c $n\left((L \cap P)' \cap (C \cup L)\right) = 9 + 1 + 3 + 25$
$$= 38$$

b i Total number $= 32 + 42 + 36$
$$= 110$$

ii a P(gold earrings) $= \frac{10}{110} = \frac{1}{11}$

b P(not a silver bracelet)
$$= \frac{110-12}{110} = \frac{98}{110} = \frac{49}{55}$$

(3) P(both silver | both necklaces)
$$= \frac{8}{42} \times \frac{7}{41}$$
$$= \frac{4}{123}$$

4 a i
$$f(-1) = a$$
$$\therefore \quad 2(-1)^2 - 6(-1) - 20 = a$$
$$\therefore \quad 2 + 6 - 20 = a$$
$$\therefore \quad a = -12$$

and $\quad f(2) = b$
$$\therefore \quad b = 2(2)^2 - 6(2) - 20$$
$$\therefore \quad b = 8 - 12 - 20$$
$$\therefore \quad b = -24$$

ii, iii
$$f(-3) = 2(-3)^2 - 6(-3) - 20$$
$$= 18 + 18 - 20$$
$$= 16$$

and $\quad f(7) = 2(7)^2 - 6(7) - 20$
$$= 98 - 42 - 20$$
$$= 36$$

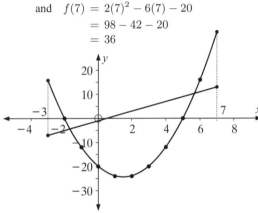

iv They meet where
$$2x^2 - 6x - 20 = 2x - 1$$
i.e., $\quad 2x^2 - 8x - 19 = 0$
$$\therefore \quad x \approx -1.67 \quad \text{or} \quad 5.67 \quad \{\text{gdc}\}$$

Points of intersection are
$$(-1.67, -4.35) \quad \text{and} \quad (5.67, 10.4).$$

b $f(x) = \frac{5}{3}x^3 + 3x^2 - 8x + 2, \quad 0 \leqslant x \leqslant 3$

i $f'(x) = 5x^2 + 6x - 8$

ii $f''(x) = 10x + 6$

iii $f'(x) = 0$ when $5x^2 + 6x - 8 = 0$
$$\therefore \quad (5x - 4)(x + 2) = 0$$
$$\therefore \quad x = \frac{4}{5} \text{ or } -2$$
$$\{\text{or use gdc}\}$$

iv $f(0.8) = -1.63$ and $f(-2) = 16.67$

But -2 is outside of the domain $0 \leqslant x \leqslant 3$.

Sketch of $f(x)$ from gdc is:

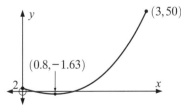

$\therefore \quad f(x)$ has largest value 50 when $x = 3$
and smallest value -1.63 when $x = 0.8$

5 a i

height	frequency	midpoint
0 - 4	0	2
5 - 9	0	7
10 - 14	2	12
15 - 19	8	17
20 - 24	20	22
25 - 29	30	27
30 - 34	24	32
35 - 39	16	37
Total	100	

ii mean $= 27.7$,   standard deviation ≈ 6.25

iii % difference in means $= \dfrac{27.7 - 23}{27.7} \times 100\%$

$$\approx 17.0\%$$

iv Height of plants $= 27.7 + 0.368 \times 6.25$

$$\approx 30 \text{ cm}$$

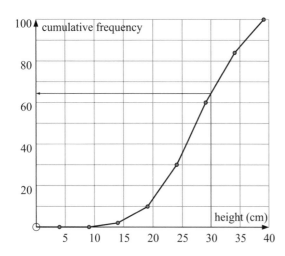

64 plants have height $\leqslant 30$ cm

$\therefore$ 36 have height > 30 cm

b i

	< 25 cm	$\geqslant$ 25 cm	
A	52	48	100
B	30	70	100
	82	118	200

ii

	< 25 cm	$\geqslant$ 25 cm	
A	41	59	e.g., $\dfrac{100 \times 118}{200}$
B	41	59	

iii $\chi^2_{\text{calc}} \approx 10.004$

iv

	< $m + 0.368s$	$\geqslant m + 0.368s$	
A	78	22	100
B	60	40	100
	138	62	200

v $\chi^2_{\text{calc}} \approx 7.57$, p-value $\approx 0.005\,92$

vi Both results suggest that the hypothesis should not be accepted.

There does appear to be a significant difference between the results for the two fields.

The calculated χ^2 values fall inside the 5% critical level.

Note: This is a guide for **students only** and not necessarily official IB policy.

PAPER 1

Paper 1 consists of **15 short questions** each worth **6 marks** for a total of **90 marks**.

Full marks are awarded for a correct answer, regardless of working. ('C' marks)

If an answer is incorrect, marks can be awarded for appropriate working **seen** ('M' marks) and for partially correct answers **seen** in the working ('A' marks).

PAPER 2

Paper 2 consists of **long questions** varying from **10 to 25 marks** to total **90 marks**.

The method/working is **expected** to be shown in this paper. Correct answers, on their own, may only be awarded the A marks, or just some of the A marks.

Note: Graphic Display Calculators (GDC's) are **expected to be used**.

The allocation of marks in the mark scheme allows for this through 'G' marks. G marks apply in situations where a candidate has not shown their working.

In some questions, there is an expectation that the GDC will be used exclusively. In these cases the mark scheme allocates G marks only. The syllabus document provides information regarding the topic areas where GDC use is expected.

The phrase "use your graphics calculator" appears in some questions in this guide. It will appear in IB Mathematical Studies examination papers in the future, but **not** for the 2006 examinations.

The general rule for students to follow is to **always** show their working where possible.

WORKING

The following presentations, seen on a student's script, would normally be awarded the mark(s) for method ('M' marks) allocated in the mark scheme.

- **A substituted formula**

  Example:

  Find the amount of money in an account which pays nominal interest of 6.8%, compounding monthly, if $3000 was placed in this account 4 years ago.

  Solution:

  $$F_v = 3000 \left(1 + \frac{6.8}{1200}\right)^{12 \times 4} \qquad \text{M1A1A1}$$

  $$\{\text{from gdc}\} = \$3934.74 \qquad \text{A1 (G3)}$$

  (M1 for substituted formula, A1 for correct monthly rate', A1 for correct periods, A1 for correct answer. G3 for correct answer with no working seen.)

- **A sketch taken from the GDC screen**

  Example:

  Find the x-intercepts for the graph of $y = 3x^2 - 9x + 4$.

  Solution:

  We sketch the graph of the function, remembering to include axes labels and an indication of scale.

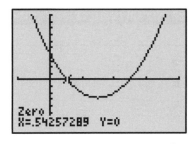

x-intercepts are (0.543, 0) and (2.46, 0)   {from GDC}

- **A mathematical statement which indicates the candidate understands the nature of the solution**

  Example:

  Given $f'(x) = 6x - 9$, find the minimum value of the function $f(x) = 3x^2 - 9x + 4$.

  Solution:

  $$6x - 9 = 0 \qquad\qquad \text{M1}$$

  $$\therefore \quad x = \frac{9}{6} \quad \left(\frac{3}{2} \text{ or } 1.5\right) \qquad \text{A1 (G1)}$$

  (M1 for setting derivative to zero.)

  Note: Answer without working is awarded G1.

  $$f(1.5) = 3(1.5)^2 - 9(1.5) + 4 \quad \text{M1}$$

  $$\text{Minimum value is} = -2.75 \qquad\qquad \text{A1ft (G2)}$$

  (M1 is for substituting their value into $f(x)$.)

  Note: Answer without working is awarded full marks, G2.

- **Follow through marks**

  Follow through marks (ft) are awarded in situations where an incorrect answer from the previous part is carried through to the subsequent part.

  If no additional errors are made, the student receives full marks for the subsequent part, provided working is shown.

  Possible follow through marks are indicated on the mark scheme.

- **Some Examination Reminders (GDC)**

  ▶ Unless told otherwise in the question, all final answers should be given correct to 3 s.f.

  ▶ For questions involving money, final answers can be given correct to 3 s.f. or nearest whole value or to 2 d.p.

  ▶ Your GDC's display can be set for 3 s.f. or various decimal places. It can also be set for scientific notation (standard form).

  ▶ Ensure your GDC is set to 'deg' i.e., degrees for problems involving trigonometry. This will need to be done if your calculator is reset. For TI calculators, 'diagnostic' also needs to be set to 'on' if the calculator is reset.

  ▶ Ensure your GDC is set to 'trig' for graphs of periodic functions (sine and cosine).

  ▶ Use sensible view windows for sketches and general problem solving with graphs. Many students begin with "std" with a domain and range of -10 to $+10$. Negative values for the domain are often not appropriate for problems simulating real situations.

  ▶ Create your own list of the many things you need to remember about using your graphic display calculator.

  ▶ Remember to **show** your **working**.

1	**a** $5, -5, \sqrt{16}$	A2	C2
	b $\frac{1}{3}, 5, -5, \sqrt{16}, 0.\dot{6}$	A2	C2
	c $5, \sqrt{16}$	A2	C2
			[6 marks]

2	**a** $f: \ x \mapsto 2x^2 + x - 3$		
		A2	C2
	b **i** domain: $-2 \leqslant x \leqslant 2, \ x \in \mathbb{Z}$	A1ftA1ft	C2
	ii range: $-2, -3, 0, 3, 7$	A1ftA1ft	C2
			[6 marks]

3	**a** Surface area $= 9.85 \times 5.90$	M1	
	$= 58.115 \text{ m}^2 \quad (= 58.1 \text{ m}^2)$	A1	C2
	b $10 \times 6 = 60$	A1	
	$\dfrac{60 - 58.115}{58.115} \times 100$	M1A1ft	
	$= 3.24\% \quad (\text{allow } 3.27)$	A1ft	C4
			[6 marks]

4	**a** $8 + 13 + 4 + x = 30$		
	5 students like both plain and chocolate milk.	A1	C1
	b	A1A1 A1ft	C3
	c P(likes only one type of milk) $= \frac{21}{30} = \frac{7}{10} \quad (= 0.7)$	A1A1ft	C2
			[6 marks]

5	**a** P(ticket costs more than \$60) $= \frac{23}{50} \quad (= 0.46)$	A1	C1
	b Mean $=$ \$60.70	A1	
	Standard deviation $=$ \$25.35	A1	C2
	c $\$60.70 + 0.722 \times 25.35 = \$79.00$	A1ft	
	% of tickets less than \$79 $= \frac{38}{50} \times 100 = 76\%$	M1A1ft	C3
			[6 marks]

6	**a** 2000×0.75	M1	
	$= 1500 \text{ GBP}$	A1	C2
	b Remaining $= 1500 - 1200$	M1	
	$= 300 \text{ GBP}$	A1ft	C2
	c $300 \times \dfrac{1}{0.80}$	M1	
	$= 375 \text{ USD}$	A1ft	C2
			[6 marks]

7	**a** $u_1 r^6 = 320, \quad u_1 r^{10} = 5120$	M1	
	$\quad$ Divide $\quad r^4 = 16$		
	$\quad\quad\quad r = 2$	A1	**C2**
	b $u_1 2^6 = 320$	M1	
	$\quad u_1 = 5$	A1ft	**C2**
	c $u_{20} = u_1 r^{19}$	M1	
	$\quad\quad = 2\,621\,440$	A1ft	**C2**
			[6 marks]
8	**a** $F_v = C\left(1 + \frac{r}{100}\right)^n$		
	$\quad = 20\,000\left(1 + \frac{6.8}{1200}\right)^{48}$	M1A1	
	$\quad = \$26\,231.59$	A1	**C3**
	b $20\,000(1.032)^4 = \$22\,685.52$	M1A1	**C2**
	c $26\,231.59 - 22\,685.52 = \$3546.07$	A1ft	**C1**
			[6 marks]
9	**a** $Q_3 = 77, \quad Q_1 = 65$	A1A1	**C2**
	b IQR $= 77 - 65 = 12$	A1ft	**C1**
	c minimum $= 45$	A1	
	$\quad 65 - 1.5(12) = 47$	M1	
	$\quad$ minimum < 47 and hence an outlier	A1ft	**C3**
			[6 marks]
10	**a** Profit $= 12.50(100) - (9.5(100) + 45)$	M1	
	$\quad\quad = \$255$	A1	**C2**
	b Breakeven when $12.5x = 9.5x + 45$	M1	
	$\quad\quad 3x = 45 \quad$ 15 boxes	A1	**C2**
	c $12.50x - (9.5x + 45) > 1000$	M1	
	$\quad\quad 3x - 45 > 1000$		
	$\quad\quad\quad x > 348.3 \quad$ 349 boxes	A1	**C2**
			[6 marks]

11 a

$p \veebar q$	$\neg(p \wedge q) \vee q$	$(p \veebar q) \Rightarrow \neg(p \wedge q) \vee q$		
F	T	T	A1	
T	T	T	A1	
T	T	T	A1	
F	T	T	A1	**C4**

b If Bozo does not have a red nose then Bozo is not a clown. $\quad$ A1A1 $\quad$ **C2**

$\quad$ **[6 marks]**

12	**a** $\quad \dfrac{3 - (-3)}{1 - (-2)} = 2$	A1	
	$\quad$ Equation AB is $\quad 2x - y = 2(1) - (3)$	M1	
	$\quad\quad\quad 2x - y + 1 = 0$	A1ft	**C3**
	b $\quad M = \left(-\frac{1}{2}, 0\right)$	A1	
	$\quad\quad m = -\frac{1}{2}$	A1ft	
	$\quad$ Equation of perpendicular bisector of AB is		
	$\quad x + 2y = \left(-\frac{1}{2}\right) + 2(0)$		
	$\quad x + 2y = -\frac{1}{2} \quad$ or $\quad 2x + 4y = -1$	A1ft	**C3**
			[6 marks]

13	**a** $f'(x) = 2ax + b$	A1	**C1**
	b $2a = 5$, $a = 2.5$ $b = -10$	A1ftA1ft	**C2**
	c $\qquad\qquad x = \dfrac{10}{5} = 2$	A1ft	
	$\quad$ Substitute into $f(x)$ $\quad -4 = 2.5(2)^2 - 10(2) + d$	M1	
	$\qquad\qquad\qquad d = 6$	A1ft	**C3**
			[6 marks]

14			
	a Equilateral triangle : diameter $= 45$ cm	A1	**C1**
	b		
	$\tan 60 = \dfrac{x}{22.5}$ $\quad x = 39.0$	M1A1ft	
	height of cone is 39 cm		
	$\quad$ Volume of cone $= \frac{1}{3}\pi r^2 h$		
	$\qquad\qquad\qquad = \frac{1}{3}\pi \times 22.5^2 \times 39$	M1A1ft	
	$\qquad\qquad\qquad = 20\,700$ cm^2 $\quad$ (3 s.f.)	A1ft	**C5**
			[6 marks]

15	**a** **i** amplitude $= 2$	A1	
	$\quad$ **ii** period $= 120°$	A1	**C2**
	b $a = 2$, $b = \dfrac{360}{120} = 3$, $c = 3$	A1A2A1	**C4**
			[6 marks]

1	**a**	Diagram reduced 50%	A1A1	2
	b	**i** Gradient BC $= \dfrac{-1-3}{3-6} = \dfrac{4}{3}$	M1A1 (G2)	
		ii Parallel lines have the same gradients.	A1	
		iii $\dfrac{d-1}{-5+2} = \dfrac{4}{3}$	M1	
		$d = -3$	A1ft (G2)	5
	c	**i** length AB $= \sqrt{(6--2)^2 + (3-1)^2}$	M1A1	
		$= \sqrt{68}$	A1 (G2)	
		ii $\cos \angle ABC = \dfrac{\sqrt{68}^2 + 5^2 - \sqrt{27}^2}{2 \times \sqrt{68} \times 5}$	M1A1ft	
		$\therefore\ \angle ABC = 36.8^\circ$	A1ft (G2)	6
	d	Area ABCD $= 2 \times$ area triangle ABC		
		$= 2 \times \frac{1}{2} \times 5 \times \sqrt{68} \sin 36.8$	M1A1ft	
		$= 24.7$ units^2	A1ft (G2)	3
				(16)
2	**a**		A4	4
	b	**i** P(B, B) $= \frac{6}{20} \times \frac{5}{19}$	M1	
		$= \frac{30}{380}$ (0.0789)	A1ft (G2)	
		ii P(B, F) + P(F, B) $= \frac{6}{20} \times \frac{9}{19} + \frac{9}{20} \times \frac{6}{19}$	M1 A1ft	
		$= \frac{108}{380}$ (0.284)	A1ft (G2)	
		iii P(both the same)		
		$= $ P(B, B) + P(F, F) + P(V, V)		
		$= \frac{6}{20} \times \frac{5}{19} + \frac{9}{20} \times \frac{8}{19} + \frac{5}{20} \times \frac{4}{19}$	M1A1ft	
		$= \frac{122}{380}$ (0.321)	A1ft (G2)	8
	c	**i** P(V, V) $= \frac{5}{20} \times \frac{5}{20} = \frac{25}{400} = \frac{1}{16}$ (0.0625)	M1A1ftA1ft (G2)	3
		ii P(both B | the two balls are same)		
		$= \dfrac{6 \times 6}{6 \times 6 + 9 \times 9 + 5 \times 5}$	M1A1ft	
		$= \frac{36}{142}$ (0.254)	A1ft (G2)	3
				(18)

3 **a i** $a = 79°$, $b = 31.1°$ | A1A1 | 2

ii $61 \times (0.95)^t + 18 = 25$ $t = 42.2$ minutes | M1A1 (G2) | 2

b

Temperature

[A1 for scale and labels, A2 for points, A1 for curve] | A1 A2ft A1 | 4

c i $t = 0$, $T_F = 53 \times (0.98)^0 + 18 = 71°$ | M1A1

ii The heat is lost at a faster rate in the plastic cup. | A1ft

iii $53 \times (0.98)^t + 18 = 61 \times (0.95)^t + 18$
$\therefore\ \ t = 4.52$ | M1 A1

The time taken for the temperature within each cup to be equal is 4.5 minutes. | A1 (G3) | 6

d The temperature will approach $18°$. | A2 | 2

(16)

4 **a i a** $r = \dfrac{s_{xy}}{s_x s_y}$

$= \dfrac{93.7}{4.78 \times 21.4}$ | M1A1

$= 0.916$ | A1 (G2)

b   A strong, positive relationship exists between the maximum temperature and the number of people attending the swimming pool. | A1ftA1ft | 5

ii $y - \bar{y} = \dfrac{s_{xy}}{s_x^2}(x - \bar{x})$

$y - 87.3 = \dfrac{93.7}{4.78^2}(x - 29.9)$ | M1A1

$y - 87.3 = 4.1(x - 29.9)$
$y = 4.1x - 35.3$ | A1A1 (G3) | 4

(attendance $= 4.1 \times$ max. temperature $- 35.3$)

iii a i   attendance $= 4.1(20) - 35.3$ | M1
$= 46.7$ i.e.,   47 people | A1ft (G2)

ii   attendance $= 4.1(40) - 35.3$
$= 128.7$ i.e.,   129 people | A1ft

b   The estimate for $20°$ is the more reliable. It is an interpolated value (within known values). | A1ftR1ft | 5

iv The manager's plan seems sensible given the high value for the coefficient of correlation. | A1ftR1ft | 2

b i H_0: Attendance by gender is independent of temperature. | A1 | 1

ii p-value $= 0.0950$ | G2 | 2

iii Do not reject H_0: Attendance by gender and temperature are independent.
$P_{calc} > 0.05$ | A1ft R1ft | 2

(21)

5	**a**	**i** $f(1) = 3(1)^3 - 4(1) + 5 = 4$	M1A1 (G2)	2
		ii $f'(x) = 9x^2 - 4$	A1A1	2
		iii $f(1) = 9(1)^2 - 4 = 5$	M1A1ft (G2)	2
		iv gradient $= 5$, through point $(1, 4)$		
		$5x - y = 5(1) - (4)$ $5x - y = 1$ $(y = 5x - 1)$	M1A1ft (G1)	2
		v (GDC) $(-2, -11)$	A1A1ft	2
	b	**i** Volume $= l \times w \times h$ $V = x^2 y$	A2	2
		ii $V = x^2 \times \dfrac{30\,000 - x^2}{2x} = 15\,000x - \dfrac{x^3}{2}$	M1A1ft (G2)	2
		iii $\dfrac{dV}{dx} = 15\,000 - \dfrac{3x^2}{2}$	A1A1ft	2
		iv minimum when $\dfrac{dV}{dx} = 0$	M1	
		$15\,000 - \dfrac{3x^2}{2} = 0$ *or* $30\,000 = 3x^2$		
		$x^2 = 10\,000$	A1	
		$x = 100$	A1ft (G2)	3
				(19)

1	**a** **C** Correct	A1	
	D Correct	A1	**C2**
	b 5.18×10^{-2}	A1A1	**C2**
	c Percentage error $= \dfrac{0.05176 - 0.0518}{0.05176} \times 100\%$	M1	
	$= 0.0773\%$ (accept negative answer)	A1	**C2**
			[6 marks]
2	**a** 40 sheep	A1	**C1**
	b mean weight $= \dfrac{2 \times 10 \ + \ 5 \times 20 \ + ...}{40}$	M1	
	$= \dfrac{1590}{40}$		
	$= 39.75$ kg	A1ft	**C2**
	c $39.75 \times 1.50 = 59.625$	A1ft	
	Percentage of sheep going to market is $\frac{8}{40} \times 100$	M1	
	$= 20\%$	A1A1ft	**C3**
			[6 marks]
3	**a** $\dfrac{DC}{100} = \cos 38$ $DC = 7.88$ cm	M1A1	**C2**
	b $\dfrac{AD}{10} = \sin 38$ $AD = 6.16$ cm	M1A1	**C2**
	$BD^2 = 8.5^2 - 6.16^2$ $BD = 5.86$ cm	M1A1ft	**C2**
			[6 marks]
4	**a** $22 \times 42.50 = €935$	A1	**C1**
	b $C(22) = 15.6 \times 22 + 245 = €588.20$	M1A1	**C2**
	c Profit $= 935 - 588.20 = €346.80$	A1ft	**C1**
	d Average profit $= \dfrac{346.80}{22} = €15.76$	M1A1ft	**C2**
			[6 marks]
5	**a** $P = \{2, 3, 5, 7, 11, 13\}$	A1A1	**C2**
	(**Note:** parentheses preferred but no penalty if missing)		
	b $Q = \{1, 2, 3, 4, 6, 8, 12\}$	A1A1	**C2**
	c $(P \cup Q)' = \{9, 10\}$	A1ftA1ft	**C2**
			[6 marks]
6	**a** P(both triangles) $= \frac{5}{10} \times \frac{4}{9} = \frac{20}{90} = \frac{2}{9}$	M1A1	**C2**
	b P(one is the rhombus)		
	$= P(t, rh) + P(re, rh) + P(rh, t) + P(rh, re)$		
	$= \frac{5}{10} \times \frac{1}{9} \ + \ \frac{4}{10} \times \frac{1}{9} \ + \ \frac{1}{10} \times \frac{5}{9} \ + \ \frac{1}{10} \times \frac{4}{9}$	M1A1	
	$= \frac{18}{90}$		
	$= \frac{1}{5}$ (0.2) or $1 - \left(\frac{9}{10} \times \frac{8}{9}\right) = \frac{1}{5}$ (0.2)	A1ft	**C3**
	c $\frac{3}{9} = \frac{1}{3}$	A1	**C1**
			[6 marks]

7	**a** domain: $-5 \leqslant x \leqslant 0$	A1A1	**C2**
	b range: $\{-8, -5, -2, 1, 4, 7\}$	A1A1	**C2**
	c $y = 3x + 7$	A1ftA1ft	**C2**
			[6 marks]

8	**a** $\quad I = \dfrac{CRN}{100}$		
	$\quad = \dfrac{2500 \times 7.5 \times 3.5}{100}$	M1A1	
	$\quad = 656.25$		
	$2500 + 656.25 = \$3156.25 \quad$ in the account.	A1ft	**C3**
	b $\quad 900 = \dfrac{2500 \times R \times 3.5}{100}$	A1M1	
	(**Note:** first A1 is for equating to 900)		
	$\quad R = 10.3\%$	A1ft	**C3**
			[6 marks]

9	**a** $\dfrac{dy}{dx} = 6x^2 - 6x - 264$	A1A1A1	**C3**
	b $6x^2 - 6x - 264 = -12$	M1	
	$\quad\quad x = -6 \quad$ and $\quad 7$	A1ftA1ft	**C3**
			[6 marks]

10	**a** $4r + 3p = 19$	A1	**C1**
	b $3r - 2p = 10$	A1	**C1**
	c $r = 4, \ p = 1$	M1A1A1ft	
	(**Note:** M1 is for algebraic method seen)		
	5 reams of paper and 5 pens would cost £25.	A1ft	**C4**
			[6 marks]

11	**a**					

	Climbing	Swimming	Mountain Biking
Female	9.3	13.2	12.4
Male	14.7	20.8	19.6

M1 / A1   **C2**

(accept integers)

	b 5.44	A1ft	**C1**
	c 0.0658	A1ft	**C1**
	d $0.05 < 0.0658$ Therefore we do not reject the null hypothesis. Activities chosen are independent of gender.	R1A1ft	**C2**
			[6 marks]

12	**a** $S_{20} = 560, \quad S_{20} = \frac{20}{2}(u_1 + 66)$		
	$\quad\quad 560 = 10(u_1 + 66)$	M1A1	
	$\quad\quad 56 = u_1 + 66$		
	$\quad\quad u_1 = -10$	A1	**C3**
	b $u_1 + 19d = 66$	M1A1ft	
	$\quad 19d = 76$		
	$\quad\quad d = 4$	A1ft	**C3**
			[6 marks]

13	**a**	A3	**C3**
	b $\sin 2x - 1 = -0.5$ $\quad\quad x = 15^\circ$ and 75°	M1 A1A1ft	**C3** **[6 marks]**
14	**a** $y = \dfrac{2^3}{3-2} = 8$	M1A1	**C2**
	b y-intercept: when $x = 0$, $\quad y = \dfrac{2^0}{0-2} = -0.5$	M1A1	**C2**
	c minimum value, $\quad x \geqslant 2 = 7.54$	A1	**C1**
	d vertical asymptote when denominator $= 0$, i.e., $x = 2$	A1	**C1** **[6 marks]**
15	**a**	A1A1	**C2**
	b $A = \frac{1}{2}(a+b)h$ $42 = \frac{1}{2}(a+2a) \times 7$ $42 = \frac{7}{2} \times 3a$ $\quad a = 4$ The parallel sides have lengths 4 cm and 8 cm.	M1A1 A1ft A1ft	 **C4** **[6 marks]**

1

a Amount $= 500 \times 1.025 + 500$ | M1A1
$= 1012.50$ USD | A1 (G2) | 3

b Amount $= 1012.50 \times 1.025 + 500$ | M1A1A1
$= 1537.81$ USD   (1540, 1538) | A1ft (G3) | 4

c **i** Amount $= 500(1.025)^1 + 500(1.025)^2 +$
$\qquad ..... + 500(1.025)^n$ | M1

$\qquad = \dfrac{512.50 \times (1.025^n - 1)}{1.025 - 1}$ | A1ft (G2)

ii Amount at the end of 11 years | A1

$\qquad = \dfrac{512.50 \times (1.025^{11} - 1)}{1.025 - 1}$ | M1

$\qquad = 6397.78$ USD   (6400) | A1ft (G2) | 5

d **i** $11 \times 500 = 5500$ USD | A1

ii $6397.78 - 5500 = 897.78$ USD | A1ft | 2

(14)

2

a
```
3 | 2 8              Key   3 | 2   means 32
4 | 0 5 5 5 5 5 8
5 | 4 5 5 8
6 | 0 0 5 5 8 8
7 | 0 5 5 5 5 8 8
8 | 0 5 5 8
```
A4 | 4

b Mean $= 1855 \div 30$ | M1
$= 61.8$ | A1ft (G2) | 2

c **i** Median $= 62.5$ | A1ft
ii Lower quartile $= 45$ | A1ft
iii Upper quartile $= 75$ | A1ft | 3

d

| A2ft
| A1ft
| A1ft | 4

(A1 for scale and label, A2 for box, A1 for whiskers)

e

Class Interval	Frequency
30 - 39	2
40 - 49	7
50 - 59	4
60 - 69	6
70 - 79	7
80 - 89	4

A2ft | 2

f 40 - 49 and 70 - 79 | A1ft | 1

g Mean $= 61.5$ | A2ft | 2

h Error $= 0.3$ | A1ft | 1

(19)

3

a

(A1 for scale and labels, A2 for points, A1 for line)   A4   4

b i L_2 parallel to L_1 ...... so gradient $k = -2$ A1

Substitute $(2, -3)$ into $y = -2x + c$ M1

$$-3 = -2(2) + c$$
$$c = 1$$
$$y = -2x + 1$$ A1ft

ii see graph   A2   5

c i Substitute $x = 3$ into $y = 5 - 2x$

$$y = 5 - 2(3) = -1$$ M1

$(3, -1)$ lies on the line L_1 A1 (G2)

ii see graph   A2   4

d i L_3 perpendicular to L_2 ...... has gradient $\frac{1}{2}$ and passes
through $(3, -1)$ A1ft

Equation L_3 is $x - 2y = (3) - 2(-1)$ M1

$$x - 2y = 5$$
$$x - 2y - 5 = 0$$ A1ft (G3)

ii L_3: $x - 2y = 5$
L_2: $2x + y = 1$ M1

Solve simultaneously $x = \frac{7}{5}$ (1.4)

$$y = -\frac{9}{5} \quad (-1.8)$$ A1A1ft (G3)   6

(19)

4

a

(A1 for 3 circles and the universal set, A1 for 8, 2, 3, 5.
A1 for 1, 5, 13 and A1 for 3 in the complement)   A1   A3ft   4

b i P(History only) $= \frac{13}{40}$ (0.325)   A1A1ft

ii P(not Music) $= \frac{24}{40}$ (0.6)   A1ft

iii P(Music or Science but not History) $= \frac{11}{40}$ (0.275)   A1A1ft

iv P(at least one subject) $= \frac{37}{40}$ (0.925)   A1ft   6

c i P$(S \cap M) = \frac{13}{40}$ (0.325)   A1A1ft

ii P$(H \cap S \cap M)' = \frac{32}{40}$ (0.8)   A1ft

iii P$(H' \cap S') = \frac{4}{40}$ (0.1)   A2ft   5

d P$(H|M) = \frac{10}{16}$ (0.625)   A1A1ft   2

e P(both like History and Science) $= \frac{11}{40} \times \frac{10}{39}$ M1A1

$$= \frac{110}{1560}$$

$$= \frac{11}{156} \quad (0.0705)$$ A1ft (G3)   3

(20)

5	a	i	$x = 0$, $y = 2^0$ y-intercept is 1	M1A1	2	
		ii	$8 - x^2 = 2^{-x}$	M1		
			GDC lines intersect at $(-2,\ 4)$ and $(2.80,\ 0.143)$	A1A1 (G3)	3	
		iii	$2^{-x} > 8 - x^2$ for $x < -2$ and $x > 2.80$	A1A1ft	2	
	b	i a	increasing for $0^o < x < 180^o$ and $540^o < x < 720^o$	A1A1 A1A1		
		b	decreasing for $180^o < x < 540^o$	A1A1	6	
		ii a	$\dfrac{dy}{dx} = 0$ when $x = 180^o$ and 540°	A1A1		
		b	gradient steepest at $x = 0^o,\ 360^o$ and 720°	A1A1A1	5	(18)

1	**a** $\dfrac{6 \times 10^4}{1.5 \times 10^8 \times 8 \times 10^2} = 5 \times 10^{-7}$	M1A1A1	C3
	b **i** 2.501	A2	
	ii 3	A1ft	C3
			[6 marks]
2	**a** Mean $= \dfrac{202}{10}$	M1	
	$= 20.2^\circ C$	A1	C2
	b 15, 15, 18, 18, 19, 20, 22, 24, 25, 26	M1	
	Median $= 19.5^\circ C$	A1	C2
	c Percentage error $= \dfrac{20.2 - 20}{20.2} \times 100\%$	M1	
	$= 0.990\% \quad (0.99\%)$	A1	C2
			[6 marks]
3	**a** If x is a prime number then x is not a factor of 12.	A1	C1
	b $x = 2$ or $x = 3$	A1	C1
	c If x is not a prime number then x is a factor of 12.	A1A1	C2
	d False, 10 is not a prime number and it is not a factor of 12.	A2	C2
			[6 marks]
4	**a** gradient $= \dfrac{5 - 2}{1 - -2}$	M1	
	$= 1$	A1	
	$y = mx + c$		
	$5 = 1 + c$	M1	
	$c = 4$		
	$y = x + 4$	A1ft	C4
	b Solve $x + y = 3$ and $y = x + 4$	M1	
	$x = -0.5 \quad y = 3.5 \quad ((-0.5, 3.5))$	A1ft	C2
			[6 marks]
5	**a** $AC^2 = 20^2 + 20^2$	M1	
	$AC = 28.3 \quad (\sqrt{800})$	A1	C2
	b $CM^2 = 10^2 + (\sqrt{800})^2$	M1	
	$= 30$	A1ft	C2
	c Angle $CMR = 2\left(\sin^{-1}(\frac{10}{30})\right)$	M1	
	$= 38.9^\circ$	A1ft	C2
			[6 marks]
6	**a** $u_n = -48$		
	$-48 = 85 + (n - 1) \times -7$	M1A1	
	$n = 20$	A1	C3
	b $S_{20} = \frac{20}{2}(2 \times 85 + 19 \times -7)$	M1A1	
	sum $= 370$	A1ft	C3
			[6 marks]
7	**a** $\frac{1}{5} = \frac{8}{40}$	M1	
	$\therefore$ there are 8 green beads	A1	C2
	b Prob $= \frac{32}{40} \times \frac{31}{39}$	M1A1	
	$= \frac{124}{195} \quad (0.636)$	A1ft	C3
	c $32 - 8 = 24$ beads	A1ft	C1
			[6 marks]

8	**a** $(x+1)$ and $(x-3)$ are factors	M1	
	$(x+1)(x-3) = x^2 - 2x - 3$		
	$a = -2, \quad b = -3$	A1A1	**C3**
	b $f'(x) = 2x - 2$	A1A1ft	**C2**
	c $(1, -4)$	A1ft	**C1**
			[6 marks]

9	**a** x any number greater than 9	A1	**C1**
	b $y = 6$	A2	**C2**
	c $\dfrac{4+6+6+4}{10+z} = 1$	M1A1	
	$\qquad z = 10$	A1	**C3**
			[6 marks]

10	**a** $\dfrac{XZ}{\sin 65} = \dfrac{5}{\sin 35}$	M1A1	
	$\quad XZ = 7.90$ km	A1	**C3**
	b $XW^2 = 5^2 + 6^2 - 2 \times 5 \times 6 \times \cos 50$	M1A1	
	$\quad XW = 4.74$ km	A1	**C3**
			[6 marks]

11	**a** $(x-7)(x+7)$	A1A1	**C2**
	b $2 + 7x - 2x^2 = 4 + 4x^2$	M1	
	$6x^2 - 7x + 2 = 0$	A1	
	$\qquad x = \frac{2}{3} \quad$ or $\quad x = 0.5$	A1A1ft	**C4**
			[6 marks]

12	**a** $r = \dfrac{s_{xy}}{s_x s_y} = \dfrac{10.6}{2.58 \times 4.35}$	M1	
	$= 0.944$	A1	**C2**
	b Strong, positive correlation	A1A1ft	**C2**
	c $y - 24 = \dfrac{10.6}{2.58^2}(x - 15.5)$	M1	
	$\quad y = 1.59x - 0.683$	A1	**C2**
			[6 marks]

| 13 | **a** | | |

p	q	$\neg q$	$p \vee \neg q$
T	T	F	T
T	F	T	T
F	T	F	F
F	F	T	T

A2   **C2**

b

p	q	$\neg q$	$p \wedge q$	$(p \wedge q) \vee \neg q$
T	T	F	T	T
T	F	T	F	T
F	T	F	F	F
F	F	T	F	T

A2   **C2**

c Yes, the two final columns are the same.   A1A1   **C2**

[6 marks]

14	**a** $\dfrac{dy}{dx} = -10x^{-2} - 2x$	A1A1A1	**C3**
	b $x = -2, \quad$ gradient $= \dfrac{-10}{4} + 4$	M1A1	
	$\qquad\qquad = 1.5$	A1ft	**C3**
			[6 marks]

15	**a** Volume $= \pi \times 4^2 \times 50$	M1	
	$\qquad = 2513 \text{ cm}^3 \text{ per second}$		
	$\qquad = \dfrac{2513 \times 60 \times 60}{1000} \text{ litres per hour}$	M1	
	$\qquad = 9050 \text{ litres}$	A1	**C3**
	b Volume $= 10 \times 4.5 \times 1.5 \times 1000 \text{ litres}$	M1	
	$\quad \text{Time} = 67\,500 \div 9047.78$	M1	
	$\qquad\quad = 7.46 \text{ hours}$	A1ft	**C3**
			[6 marks]

1	**a i** (A1 for 3 labelled circles and the Universal set, A1 for 5, A1ft for 10, 15, 20 in P intersect C, A1ft for 35, 40 and 10)	A4	4
	ii $150 - 135 = 15$	A1ft	1
	iii $\frac{70}{150}$ (0.467)	A1ftA1	2
	iv $\frac{45 + 25}{150} = \frac{70}{150}$ (0.467)	M1A1ft (G1)	2
	v $\frac{20}{50}$ (0.4)	A1A1ft	2
	b i Belonging to a club is independent of gender. (There is no difference between males and females regarding membership of a club.)	A1	1
	ii Expected value $= \dfrac{100 \times 110}{250}$ $= 44$	A1A1 AG	2
	iii 25.4	G2	2
	iv Reject the null hypothesis, there is a difference between males and females. p value $= 3.04 \times 10^{-6} < 0.05$ or χ^2 critical value $< \chi^2$ test statistic. (**Note:** both marks are lost if there is no reason given.)	A1ft R1ft	2
			(18)
2	**a** Number $= 10 \times 1.2$ $= 12$	M1 A1 (G2)	2
	b Number $= 10 \times (1.2)^7$ $= 35.8$ Answer 36	M1 A1ft (G1) A1ft (G2)	3
	c i $N = 10$	A1ft	
	ii $a = 1.2$	A2ft	3
	d (A1 for scale indicated and labels, A2 for curve, A1 for intercept)	A4ft	4
	e Range is the interval $2 \leqslant y \leqslant 383$ (0, 383]	A1A1A1ft	3
	f $y = 0$	A1A1ft	2
			(17)

3	**a** $24°C$	A1	1
	b $23.5°C$	A1	1
	c Range $= 5°$, interquartile range $= 1.5°C$	A1A2	3
	d Nice	A1	1
	e The middle half of the days have temperatures more dispersed in Geneva.	A1A1	2
	f i There are 30 days in September.	A1	
	There are 7 days above upper quartile (25%)	A1	
	Nice maximum = Geneva upper quartile value		
	Smallest number of days $= 1$	A1	
	ii Largest number of days $= 7$	A2	5
			(13)

4	**a** Amount $= 10\,000(1.035)^5$	M1A1	
	$= 11\,876.86$	A1	
	$= 11\,900$ AUD	AG	3
	b $20\,000 = 10\,000(1.035)^n$	M1A1	
	$n = 21$ years	A1 (G2)	3
	c $\quad 2 = (x)^{12}$ where $x = 1 + \frac{r}{100}$	M1	
	$x = \sqrt[12]{2}$	A1	
	$= 1.059\,46$	A1	
	$\therefore\quad r = 5.95\%$	A1 (G3)	4
	d Interest $= 5000(1.0075)^{24} - 5000$	M1A1A1	
	$= 982.07$ AUD (982, 980)	A1 (G3)	4
	(**Note:** first two A1's are for n and r seen)		
	e $5000 \times 1.35 = 6750$ AUD	M1A1 (G2)	
	Amount $= 6750 \times 1.015$	M1	
	$= 6851.25$ AUD	A1ft (G2)	
	(G3 for the case when **only** the final answer is given)	(G3)	4
			(18)

5	**a i**		
	(A1 for axes and labels, A2 for points, A1 for curve, A1 for domain)	A5	5
	ii a Amplitude $= 10$, Period $= 12$	A1A1	
	b $a = 10$, $b = \frac{360}{12} = 30$, $c = 12$	A1A2A1	6
	b i PQ $= (20 - 2x)$ cm	A2	2
	ii $V = x(20 - 2x)(20 - 2x)$	A2	
	$= x(400 - 40x - 40x + 4x^2)$	M1	
	$= 4x^3 - 80x^2 + 400x$	AG	3
	iii $\frac{dV}{dx} = 12x^2 - 160x + 400$	A1A1A1	3
	iv $3x^2 - 40x + 100 = 0$	M1	
	$x = \frac{10}{3}$ or $x = 10$	A1A1 (G3)	3
	v $x = 10$ not possible $x = 3\frac{1}{3}$ cm	A1ftA1ft	2
			(24)

1	50.438 399 11		
	a 50.44	A1	C1
	b 50	A1ft	C1
	c 50.4384	A1ft	C1
	d 50.4384	A1ft	C1
	e 5.04×10^1	A1ftA1ft	C2
			[6 marks]

2	**a** **i** If Joshua did not study hard at Mathematics then Joshua did not pass Mathematics.	A1A1	
	ii Joshua did not study hard at Mathematics and Joshua passed Mathematics.	A1ftA1	C4
	b **i** $q \Rightarrow p$	A1	
	ii converse	A1ft	C2
			[6 marks]

3	**a** $2400 \times 46.184 \times 0.985 = 109\,178.98$ Baht	M1A1A1	C3
	b $\qquad 109\,178.98 \times 0.10 = 10\,917.90$	A1ft	
	$10\,917.90 \times \dfrac{1}{45.865} \times 0.985 = 234.47$ Euro	M1A1ft	C3
			[6 marks]

4	**a**		
		A1A1ft	C2
	b $P(E \text{ and } MS) = \frac{7}{28} = \frac{1}{4}$ (0.25)	A1ftA1ft	C2
	c $P(E \mid E \text{ or } MS \text{ not both}) = \frac{5}{15} = \frac{1}{3}$ (0.333)	A1ftA1ft	C2
			[6 marks]

5	**a** $AC^2 = 7.1^2 + 4.7^2 - 2 \times 7.1 \times 4.7 \cos 92.7$	M1A1	
	$\qquad AC = 8.70$ cm	A1	C3
	b $\dfrac{8.70}{\sin 92.7} = \dfrac{4.7}{\sin \angle CAB}$	M1A1ft	
	$\qquad \angle CAB = 32.7^o$	A1ft	C3
			[6 marks]

6	**a** $t = 0$. Population in 1960 is 360.	A1	C1
	b $t = 45$, $P = 360(1.045)^{\frac{45}{2}}$	M1	
	$\qquad\quad = 969$	A1	C2
	(**Note:** a decimal answer is an error, not an AP)		
	c $800 = 360(1.045)^{\frac{t}{2}}$	M1	
	$\qquad t = 36.28$	A1	
	Population reached 800 in 1997.	A1ft	C3
			[6 marks]

7	**a**		

Number of letters	1	2	3	4	5	6	7
Number of words	3	**11**	12	11	5	5	4

		A2	C2
b	(A1 for scale and labels, A2 for points, A1 for line)	A4	C4
			[6 marks]

8	**a** $I = \dfrac{2500 \times 3.2 \times 5}{100} = 400$ JPY	M1A1	C2
	b $I = 2500\left(1 + \dfrac{3.2}{400}\right)^{5 \times 4} - 2500$	M1A1A1	
	$\qquad = 432$ JPY	A1	C4
			[6 marks]
9	**a i** Domain is $\{-2, -1, 0, 1\}$	A1	
	ii Range is $\{-1.5, 6, 18.5, 36\}$	A1ft	C2
	(only lists needed, not $\{\}$)		
	b $c = 6$, when $x = 1$, $a + b + 6 = -1.5$	A1	
	$\qquad\qquad\qquad\qquad a + b = -7.5$	M1	
	when $x = -2$, $4a - 2b + 6 = 36$		
	$\qquad\qquad\qquad 4a - 2b = 30$		
	Solve simultaneously, $a = 2.5$, $b = -10$	A1ftA1ft	C4
			[6 marks]
10	**a i** P(long and light) $= \frac{5}{58}$ $\quad(0.0862)$	A1A1	C2
	ii P(not medium) $= \frac{26}{41}$ $\quad(0.634)$	A1A1ft	C2
	b P(both short, heavy) $= \frac{2}{58} \times \frac{1}{57}$	M1	
	$\qquad\qquad = \frac{2}{3306}$		
	$\qquad\qquad = \frac{1}{1653}$ $\quad(0.000\,605)$	A1	C2
			[6 marks]
11	**a** Profit $= 50\,000(1.015)^9$	M1	
	$\qquad = 57\,169.50$ MAR $\quad(57170, 57200)$	A1	C2
	b Total profit $= 50\,000 + 50\,000 \times 1.015 + 50\,000 \times 1.015^2$		
	$\qquad\qquad + \ldots\ldots + 50\,000 \times 1.015^9$	M1	
	$\qquad = \dfrac{50\,000(1.015^{10} - 1)}{(1.015 - 1)}$	M1	
	$\qquad = 535\,136.08$	A1	
	$\qquad = 535\,000$ MAR	A1ft	C4
			[6 marks]
12	**a** $(x + 3)$	A1	C1
	b $x(x + 3) = 108$	A1ft	C1
	c $\qquad x(x + 3) = 108$		
	$\quad x^2 + 3x - 108 = 0$		
	$\qquad\qquad x = -12$ and 9	A1ftA1ft	C2
	d Width is 9 cm, length is 12 cm	A1ftA1ft	C2
	(ft only for sensible positive values)		**[6 marks]**
13	**a** $45\,000 \times 0.80 = \$36\,000$	M1A1	C2
	b $36\,000(0.88)^2 = \$27\,878.40$ $\quad(27\,900, 27\,878)$	M1A1ft	C2
	c $\qquad 45\,000 \div 3 = 15\,000$		
	$\qquad 36\,000(0.88)^n < 15\,000$	M1	
	$\qquad\qquad\qquad n \geqslant 6.85$		
	Number of years $= 7 + 1$		
	$\qquad\qquad\qquad = 8$	A1ft	C2
			[6 marks]

14	$y = (x-2)(x-2) - 5$ $\quad = x^2 - 4x - 1$	A1	
	a $\dfrac{dy}{dx} = 2x - 4$	A1A1ft	**C3**
	b at $x = 3$, gradient of tangent $= 2(3) - 4$ $\qquad\qquad\qquad\qquad\qquad\qquad = 2$	A1ft	**C1**
	c Equation of the tangent at $x = 3$ is $\qquad 2x - y = 2(3) - (-4)$ $\qquad 2x - y = 10$	M1 A1ft	**C2** **[6 marks]**
15	**a** Sum angles $= 3 \times 180 = 540^o$ Each angle is $\quad \frac{540}{5} = 108^o$	M1 A1ft	**C2**
	b Area triangle EAB $= \frac{1}{2} \times 15 \times 15 \times \sin 108^o$ $\qquad\qquad\qquad\quad = 106.99 \text{ cm}^2$	M1 A1ft	
	$\qquad$ Area pentagon $= 2 \times 106.99 + 173.12$ $\qquad\qquad\qquad\qquad = 387.10 \text{ cm}^2 \quad (387)$	M1 A1ft	**C4** **[6 marks]**

1	**a** **i** $25 \times 1.04 = 26$ employees	A1		
	ii $25 \times 1.04^{15} = 45.02$	M1		
	$= 45$ employees	A1 (G2)	3	
	b $25 \times 1.04^6 = 31.63$ (32)	M1AG	1	
	c $a = 1.045^{15} = 1.935$	A1		
	$\left(1 + \dfrac{b}{100}\right)^{10} = 1.877$	M1		
	$b = 6.50\%$	A1 (G2)	3	
	d $18\,000 \times 2.232 = 40\,176$ NZD	M1A1(G2)	2	
	e $30\,000 = 18\,000 \times 1.045^n$ $n = 11.6$	M1A1		
	In the 12th year.	A1 (G2)	3	
				(12)

2	**a** **i** $6 \mid 6\ 7\ 7\ 8$ Key $6 \mid 7$ means 67	A1		
	$7 \mid 0\ 1\ 3\ 3\ 3\ 5\ 8\ 9$	A1		
	$8 \mid 3\ 4\ 7$	A1	3	
	ii **a** Median $= 73$	A1ft		
	b Interquartile range $= 79 - 68$	M1		
	$= 11$	A1ft (G2)	3	
	iii Mean score $= \dfrac{66 + 67 + 67 + \ldots}{15}$	M1		
	$= 74.2666$ (74.3)	A1 (G2)	2	
	iv Frequency $= 4, 8, 3$	A1ftA1ft	2	
	v Mean $= (4 \times 64.5 + 8 \times 74.5 + 3 \times 84.5) \div 15$	M1		
	$= 73.8333$ (73.8)	A1ft (G2)	2	
	vi Percentage error $= \dfrac{73.83 - 74.27}{74.27} \times 100$	M1		
	$= 0.592\%$	A1ft (G2)	2	
	(**Note:** Allow $74.3 - 73.8$ as numerator ($= 0.673\%$). Allow negative.)			
	b **i** cumulative frequencies: 97, 121, 143	A1ftA1ft	2	
	ii			
	(A1 for scale and labels, A1A1ft for points (the first A1 is for setting against the end point of each class) A1 for curve)	A1 A1A1ft A1	4	
	iii **a** Median 72nd vehicle ...... approx. 9:15 am	A1ft		
	b 100th vehicle ...... approx. 10:10 am	A1ft		
	c 9:30 - 11:30 am ...... $132 - 80 = 52$ vehicles	A1ft		
	d 25th percentile $= 36$th vehicle .... approx. 8:30 am	A1ft	4	
				(24)

3	a	$\dfrac{DE}{57} = \cos 6.2$		
		$DE = 57 \times \cos 6.2$	M1	
		$= 56.7$ m	A1	
		Poles are $200 - 56.7 = 143$ m apart.	A1ft	3
	b	$\dfrac{200}{DH} = \cos 6.2$		
		$DH = \dfrac{200}{\cos 6.2}$	M1	
		$= 201$ m	A1	
		Slant distance $GH = 201 - 57$		
		$= 144$ m	A1ft	3
	c	$\dfrac{FH}{200} = \tan 6.2$		
		$FH = 200 \times \tan 6.2$	M1	
		$= 21.7$ m	A1	
		$\tan \angle FEH = \dfrac{21.7}{143}$	M1	
		$\angle FEH = 8.63^{o}$ (8.62)	A1ft	4
	d	$\dfrac{EG}{57} = \sin 6.2$		
		$EG = 57 \times \sin 6.2$	M1	
		$= 6.16$ m	A1	2
	e	$\angle HGE = 90^{o} + 6.2^{o} = 96.2^{o}$	A1	
		Area $GEH = \frac{1}{2} \times 6.16 \times 144 \times \sin 96.2$	M1A1ft	
		$= 441$ m^{2}	A1ft	4
				(16)

4	a	i			

$(p \wedge q) \Rightarrow r$	$(\neg p \vee \neg q)$	$\neg p \vee \neg q \Rightarrow \neg r$
T	F	T
F	F	T
T	T	F
T	T	T
T	T	F
T	T	T
T	T	F
T	T	T

				A1A1A1ft	3
		ii none of these		A1ft	1
		iii If the weather is not fine or the bus is not late then I will not walk to school.		A1A1	2
		iv If the bus is not late then I will walk to school.		A1A1	2
	b	i P(fine, fine) $= 0.7 \times 0.7 = 0.49$		M1A1 (G2)	2
		ii P(bus early) $= 0.6$		A1	
		P(fine and not late for 2 days)			
		$= (0.7 \times 0.6) \times (0.7 \times 0.6)$		M1A1	
		$= 0.176$		A1ft (G2)	4
					(14)

5 **a**

(A1 for scale indicated and labels, A1 for approx. intercepts, A1 for curve)   A1A1A1   3

b **i** $H(t) = 0$, $1600 - 4t^2 = 0$ M1

$$4t^2 = 1600$$

$$t = \sqrt{\frac{1600}{4}}$$ M1

$$= 20 \text{ seconds}$$ (AG)   2

ii $t = 0$, $H(t) = 1600 - (0)^2$ M1

$$= 1600 \text{ m}$$ A1 (G2)   2

iii average speed $= \dfrac{1600}{20} = 80 \text{ ms}^{-1}$ M1A1 (G2)   2

c **i** $H(10) = 1600 - 4(10)^2$ M1

$$= 1200 \text{ m}$$ A1 (G2)   2

ii $H(10 + h) = 1600 - 4(10 + h)^2$ M1

$$= 1600 - 4(100 + 20h + h^2)$$ M1

$$= 1600 - 400 - 80h - 4h^2$$ M1

$$= 1200 - 80h - 4h^2$$ (AG)   3

iii $\dfrac{H(10 + h) - H(10)}{h} = \dfrac{(1200 - 80h - 4h^2) - 1200}{h}$ M1

$$= \frac{-80h - 4h^2}{h}$$

$$= \frac{h(-80 - 4h)}{h}$$

$$= -80 - 4h$$ A1   2

d **i** $H'(t) = -8t$ A1A1   2

ii Decreasing function. Gradient is negative.   A1R1   2

iii $H'(5) = -40$, $H'(10) = -80$ A1A1   2

iv The gradient of the curve at $t = 10$ is steeper than the gradient at $t = 5$.   A2   2

(**Note:**   Motion is not part of the syllabus. An answer of "speed increasing" or something similar will be awarded full marks but it is not required.)

(24)

1	**a** $5^2 \times 12 \times 100^3 = 300\,000\,000$	M1A1	**C2**
	b 3×10^8	A1ftA1ft	**C2**
	c $\sqrt{300\,000\,000} = 17\,320.51 \quad 17\,300 \text{ 3 s.f.}$	A1ft	**C1**
	d $17\,000$	A1ft	**C1**
			[6 marks]
2	**a** $38, 35, 32, 32, 30, 28, 27, 24, 19, 18$	A1	**C1**
	b Median $= \dfrac{28 + 30}{2} = 29$	A1ft	**C1**
	c $\frac{6}{10}$ (0.6)	A1A1ft	**C2**
	d $\frac{4}{10} \times \frac{3}{9} = \frac{12}{90}$	M1	
	$= \frac{2}{15}$ (0.133)	A1ft	**C2**
			[6 marks]
3	**a** {Equilateral, Isosceles} or equivalent	A1A1	**C2**
	b Pentagon or equivalent	A1	**C1**
	c		
	$U = $ Polygons	A2	**C2**
	d $n(A \cap B) = 0$	A1	**C1**
			[6 marks]
4	**a**		

$(q \wedge \neg p)$	$(\neg q \vee p)$	$(q \wedge \neg p) \Rightarrow (\neg q \vee p)$		
F	T	T		
F	T	T	A1	
T	F	F	A1ft	
F	T	T	A1ft	**C3**

	b Not a contradiction. (All the entries are not F.)	A1ft	**C1**
	c $\neg(\neg q \vee p) \Rightarrow \neg(q \wedge \neg p)$	A1A1	**C2**
			[6 marks]
5	**a** $(m - 9)(m + 3)$	A1A1	**C2**
	b zero are 1.4 and -12	A1A1	**C2**
	c $v = 4$ or $\frac{2}{3}$	A1A1	**C2**
			[6 marks]
6	**a**	A1 A1 A1	**C3**
	b	A1 A1 A1	**C3**
			[6 marks]

7	**a**		
	(**Note:** marks are for m and c)	A1A1A1	**C3**
	b $2x - 3 = \frac{3}{2}$ $x = \frac{9}{4}$	M1A1	**C2**
	c distance is $\frac{3}{2}$ units	A1	**C1** [6 marks]
8	**a** $r = 2$	A1	**C1**
	b $256 = u_1 r^{n-1}$ $256 = \frac{1}{64} \times 2^{n-1}$	M1	
	$n = 15$ There are 15 terms.	A1ft	**C2**
	c $S_{15} = \dfrac{\frac{1}{64} \times (2^{15} - 1)}{2 - 1}$	M1A1ft	
	$= 511.984\,375$ (exact answer)		
	$= 512$	A1ft	**C3** [6 marks]
9	**a** 19 seedlings	A1	**C1**
	b **i** $Q_1 = 78$ cm **ii** Med $= 88$ cm **iii** $Q_3 = 103$ cm	A1A1A1	**C3**
	c	A2ft	**C2** [6 marks]
10	**a** **i** $P = R - C$		
	$= (2000 \times 30) - (46\,000 + 11.50 \times 2000)$	M1	
	loss of \$9000	A1	**C2**
	ii $(5000 \times 30) - (46\,000 + 11.50 \times 5000)$	M1	
	profit of \$46\,500	A1	**C2**
	b $R = C$		
	$30x = 46\,000 + 11.5x$	M1	
	$x = 2486.5$		
	Break even when 2490 books are sold (2487)	A1	**C2** [6 marks]
11	**a** Cosine rule:		
	$\cos \angle BCA = \dfrac{650^2 + 700^2 - 400^2}{2 \times 650 \times 700}$	M1A1	
	$\angle BCA = 34.2^o$	A1	**C3**
	b Area $= \frac{1}{2} \times 650 \times 700 \times \sin 34.2^o$	M1A1ft	
	$= 127\,926.6768$		
	$= 128\,000$ m^2	A1ft	**C3** [6 marks]
12	**a** **i** $I = \dfrac{3500 \times 5.2 \times 7}{100} = 1274$	M1	
	Investment is worth 4774 AUD	A1	**C2**
	ii $A = 3500 \left(1 + \frac{5.2}{1200}\right)^{7 \times 12}$	M1A1	
	Investment is worth 5032.80 AUD	A1	**C3**
	b Difference is 258.80 AUD	A1ft	**C1**
	(can ft for difference of wrong amounts but do not accept 0 AUD)		[6 marks]

13	**a** Intercepts at $(-3, 0)$ and $(4, 0)$	A1	**C1**
	b $\dfrac{-3+4}{2}$ $\quad x = \frac{1}{2}$	A1ft	**C1**
	c $y = a(x+3)(x-4)$	M1	
	y-intercept is -24, hence $a = 2$		
	$y = 2(x+3)(x-4)$	A1ft	**C2**
	d minimum when $x = \frac{1}{2}$,	M1	
	$y = 2\left(\frac{1}{2}+3\right)\left(\frac{1}{2}-4\right) = -24.5$	A1ft	**C2** [6 marks]
14	**a** $Q = -0.543P + 74.3$	A1	
	$r = -0.642$	A1	**C2**
	b $Q = -0.614P + 82.2$	A1	
	$r = -0.897$	A1	**C2**
	c Gradient is steeper. Relationship is stronger.	A1ftA1ft	**C2** [6 marks]
15	**a** **i** $x < b$ and $x > c$	A1A1	**C2**
	ii $b < x < c$	A1ftA1ft	**C2**
	b $f'(x) = 0$ when $x = b$ and $x = c$	A1A1	**C2** [6 marks]

1	**a**	**i** $3 \times 700 \times 12 = 25\,200$ USD		A1	1
		ii $25\,200 \times 0.028 = 705.60$ USD		M1A1ft (G2)	2
		iii $700 \times 12 \times 1.028 \times 1.033 = 8920.16$ USD		M1M1A1ft (G3)	3
	b	**i** $u_4 = 800 + 4 \times 40$		M1	
		$= 960$ employees		A1 (G2)	2
		ii Number $= 800 - 5 \times 40$		M1	
		$= 600$		A1 (G2)	2
		iii $800 + (n-1) \times 40 > 1000$ (or equivalent)		M1	
		$n > 6$ Year 2011		A1A1 (G2)	3
					(13)

2	**a**	**i** length is $(x+5)$ cm		A1	1
		ii $A = x(x+5)$ or (x^2+5x)		A1A1ft	2
		iii $x(x+5) = 204$		M1	
		$x^2 + 5x - 204 = 0$			
		$(x+17)(x-12) = 0$			
		$x = -17$ or 12		A1ft (G2)	2
		iv length is 17 cm, width is 12 cm		A1ftA1ft	2
	b	**i** $\frac{1}{2} \times \frac{4}{3}\pi r^3 = 7068$		M1A1	
		$r^3 = \dfrac{7068 \times 6}{4\pi}$			
		$r = 15.0$ m		A1 (G2)	3
		ii Surface area $= 2 \times \pi \times 15^2$		M1A1ft	
		$= 1413.72$			
		$= 1410$ m^2		A1ft (G1)	3
		iii Cost $= 23.45 \times 142$		M1	
		$= \$3329.90$ (**Note:** must be 142)		A1ft (G2)	2

c **i** Base of the box

$AC^2 = 12.7^2 + 10.8^2 \qquad AC = 16.7$ cm

$AD^2 = 16.7^2 + 6.45^2 \qquad AD = 17.9$ cm

(**Note:** maximum G2 for answer with no working or diagram)

M1A1 (G1)		
M1A1ft (G2)	4	

ii $\tan\theta = \dfrac{6.45}{16.7} \qquad \theta = 21.1°$ — M1A1ft (G1) — 2

(21)

3	**a** **i**			

$U = 60$

(A1 for 1, 4, 25   A1 for 3, 6, 9   A1 for 5)

			A1A1A1	**3**

ii **a** $n(P \cap C) = 32$ — A1ft

b $n(P \cup C') = 56$ — A1ft

c $n((L \cap P)' \cap (C \cup L)) = 38$ — A1ftA1ft — **4**

b **i** 110 items — A1 — **1**

ii **a** P(gold earings) $= \frac{10}{110} = \frac{1}{11}$ (0.0909) — A1A1 (G2) — **2**

b P(not a silver bracelet) $= \frac{98}{110} = \frac{49}{55}$ (0.891) — A1A1 (G2) — **2**

iii P(both silver given both were necklaces)

$= \frac{8}{42} \times \frac{7}{41} = \frac{56}{1722} = \frac{4}{123}$ (0.0325) — M1A1A1 (G2) — **3**

(15)

4	**a** **i** $a = -12$, $b = -24$	A1A1	**2**

ii

(A1 for scale and labels, A2 for points, A1 for curve) — A1A2ft A1ft — **4**

iii on graph   (A1 for intercept, A1 for gradient) — A2 — **2**

iv $(-1.67, -4.35)$ and $(5.67, 10.4)$ — A1A1 — **2**

accept $(-2, -4)$ and $(5.5, 10)$ from graph

b **i** $f'(x) = 5x^2 + 6x - 8$ — A1A1A1 — **3**

ii $f''(x) = 10x + 6$ — A1ftA1ft — **2**

iii $5x^2 + 6x - 8 = 0$ — M1

$x = -2$ or $x = \frac{4}{5}$ (0.8) — A1ftA1ft (G3) — **3**

iv -2 is outside of domain — A1ft

$(0.8, -1.63)$ is a local minimum and -1.63 is the smallest value in the given domain. 50 is the largest value in the given domain. — A1A1ft

A2ft — **5**

(23)

5 a i

height (cm)	freq.
0 - 4	0
5 - 9	0
10 - 14	2
15 - 19	8
20 - 24	20
25 - 29	30
30 - 34	24
35 - 39	16
Total	100

accept 25 and 15 for last 2 entries

A1A1   2

ii Mean $= 27.7$ Standard deviation $= 6.25$ (6.19)

A1ftA1ft   2

iii $\dfrac{27.7 - 23}{27.7} \times 100 = 16.967 = 17.0\%$

M1A1ft (G1)   2

iv $6.25 \times 0.368 + 27.7 = 30$ cm

M1

36 plants

A1ft (G2)   2

b i

52	48
30	70

A1   1

ii

41	59
41	59

A2ft   2

iii $\chi^2 = 10.004$

A2ft   2

iv

	$< m + 0.368\ s$	$\geqslant m + 0.368\ s$
Plot A	78	22
Plot B	60	40

A1ft   1

v p-value $= 0.005\,92$

A2ft   2

c Both results suggest that the hypothesis should not be accepted. There does appear to be a significant difference between the results for the two fields.

A1

Calculated χ^2 values fall inside the 5% critical level.

R1ft   2

(18)